Shell Connections 2006

NEW PLAYS
FOR YOUNG PEOPLE

For a complete list of volumes and individual titles available in the Connections *series, see page 725*

Shell Connections 2006

NEW PLAYS
FOR YOUNG PEOPLE

Broken Hallelujah

Feather Boy

Liar

The Miracle

Pack Up Your Troubles

Pass It On

School Journey to the Centre of the Earth

The Shoemaker's Incredible Wife

Shut Up

The Spider Men

ff

faber and faber

First published in 2006
by Faber and Faber Limited, 3 Queen Square, London WC1N 3AU

Typeset by Country Setting, Kingsdown, Kent CT14 8ES
Printed in England by Mackays of Chatham plc, Chatham, Kent

This collection © Faber and Faber Ltd 2006

Introduction and Notes © Suzy Graham-Adriani 2006

Interviews © Jim Mulligan 2006

Broken Hallelujah © Sharman Macdonald, 2006

Feather Boy: the Musical © Nicky Singer, Peter Tabern,
Don Black and Debbie Wiseman, 2006

Liar © Gregory Burke, 2006

The Miracle © Lin Coghlan, 2006

Pack Up Your Troubles © Pack Up Your Troubles Ltd, 1998, 2006

Pass It On © Doug Lucie, 2006

School Journey to the Centre of the Earth © Daisy Campbell, 2006

La zapatera prodigiosa by Federico Garcia Lorca
© Herederos de Federico Garcia Lorca. English adaptation by
Lucinda Coxon (*The Shoemaker's Incredible Wife*)
© Lucinda Coxon and Herederos de Federico Garcia Lorca.
All rights, including performance rights, are reserved throughout
the world by Herederos de Federico Garcia Lorca and Lucinda Coxon.

Shut Up © Andrew Payne, 2006

The Spider Men © Ursula Rani Sarma, 2006

The rights of Gregory Burke, Daisy Campbell, Lin Coghlan, Lucinda
Coxon, Federico Garcia Lorca, Doug Lucie, Sharman Macdonald, Andrew
Payne, Aubrey Powell, Ursula Rani Sarma, Nicky Singer, Peter Tabern and
Snoo Wilson to be identified as the authors of these works have been asserted
in accordance with Section 77 of the Copyright, Designs and Patents Act 1988

Information regarding applications for performance
will be found preceding the individual plays

A CIP record for this book is available from the British Library

978-0-571-23398-4 / 0-571-23398-8

2 4 6 8 10 9 7 5 3 1

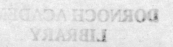

Contents

SHELL CONNECTIONS 2006

Introduction

The Shell Connections programme is part of the National's DNA. Each year it commissions and develops ten new works for and about teenagers. This dazzling anthology of eight plays and two new musicals was workshopped by around three hundred directors during a record-breaking retreat hosted by Bath Theatre Royal last November. The works in their present form are now available for you to read or, better still, produce.

There are tales of conspiracy, mysterious disappearances and searches for truth and self-identity. Settings encompass a wealth of imaginative worlds. In Sharman Macdonald's *Broken Hallelujah*, set in the smoky hollows of Virginia during the American Civil War, two girls have a life-altering encounter with Confederate and Union soldiers. The effects of war on young people are explored in a play as timely as today's newspaper headlines.

In *Feather Boy* (book by Nicky Singer and Peter Tabern, lyrics by Don Black, music by Debbie Wiseman), no one's more surprised than Robert, the class nerd, when a strange old lady sends him on a quest to the derelict Chance House. Legend has it that a boy once fell to his death from an upper window. To get to the truth, Robert must learn what it really means to fly. Here we have a musical with big show routines, tender lyrical numbers and a Firebird undercurrent of myth and magic.

In *Liar*, a warm-hearted comedy by Gregory Burke, Donnie is the new boy at school – he is also a liar. In fact, he's not even called Donnie, he's really called Ronnie, but he thinks that's the sort of name a girl like Katie (a bit of a goddess with a brain) will go for. Unfortunately, he has a tendency to get caught out. Ronnie picks his way through the social minefield and myriad teenage tribes of an average British high school.

Pack Up Your Troubles (book by Snoo Wilson, based on an idea by Aubrey Powell) is a musical based on the life and death of Felix Powell, composer of the famous First World War marching song. Felix and his brother George were stars of the music hall. Their song 'Pack Up Your Troubles' played countless British and Empire soldiers 'over the top' to their deaths – something which preyed on Felix's mind in later years. The musical charts the lives of the brothers through to the Second World War; haunted by an unhappy love affair, embezzlement and a new musical doomed when its London theatre was bombed on opening night, Felix was found shot through the heart from his own rifle, in the uniform of the Peacehaven Home Guard.

War continues as a theme in *Pass It On* by Doug Lucie. This looks at some of the ways in which war impacts on the lives of teenagers, beginning with Irish rebel Nev in 1971, moving to squaddies Chris and Glen in Iraq in 2004, via warring sisters Kelly and Monique – whose dad has just sailed on the Falklands Task Force in 1982 – and Giles in 1997, who sees New Labour's General Election victory as the end of his dream of an army career.

Join Tricia and her classmates on their odyssey into the paranoid, unscrupulous and hilarious world of the eight-year-old imagination in the Connections revival of *School Journey to the Centre of the Earth* by Daisy Campbell with Ken Campbell, which originally formed part of the very first series. Is their teacher kidnapping them as part of a worldwide conspiracy? Are they going to have to face The Doctor? Is Tricia really a schoolgirl spy? Or are they simply on a day trip to Alton Towers?

In Andrew Payne's *Shut Up*, it's exactly eleven months, two days and thirteen hours since Dexter shut up. Since then he's been nagged, cajoled, counselled, therapised and generally messed about . . . but Dexter still isn't talking. But if things were bad when Dexter kept his mouth shut, they only get worse when he starts talking – and we find out why he became silent in the first place.

When the canal broke its banks and a holy statue burst up through the floor of twelve-year-old Veronica Sheehan's bedroom in Lin Coghlan's *The Miracle*, no one was more surprised than she was. With the enthusiastic support of best friend Zelda, the two girls set about using their new-found skills to help their ailing community, as the townspeople find themselves hungering unknowingly for something magical to come into their lives.

The two central characters in *The Shoemaker's Incredible Wife* by Federico Garcia Lorca, translated by Lucinda Coxon, are a combustible young woman and a staid old man who are locked together in a marriage of tragi-comic misery. Eventually, the husband heeds his wife's seemingly heartfelt wish that he should leave her. But with her husband departed, the young wife appears to discover a hitherto unimagined depth of feeling for him, and holds off a variety of suitors, until one day a travelling puppet show arrives in the village with a puppeteer who bears a striking resemblance to her long-lost husband . . .

An act of rebellion goes horribly wrong in *The Spider Men* by Ursula Rani Sarma. David wants Michael to camp in the woods all night to teach their parents a lesson, but Michael just wants to go home. The boys' disappearance and the eventual realisation that David is never coming back force their friends to reassess their values, to find their own identity beyond the whitewash of the label 'teenager', and to search for their own truth amidst the chaos of peer pressure, a sometimes dangerous world and the need to be loved.

All of the plays were premiered in March 2006. The team visited every one of the 284 productions in their own venues (listed at the back of this book). Most transferred their shows and were part of the Connections festival season which began at Plymouth Theatre Royal and continued to The Castle, Wellingborough; Southampton Nuffield; The Playhouse and The Garage; Nuffield, Brewery Arts Centre; Stephen Joseph Theatre, Scarborough; Watford Palace Theatre; The Lowry, Manchester; Everyman Palace Theatre, Cork, Ireland; Greenwich Theatre; Teatro Limonaia, Florence, Italy; Clwyd Theatr Cymru, Wales; Cultergest Theatre, Lisbon, Portugal; Bath Theatre Royal; Newcastle Theatre Royal; Royal Lyceum, Edinburgh, Scotland; the Albany Theatre and Lyric Theatre, London; and Brighton Dome. The season culminated at the National in July.

As I write, three of last season's plays – *Chatroom* by Enda Welsh, *Burn* by Deborah Gearing and Mark Ravenhill's *Citizenship* – are part of the National's main repertoire in the Cottesloe. And the next series is a long way into development. If you would like to be part of the programme, you can be.

SUZY GRAHAM-ADRIANI

National Theatre
March 2006

BROKEN HALLELUJAH

Sharman Macdonald

Sharman Macdonald's plays include *After Juliet* for Connections, *When I Was A Girl I Used to Scream and Shout*, *The Brave*, *When We Were Women*, *All Things Nice*, *Shades*, *The Winter Guest*, *Sea Urchins*, *Soft Fall The Sands of Eden* and *Girl with Red Hair*. She is also the author of two novels, *The Beast* and *Night Night*, the opera libretto *Hey Persephone!* and the screenplays for *Wild Flowers*, *The Winter Guest* and *Best Times of Our Lives*.

Characters

Stewart
a Northern soldier

Hosgood
a Northern soldier

Hancock
a Northern soldier

Rowatt
a Southern soldier

Loren
a Southern girl

Maureen
a Southern girl

Bridh
an Irish girl

Broken Hallelujah was originally commissioned and produced by American Conservatory Theater Young Conservatory New Plays Program, San Francisco, California

*The morning of 5 September 1864 at the siege of
Petersburg, Virginia.*

*A gleam of sunlight shines on Northern lines. It hits
Stewart in a slum of a dugout, sordid and dirty, beyond
the outer defences of the town.*

*A Northern soldier, Hosgood, runs low back from the
town, leaps roaring onto the lip of the dugout. Stays for
three seconds, rolls down into the dugout.*

Hosgood Gone, see. No Southern trash planter slave-
   owning son-of-a-whoring-bitch sniper there. Gone. I'm
   telling you, gone.
Stewart Where've you been?

*Hosgood waggles a stick with a hat on the end up
there.*

Hosgood There's ways into that town. I could get a
   whole army in there. Sack old Useless, put me in
   charge, and I could.
Stewart You'd have us all dead with your 'ways'.
Hosgood Stewart, you are suffering from what is called
   the siege mentality.
Stewart Boredom I'm suffering from. Hunger I'm suffering
   from. The desire to stay alive at all costs I'm suffering
   from.
Hosgood Like I said.

The stick with the hat waggles furiously.

Stewart Think he's stupid, your Southern boy?

Hosgood Think he's gone is all.

Stewart That's a stick with a hat on the end.

Hosgood I was up there. I was up there for all to see.

Stewart He's not going to waste shot on a hat and a stick, is he?

Hosgood Didn't take a pop at me, did he?

Stewart Getting his aim set is all.

Hosgood He's not there.

Stewart You're lucky you got through the lines alive. You go back up there now he'll shoot you dead.

The hat on the stick stabs the air.

Hosgood He. Is. Not. There.

Stewart He's waitin'. Like he's fishin' for a fat catfish in a pool. Patience itself he is, sittin' there.

Hosgood I'm going to prove it to you.

Stewart I don't need proof.

Hosgood I'll make a bet with you.

Stewart You've got nothing I want.

Hosgood Have though.

Stewart You've got nothing and I've got nothing. We both got nothing. Nothing to bet.

Hosgood I have something you truly do want and need.

Stewart You got an itch, that's what you got. And there's a Southern boy out there waitin' and willin' to scratch it.

Hosgood Suppose I said I had bacon?

Stewart You have not got bacon.

Hosgood I got bacon with plenty fat on it and I don't mean army issue. Been through the gates of Hell itself to get it. I mean sweet bacon, whole bacon that doesn't turn to string in your mouth and swell up there with spit till you can't swallow it, then you do and it rests down in your intestinal tract like a wad of filthy rag waitin' to turn your bowels to water. Know what I'm saying? Saw a man with his stomach shot out, lying there with his stomach in his hands all open to the sky with the contents plain for all to see. Wads of bacon lyin' in it. If he hadn't a been shot the way he was, the bacon would've killed him. Given him a blockage lyin' in there like that and strangulated him. Lucky he was shot. Smoke-house bacon I've got here; 'nough fat on it. This bacon I've got, it's the best bacon I've ever had the pleasure to behold. Not only does it do honour to the pig that it came from but to all pig-kind. My mouth waters at the thought of this bacon. I am salivating. This bacon. There's a yard on the edge of that town. And in that yard there is a secret larder. And in that larder . . . I will wager you this bacon that that sniper has gone.

Stewart Bacon, you say?

Hosgood Sweet smoked bacon.

Stewart Man might die happy if he had a good few rashers of bacon inside him.

Hosgood Might at that.

Stewart Suppose I was to take your bet?

Hosgood Your boots against my bacon.

Stewart You ain't getting my boots.

Hosgood I'll give you mine.

Stewart I got these off of a dying man. Made my heart cry to take them off him. Dying the way he was. Though he was my enemy. We're all soldiers and he blessed me for giving him a drink as he lay dying and he let me take these boots.

Hosgood Didn't have a choice, did he?

Stewart We're all soldiers in this war one side or the other. Way I see it doesn't matter what side you're on. We're all in the same boat. War won't be over till every last soldier of us is dead. That's what they're aiming at. Only man that valued a soldier's life was General George McLellan whom I take my hat off to. May he be elected president. He'll bring peace. Old Lincoln now, he gets back in for a second term we're all dead and gone.

Hosgood You want this bacon?

Stewart I got a Bible here.

Hosgood I don't want a Bible.

Stewart You hear about this Bible, you'll want it.

Hosgood The sniper hasn't gone you're telling me. If he hasn't gone why don't you wager your boots? You so sure he's not gone you are not going to lose them? No danger.

Stewart This Bible was my ma's Bible. I was saying goodbye to her. Course she didn't want me to go but this man paid me three hundred dollars to take his son's place, be his surrogate, my ma knows the value of money.

Hosgood Knew a man was old Abe Lincoln's surrogate.

Stewart She knows the value of money, my ma. Blessed this Bible, put it next to my heart to keep me safe.

Hosgood We're talking about bacon here. Boots we're talking about.

Stewart This is a lucky Bible.

Hosgood I know, been hit three times, Bible's taken the bullet, heart's gone on beating.

Stewart Only one left of all I enlisted with. Odds are my time is running out. Wouldn't get a betting man to bet on me surviving the next push.

Hosgood Nor any one of the rest of us.

Stewart I got my Bible though. And I'm saying you got a chance of having it.

Hosgood You're trying just too hard to keep your boots. You know that sniper's gone.

Stewart You get up there on that ridge you'll come back down dead, I'll get your bacon anyway, you won't get my boots. I'll open my Bible and say a few words over you. How about that?

Hosgood There is no one there.

Stewart So why don't you get up there then and do your roaring thing, your sounding-like-a-stuck-pig thing.

Hosgood That's my yell.

Stewart Rebs have a yell much better than that.

Hosgood Says who?

Stewart Turns your blood cold when they yell. I've seen men freeze in the ranks.

Hosgood Not me.

Stewart You going to get up on that parapet?

Hosgood Bet me your boots.

Stewart I'm not risking my boots even on a sure thing, even to win some bacon.

Hosgood This quiet gets to me. How come it doesn't get to you?

Beat.

Sun's shining.

Hosgood roars and leaps.

Stewart Hosgood! Hosgood!

The sunlight's bright, almost white. A shot rings out.

Hosgood!

Hosgood leaps back down.

Hosgood You were right. He was there.

Stewart He get you?

Hosgood What?

Stewart Are you hit, man?

Hosgood I wouldn't be a sniper. Would you be a sniper? Dirty thing a sniper. Fighting right out front. That's a man's way. You remember Pickett's Charge? That was a beautiful thing. Watching from up Little Round Top, you and me. Watching the pattern of those troops unfold. Wave on wave. They were the enemy sure enough but you had to admire them for the beauty of their form. That's fighting. Sneaky little runt a sniper. I could've sworn he wasn't there.

He puts his hand up to the left side of his chest.
Touches, looks.

Can't be blood, can it?

Stewart and Hosgood stare at each other.

Stewart You're hit, man.

Hosgood runs.

Hey. Hey, Hosgood. C'mere, man. Come on. I'm not
going to hurt you. Come here.

Stewart catches him. Hosgood struggles.

Hosgood Nicked me, that's all. Flesh wound, that's all.
I'll just sit still a while, I'll be fine.
Stewart What d'you do it for, eh?
Hosgood Have to do something.
Stewart We need to get you seen to.
Hosgood I'm not going to hospital. I'm not moving from
here. More men die in hospital. You get gangrene in
hospital. You get fever. It smells bad in there, man. The
only place you go from there's the embalming tent if
you're rich, the shallow earth if you're not. To come
popping back up when the rain sets in.
Stewart More chance there, man, in the hospital even so.

Stewart starts to lift Hosgood. Hosgood gathers
himself. Whips out half a side of bacon.

Hosgood I had you there, man? I had you.
Stewart Eh?
Hosgood I'm not hit.
Stewart You're hit.
Hosgood I'm not hit, man. Here. My daddy told me
always to pay my debts of honour.
Stewart I'm not taking it.
Hosgood You think I'm a liar?

Stewart Eh?

Hosgood You don't believe I'm not shot?

Stewart Come on, Hosgood.

Hosgood I take exception, Stewart, I do.

Stewart Hosgood, I need you . . .

Hosgood They shot my bacon. Risked my life to get this and they shot it. The fat lady I got it from . . . Risked my very soul. There is the bullet hole.

Stewart Goes in one side, comes out the other. Where's the bullet?

Hosgood My bacon is now your bacon.

He puts it down on a stone. Walks to the edge of the dugout.

Stewart Where are you going?

Hosgood Taking a constitutional.

Stewart You're on duty.

Hosgood Why don't you . . . cook your bacon. That's it, Stewart, cook your bloody bacon. You won it fair and square.

He slides out of the back of the dugout and he runs, keeping low, hand tight to his chest. Stewart crawls after him.

Stewart Hosgood. Hosgood.

Then he stops. Picks up the bacon.

Bright, bright sunlight. So bright nothing can be seen except light.
A yard in Petersburg.
Southern voices.

Maureen (*whispering*) R–A–P–E.

Loren I can spell.

Maureen Didn't say you couldn't.

Loren You mean 'rape'. You say 'rape'.

Two girls from the town walk in a huge yard in the heat. The earth's dry. Now and again Loren scrabbles at the earth. Sometimes she stamps. Listens.

Maureen Keep your voice down. Ma Tyler hears you, she'll be out here with her shotgun. She don't take so kindly to trespassers in her yard. Let alone thieves, Loren Maeve.

Loren You mean it, you say it.

Maureen My mother she'd make me wash my mouth out if ever I let a word like that escape from it all in one piece.

Loren Your mother . . .

Maureen Don't you use that tone of voice about any member of my family. I've come along to help you out. Help you out with your thievin', which is a sin. I can go home just as easy. I can go home right now and be a sinner no more.

Loren You have to say what you mean. You have to say it out loud. That's what I believe. If it's 'rape' you mean, it's 'rape' you say.

Maureen You're not old enough to have beliefs. We neither of us are.

Loren Your mother tell you that too?

Maureen Stay young as long as you can, my mother says. Even in these days.

Loren Go on then, go home.

Maureen Well, I will.

Loren Go on then.

Maureen If I want to, I will.

Loren Well then?

Maureen I don't want to, do I? Do I?

Loren You needn't think I need you. I don't need you.

12

Ma Tyler's got a larder in this yard. And it's just filled with bacon way I hear it. And I'm going to find her larder and I'm going to take that bacon from it to feed my little brother with. She's just a fat old lady after all. And there is no fat old lady on this earth that can scare me.

Beat.

Maureen R–A–P–E. They say it that way so's you don't know.

Loren Don't know what?

Maureen You and me and all the rest of us if they get into the town. If the town falls, what they'll do.

Loren I ain't scared of any Yankees.

Maureen Well, I'm not either.

Loren Never said you were, did I?

Beat.

Maureen It's what they've been doing. Rape. Way I hear it, anyway. Everywhere they've been. Because they're dogs the Yankees, no better than. You can tell a Yankee by his smell and of course they don't have much intelligence, for which we must pity them. It's an accident of birth, after all. What they do, coming into our land, they do it because they know no better.

Loren You ever met anybody they've done it to, this rape thing you're telling me of?

Maureen Not exactly.

Loren Has your mother?

Maureen Well now, I do not think she would tell me if she had.

Loren I don't see we've got the proof then that they'd do it.

Maureen It's what mean people do do. Folks they have in their power, they cause them harm.

Loren I don't see the proof, is all I'm saying.

Maureen You don't know what it is, do you?
Loren R–A–P–E, you said.
Maureen You don't know.
Loren And you do, I suppose?
Maureen You just ask me. Go on. Ask me.

Beat.

Loren Anyway . . .
Maureen What?
Loren General Robert E. Lee will not let Petersburg fall, I bet.
Maureen He'll sacrifice us, is what I hear.
Loren He loses Petersburg, he'll lose Richmond. We're his last bastion's what I hear. So I'm not scared of rape or anything any Yankee's going to do when he gets into Petersburg because he just will not be allowed to get in. Besides which, we are all a part of human kind.
Maureen Apart from Yankees.

Beat. Loren stamps hard on the ground.

Loren It's hollow somewhere, I know it is. That larder's somewhere here and the bacon that's in it.
Maureen They don't shoot. You know that? You know they don't shoot?
Loren Who?
Maureen Neither the one side nor the other shoot.
Loren We got a shell through one of the pillars on the porch, near brought the whole house down. I call that shooting.
Maureen That's the big guns. I'm not talking about the big guns. That's shooting at us citizens. They can't see us. Don't mind shooting at what they can't see, do they? I'm talking about the soldiers facing each other. All the long lines of them facing. They don't exactly shoot as we understand it. Not as we'd think it.
Loren Thought you said they were animals.

14

Maureen What they do is . . . What they do is, they load
their guns but they don't fire them off or, if they do,
they fire to the side, you know, to the side. There were
rifles they picked up after . . .

Loren Who picked up? Who's they? After what?

Maureen You know what I'm going to say?

Loren What?

Maureen You want to know what I'm going to say?

Loren Eh?

Maureen You want to know what I'm going to say, you
have to let me say it. You have to shut your mouth and
let me say it.

Loren So?

Maureen I could name you battles. I could name you
many a battle. The battles I could name you that they
picked up rifles after. They picked up rifles and they
had never been fired. Gettysburg. Antietam, Cold
Harbor even.

Loren Benjamin's brother, he died. And his father. My
Uncle Samuel died. And Solomon Kirk got his leg
chopped off because the bone was smashed into by a
lead bullet from an Enfield rifle that the British made
and it was so splintered the bone, they couldn't do
nothing but take the leg off and he didn't have any
ether to take the pain away when they cut. And then
they threw his leg onto a bundle with feet and arms
and things. And he said he ain't afraid of Hell no more
because he's been to a far worser place. You think he
imagined the bullet in his leg? You think he plain
imagined it?

Maureen They faced each other and they never fired.

Loren If I was in a battle and I had a rifle and it was
loaded and there was a man all lined up opposite me
and he had a rifle and it was loaded and he was
pointing his rifle at me, I'd fire my rifle. Damn an'
I would.

Maureen Don't say that word.

Loren Right at him, I would damn well fire it, make no damn mistake.

Maureen You shouldn't say that word, God Almighty will cast you out of Heaven.

Loren I'm not dead.

Maureen And you'll fall. All the way you'll fall down to the other place that's the Devil's Kingdom.

Loren I'm not dead yet.

Maureen And the Devil'll get you and he'll take you and he'll roast you on his spits over the fires of Hell. That's what he'll do an' you say that word.

Loren No he won't.

Maureen An' you say that word he will.

Loren I'll say what I damn well like.

Maureen It doesn't sit nice in the mouth of a lady.

Loren And you know all about ladies. I expect your lady mother taught you.

Maureen I know what I hear is all. I know what I'm told. I listen, Loren Maeve. Which is more than you do. You leave off my mother.

Loren She cries every day, don't she?

Maureen She's frightened.

Loren We're all frightened, we don't cry. No honour in tears.

Maureen My mother's heard too much about honour. And I have. Too damn much.

Loren Too 'damn' much?

They giggle.

Maureen Aren't you the least scared of the Almighty?

Loren I can't see Him, can I? I can't feel Him. I can't touch Him and He doesn't touch me. Don't seem to me I have much to be scared of.

Maureen Don't you pray?

Loren I'm more scared of the Feds than I am of God.

And I ain't scared of them at all.

Maureen Don't you pray for your brother?

Loren Even General Grant I ain't scared of, nor Abe Lincoln himself. Being scared doesn't change what's going to happen way I see it. And it's uncomfortable in your stomach. Might as well not be scared.

Maureen Don't you love your brother?

Loren He's my darling and my mother's darling and my father's darling.

Maureen You should pray. If he dies . . . If your little brother dies and you ain't prayed, it will be your fault he dies.

Loren I held him first when he was born.

Maureen I'll pray for him for you.

Loren I don't want you to do that.

Maureen I'd do anything for you. In the cause of friendship.

Loren I hear men screaming out there. I hear them screaming in the night sometimes. Don't you pray. Don't you pray to Something that's bad to my brother. Don't you pray to Something that lets men scream like that, all alone in the night. That's Something not worth praying to.

Maureen They're mostly just Yankees.

Loren Doesn't matter.

Maureen Our cause is sacred to God.

Loren He come down and whisper that in your ear, God?

Maureen Everybody says it is.

Loren God came down from the sky and told 'everybody' that, did he?

Maureen I'm stopping my ears, Loren. I'm stopping my ears so I don't hear you. I could go to Hell for hearing you.

Loren Why is he sick, my little brother?

Maureen He's hungry.

Loren He never did anything to anybody, my little brother.

Maureen Folk get sick when they're hungry is all.

Loren I don't see the Almighty making my brother better, not for all my prayers.

Maureen You did pray, then. You did pray.

Loren Not any more.

Loren stamps on the ground again.

Maureen There's no larder here. Nor no bacon neither.

Loren How come Mrs Tyler's fat as a hog?

Maureen God made her that way.

Loren She's ate herself that way. That's how come. The whole town says there's bacon.

Maureen Send her to prisoner camp. They don't come out of there fat. Good as a reducing diet, going to prisoner camp. Never seen a fat prisoner yet, my ma says. Skeletal, my ma says.

Loren Doin' her a favour then. Taking her bacon.

Maureen If we find it.

Loren I have to find it. My brother'll die else.

Maureen There are towns south of here. In Tennessee there are towns. In Alabama there are towns and the towns are empty of men. They're just empty of men. All the men from the towns are dead. And the ladies have no husbands. And the children have no fathers. And the girls have no sweethearts. I hear the war will go on and on till all the towns are like that. Till there's only women left in all the towns of the Confederacy. Only then will the war end.

Loren How come?

Maureen How come what?

Loren If the soldiers don't shoot like you said they don't. If none of the soldiers shoot, how come there's all these dead men?

Maureen You have to have a man's weight behind the lead, and then the men die. It's the big guns like I said. You don't listen, Loren Maeve. The big guns just tear men apart and spread their vitals over the earth till there's lakes of blood and bridges to walk on over the lakes of blood and these bridges they are made of flesh.

A thud.

Loren There.
Maureen You heard hollow?
Loren You didn't believe me, did you?
Maureen I didn't hear hollow.

Still morning. Still bright.
In the dugout, Stewart's beginning to cook over a wood fire. Setting stones to heat round it. Putting a trestle over the flames. Taking out a twist of greasy paper with a precious lump of fat in it. Sliding the fat into the slowly heating pan, talking to Hancock, standing watching all the while.

Stewart Then she says, my ma says, 'I'm going to buy the clothes to put upon my back. Just like I'll buy the food we eat. I've cooked all my life,' she says. 'I'm cooking no more. Your grandma,' my ma says, 'she wore herself out. She span the thread, she wove the cloth, she made the clothes, she hoed, she planted, she washed, she scrubbed, she cooked, she died. I don't remember your grandma once singing a song for pure joy,' my ma says. 'Plenty hymns she sang begging the good Lord above for joy in the life to come. Not a one for joy in the here and now do I remember. Well not me,' my ma says. She says, 'I'm going to have some joy. Right here. Right now. In this life. For I'm not so sure there is a life to come.'
Hancock That bacon fat?

Stewart She wasn't so sure and neither am I.

Hancock Should use that fat on all the seams of your clothes. All the seams. Keep the chiggers from biting you.

Stewart You look at them, corpses, lying there, lying where they fall. Watch them swelling up. Watch them rotting. You know there's nothing else. Man's dead, he's dead.

Hancock I count that blasphemy.

Stewart My fire, my blasphemy, your choice.

Hancock Eh?

Stewart Stay or go.

Beat.

Hancock Course you could rub it on your skin, the fat.

Stewart Still be there when the cooking's done.

Hancock Near as good as salt, bacon fat. Salt-water bathing, that would be the thing, keep the beasts from biting you. I'd like to swim in some salt water. We had a water hole back home. Used to swim there in the summertime.

Stewart Wouldn't be salt.

Hancock Cool though.

Stewart You've got the James River running over there. Go on down to the river, why don't you?

Hancock Sniper'd get me.

Stewart Maybe not.

Hancock I'd get to that river if I could. See if I wouldn't. I had some salt I'd get there. Wouldn't care though it's fresh water. Rub the salt on my skin, see. Use it like soap.

Stewart No salt, not for any money.

Hancock Think it's green do you, the James? Shady green water? Willows dipping in. Green with silver in it where there's light. Or gold from the sun. Gold and green.

Stewart No use talking.

Hancock Been quiet today.

Stewart Quiet enough.

Hancock Don't like the quiet. See my hands. (*Holds them out. They're trembling.*) Like an old man's hands. Like my grandfather's hands. See. See.

Stewart You want to take up whittling.

Hancock We been judged's what it is. We been judged alright. We been found wanting, else what is all this that's been brought on us? I'm a good man.

Stewart What's that mean, goodness? Don't mean anything to me. Let them in charge think about goodness, I just do what I'm told best as I'm able. I follow orders. One step at a time's enough for me. Right now my orders is to stay put. So I'm staying. I'm heating a pan. When the fat's melted, if I live till then, I'll cook some bacon. If I live till it's fried I'll eat the bacon. Right now I'm living each melt of the fat in my pan. I'm savouring the melt of the fat. I'm breathing each breath like the precious thing it is.

Hancock Knew a man that cooked. Orderly. Used to be a butler. Mid-battle this was. Cold Harbor maybe. They merge. They all merge. Ask me Grant's a butcher. Bring back McLellan, he didn't waste men's lives. Had the pack shot off me at Bull Run. Shell took the pack right off my back. Not a scratch on me. Not a scratch. Miracle, they called it. I don't know, though. See my hands. See them shaking. My hands think I've had my miracle. I've run out of miracles. Anyway this orderly, my friend the butler. Brass come in for lunch. He has chicken cooked, this orderly, this butler. Old chickens but chickens all the same. Don't know where he got them. He has potatoes cooked. And bread he has. All ready and laid out it is beneath the trees. Hot and savoury as a man could want. Battle makes you hungry. Never understood that. Men dying all around you.

They can be friends, even. You get hungry. All sorts of hungry. What do you think that is? What do you think?

Stewart I don't get hungry.

Hancock Hungry, thirsty.

Stewart I get thirsty.

Hancock Bound to get thirsty.

Stewart Talking about chickens.

Hancock Brass sits down as well as they can. Aren't enough chairs so they sit on the grass, some of them. Barrage starts up just as he's passing the butter, my friend the orderly. For the new-baked bread. Shell near cuts him in half, butter in his hand. You'd think a man would die fast cut in two like that. He has time to look around him. See the state he's in.

Stewart Could put you off butter.

Hancock One way or another it fucked up dinner.

Stewart They eat the meal?

Hancock Would you?

Stewart Man spent his last hours cooking it.

Hancock That's so.

Stewart I'd eat it.

Hancock Man's cut in half, though. Not too pretty.

Stewart Could bury him.

Hancock Dinner would be cold an' you did that.

Stewart What'd they do?

Hancock Nice question. Nice question.

Stewart So?

Hancock They left him there. They ate. And they savoured every last mouthful. In his honour. He was nice and fresh and dead, see. You don't get that smell, not when they're fresh. Buried him after. Proper bacon you got there. Good and proper. Look like you know what you're doing.

Stewart 'You've all got hands to cook and clean with,' my ma says. 'You get on with it. And while you're

about it you can cook and clean for me,' she says. 'I'm
going to read a book, that's what I'm going to do,
while I've got eyes to see with. I'm going to read a
book in the sun.' Read a book, then another and
another. Came to Mrs Beecher Stowe's work that the
voice of God Himself gave to her, if you can believe
that. Read *Uncle Tom's Cabin*, became an abolitionist.
That woman is a political woman. 'All men are created
equal.' 'All men,' she says. Then that stuck in her craw.
No mention of womankind, see.

Hancock This quiet, man. Makes you hear things. Voices
you hear. Like home.

Stewart I loved my ma's cooking. The soups she made,
the tarts she made. Gooseberry fool. Elderberry she
put in it. Said it was part of the great plan that
elderberries came out when the gooseberries did to
keep them company in a fool. Like sweet cicely and
rhubarb. Almost made her believe in God again.

Hancock Men dying, you hear them. Call for their
mothers, all the dying men. I can't abide quiet. Makes
you soft. You get soft you don't last till the next sunset.
(*He holds out his hand, tries to stop it shaking.*) Don't
know where I am. What part of the year I'm in. When
the sun last shone on me. What day it is. The big tree
back home. I don't know if it's flowering. See this quiet.

Beat.

I'm remembering July Fourth. You remember? We gave
them something to think about July Fourth. Man, that
was truly something. That was truly something. Nice
boots.

Stewart Lucky to have them.

Hancock Boots, bacon an' all. You're a very lucky man.

Stewart Must've spit in a moon-filled puddle.

Hancock You planning on cooking all that bacon?
Cutting it down and cooking it?

Stewart Thought I would.

Hancock All of it?

Stewart Why not?

Hancock Can't eat all that yourself, can you?

Stewart 'Feast all you can. Feast when you can,' my ma says. 'You got plenty, you eat plenty. Indulge now and then in excess,' my ma says, 'so you know what it is. You could be dead tomorrow.'

Hancock Touch wood when you say that. Throw salt over your shoulder.

Stewart Leave that to you, will I?

Hancock spits.

Hancock Feast, you say?

Stewart I do.

Hancock Man could get melancholy if he feasted alone.

Stewart Could he?

Hancock Mind if I hang around?

Stewart I do not.

Hancock Well . . .

Stewart You care for flat bread?

Hancock I am salivating.

Hancock pokes at the piece of bacon.

Where'd you come upon this?

Stewart Got left it, see, so's to speak.

Hancock Like in a fella's last will and testament?

Stewart That's the way of it.

Hancock That a bullet hole?

Stewart Quit fingering my bacon.

Hancock Bullet hole goes right the way through.

Stewart Quit mauling it.

Hancock Could say I'm tenderising it.

Stewart Tender enough, I'd say.

Hancock Pan hot, is it? Stones hot?

Stewart Bit to go yet. Bit to go.

Hancock takes a flask from inside his tunic.

Hancock While we're waiting.

He offers Stewart the flask.

Stewart Hear the Rebs put meat in their brew, give it body. Meat 'mongst other things.

Hancock Don't know what's in this. Don't care. Makes the quiet more bearable, that's all.

Stewart That fire heats up some. That pan heats up. You won't have quiet any more – you'll have the sizzle of meat cooking to fill your quiet. The smell of home you'll have. And the smell of home.

Still hot in the yard.

Loren There.

She stamps.

You hear it. You hear it now?

Maureen They're going to say we stole it. Mrs Tyler will.

Loren We're not taking it for us.

Maureen They'll say we stole it anyway.

Loren Why should she have food?

Maureen I'm saying what they'll say is all.

Loren I'm doing this. Alone if I have to. I won't see my brother die and not lift a hand.

Beat.

Maureen I'll dig if you want.

Loren Won't take much digging.

Maureen I will if you want.

Loren You see no one comes.

Maureen I can dig as well as you can.

Loren You can tell me if someone's coming, that's what you can do for me.

Loren digs with her hands.

Maureen Could feed him rat.

Beat.

My mother puts pepper on them. Pepper a rat enough and it tastes like chicken, my mother says.

Loren She stop crying long enough to cook, does she?

Maureen You are plain nasty sometimes, you know that, Loren Maeve? There is no other word for the way you talk to me.

Beat.

Loren I'm sorry.

Maureen That's just a word.

Beat.

Loren You really think it tastes like chicken, rat?

Maureen Been a while. Been a while since I ate chicken, me. Course my mother won't catch the rats. And my brother won't.

Loren stares at Maureen.

What?

Beat.

What?

Loren What'll she do when the pepper runs out?

Maureen I'm not going to think about that.

Loren I'm never eating rat meat. Never.

Maureen Young rat, maybe that's like chicken. Old rats though. Old rats, they need molasses on them.

Loren I near can smell the bacon down there.

Maureen You steep an old rat in molasses. Molasses and . . . something . . . old rat needs steeping in

molasses and . . . something, I forget . . . to make it
tender.

Loren You got molasses?

Maureen No.

Loren They eat the dead bodies, the rats.

Maureen When I'm hungry I just close my eyes and I eat
anything mostly. Guess a hungry rat feels just the same
way.

Loren You eat rats, you're eating soldiers. Maybe even
Confederate soldiers. Maybe even someone you know,
you're eating, if you eat rats.

Maureen I'm always hungry.

There's a trapdoor laid bare by Loren's scrabbling.

Loren See, now this should just open up.

She heaves but the door doesn't budge.

Maureen Someone's shut that hard.

Loren You could help me.

They heave together. Nothing happens.

Maureen What we need is a lever.

She works a long stick under the gap in the trap door.

Maureen A woman's ingenuity is a gift from the
Almighty, my mother says.

Loren Whatever I find down there, I'm taking.

She heaves on the stick. It breaks.

Maureen You hurt?

Loren Split my palms is all. No calluses on my hands.
A good hand has calluses on. We need something
stronger than a stick.

She searches in the grass for another tool.

Maureen The biggest enemy of a soldier is his bowels,

and his feet, and his lungs. You hear their lungs. In the
morning when their drums roll to wake them up you
hear the whole army cough. Thousands of men
coughing all at once – coughing so hard you can't hear
the drums anymore. Can you tell a Confederate cough
from a Yankee cough? I can't. That's the strangest
thing. We think different, we talk different, we smell
different. Wouldn't you think we'd cough different?
Measles have killed more men than ever the guns have.

Loren Where do you get it from?

Maureen I listen.

Loren You never stop talking, where d'you get time to
listen?

Maureen I'm just going to ignore that, Loren Maeve. I'm
going to ignore your insult to me and put it down to a
cruelty born of your concern over your dying little
brother.

Loren Don't say he's dying.

Maureen Need to call a thing by it's name, that's what
you said.

Loren Don't you say it.

Beat.

Maureen More men have died of dysentery and scarlet
fever and mumps and the typhus than ever died of
bullet wounds. There's a band from a barrel there.
In the grass there. You wrap your hands in something
case the rust gets in that cut. You get rust in an open
wound you'll get the lockjaw.

Loren I need your weight here.

Maureen There are prettier ways to die than with the
lockjaw.

*Loren tears the hem of her petticoat into a strip. Wraps
it round her hands. Maureen swings on the metal.*

I'm half the girl I was, now September's come. I'm half

the girl I was on the fifteenth of June when these people started besieging us, my mother says. I'll be half again by the time they go. Then no man will ever want me. A man wants flesh on the bones he holds in his arms. Man sees me half the weight I am now, he'll think I've got the galloping consumption and he'll never marry me.

Loren's finished wrapping her hands. The two girls swing down hard on the metal spar.

Loren I don't want to marry. Marriage brings children. Children bring trouble.

The trap door swings up. The girls fall.

You alright?
Maureen I've got a bruise. I've bruised my butt.
Loren It's dark down there.
Maureen I'm scared of the dark.
Loren I am so sick of the sound of that word.
Maureen 'Scared'?
Loren Maybe if you didn't say it so often you wouldn't feel it so much.

She lowers herself into the hole.

Maureen It's not so bad for you. See, I'm a sinner. I'm already a sinner. Sinners can't go in dark places. One of them might just be the doorway to Hell and a sinner doesn't even need a key to that door. It just flings itself wide open for him and swallows him in.
Loren You're not a sinner.
Maureen I am.
Loren You are not.
Maureen I am no longer lilywhite in the face of the Lord.
Loren I'm going down there and get Mrs Tyler's bacon that was cured from her prize hog. That animal had as sweet a disposition as you could wish.

Maureen I am no longer lilywhite.

Loren A sweet-tempered hog makes the best bacon, I just bet you he does.

Maureen Don't you want to know why?

Beat.

Jem Matthenson put his hand on me.

Beat.

I said he put his hand on me.

Loren I heard you.

Maureen His father died at Cold Harbor.

Loren Doesn't mean he can put his hand on you.

Maureen Think I'll go to Hell?

Loren's down below. Maureen lies over the hole in the ground calling down to her.

His father was embalmed, you know? They put fluid in his veins instead of the blood and sent him home looking like he was alive. That's what Jem Matthenson said. They made Jem kiss his father's dead flesh though he'd died more 'n three weeks before. So I let Jem Matthenson put his hand on me when he asked. It was the least I could do. An' I let Jem kiss me too. 'Tisn't right that a boy should have the taste of dead flesh on his lips so I gave him a living kiss to take the taste away.

Loren You'll go to Heaven for it. The Almighty will give you wings.

Maureen You find the bacon?

Loren No.

Beat.

Maureen You find it yet?

Loren There's nothing here, practically.

Maureen Why'd you ever think there would be? My belt's pulled in three notches from where it used to be.

Loren Somebody's taken it.
Maureen What're you talking about?
Loren The bacon. Somebody's stolen it maybe.

A small sack's chucked out of the hole.

Maureen Think it's flour?
Loren Open it and tell me.

Maureen unties the sack.

Maureen It's crawling, Loren.
Loren I don't care about that.
Maureen You can't use it crawling.
Loren Pick them out, the crawlers.
Maureen Look like maggots to me.
Loren Pick 'em out, anyway.
Maureen You pick 'em.

Loren heaves herself out of the hole.

Loren Look what else.
Maureen Lord, Loren, that's honey.
Loren What can I do? What am I going to do? I needed that bacon for my little brother, to save him. I needed it.
Maureen You got honey. Honey's good for a person. We could make a cake. All we need's eggs and some fat.
Loren There isn't a chicken left or a duck on a pond to get eggs from.
Maureen Pie crust. We could make pie crust. And I know where there's blueberries.
Loren Blueberries?
Maureen Big fat ones. Down by the river, they are. You know? Where it pools deep and the big willow is. Jem Matthenson told me. Said he'd take me.
Loren I don't know.
Maureen Better than nothing, Loren. Come on.

She walks away. Loren bangs the trapdoor shut.

You bring that flour now.

Loren grabs the sack, runs after Maureen.

Loren Where'd he put his hand? What part of your anatomy?

Maureen Who?

Loren How many have you let touch you?

Maureen Loren Maeve, what are you accusing me of?

Loren Jem Matthenson you told me.

Maureen It was a sweet moment, Loren Maeve, and I'm not going to indulge in the kind of gossip that will sour it's memory. For gossip is a pleasure of the moment only, memory lasts for ever.

Beat.

Promise you won't tell.

Loren I won't tell.

Maureen Promise, or I won't show you where the blueberries are.

There are sudden tears running down Loren's face.

What're you blubbing for?

Loren Ma Tyler ate a whole hog to herself. She could've left one bit. One little bit.

Maureen Keep walking, Loren Maeve.

Loren It's going on for ever. All . . . this.

Beat.

Feel the quiet.

Maureen wipes the tears away with the hem of her dress.

Maureen Don't you give in to despair.

Beat.

Say, I promise not to tell about Jem Matthenson.

Loren I promise.

Maureen Say,' If I break my word may the Devil take me and roast me on the fiery spits of Hell.'

Loren May he roast me.

Maureen On my buttocks he touched me, then. And on my chest. My left chest. Here. And I don't care a bit that he did. It was a good bit of my life. I treasure the good bits.

In the dappled light under the willows by the pond there's a figure. Seems like a young boy. A Northern soldier, far too young to be in uniform. The figure bends down, lifts water in its hands. Holds it there for a moment. Splashes it into the air so that drops sparkle in the sunlight. There's grace in the movement. The soldier unbuttons a faded blue shirt. There's a glimpse of lace beneath.

The fire flares in the dugout.

Hancock You ever made love to a woman?

Stewart These stones hot enough for dough?

Hancock I'm asking you a question, man.

Stewart Course, I'm in love with womankind. If my ma taught me anything she taught me that. To love womankind every last one of them. To hold them in reverence and awe on the one hand and on the other to treat them as wantons.

Beat.

Hancock Ever made love to a woman?

Stewart To a girl I made love.

Hancock Can't have been a good girl.

Stewart Good enough not to want me to die and never have known what it was to make love.

Hancock When'd you last see her?
Stewart I see her all the time.
Hancock In the flesh, man. Not in your mind's eye.

Beat.

I'm going to tell you something about your precious
  womankind. Once you awaken that appetite in them.
  'Appetite', you know what I mean? Once that appetite
  is awakened, it becomes a fever that has to be sated.
  Your wanton that you so reverence will be off with
  any man who so much as looks at her. You given her
  an itch, man. She just got to scratch it.

Stewart leaps up and grabs Hancock.

Stewart Take that back.
Hancock I'm telling you, man.
Stewart Take it back.
Hancock I'm telling you for your own good.
Stewart You'll feel my knife in your throat.
Hancock For your own good, man.
Stewart Now you take back your words.
Hancock I'm telling you the truth.

*Stewart throws him down on the ground, sits astride
  him, forces dirt into his mouth. Hancock chokes.*

Stewart You swallow then. Swallow the . . . Swallow it.
  Choke on it.

Hancock's gagging.

*Stewart drags Hancock to a sitting position. Hancock
  spits. Wipes the dirt from his mouth. Watches Stewart.
  His voice is hoarse when he speaks.*

Hancock Need something to keep you alive, I guess. We
  all do.
Stewart I'll take that for an apology.

Beat. Hancock nods.

Stones are hot enough for bread. Put some water in that
    flour. Some bacon fat. Nice and clear, see.
Hancock Nothing like a girl to keep you alive.
Stewart Work it to a dough why don't you?

*In the dappled light under the willow by the pool, a girl
wearing a lace-trimmed chemise walks into the water. She
ducks under. Comes up into the light shaking the wet
from her hair, shorn as if from a recent fever.*

    *Loren and Maureen come out from under the shadow
of the willows.*

Loren Got enough now, d'you think?
Maureen What d'you think?
Loren You're the cook.

    She's carrying a straw hat full of blueberries.

Maureen?

    *Maureen's picking through the clothes lying beside the
water.*

They soldier's clothes?

    Beat.

Maureen We got a Fed here.
Loren Where is he?
Maureen He finds us, he's going to kill us.
Loren He's got no clothes on, Maureen. He won't kill
    us – not without his clothes on.
Maureen The good Lord knows what worse he might do
    to us.
Loren Not without his clothes.

Maureen What difference does that make?

Loren There's no dignity in it.

Maureen Dignity? Feds, Loren. They don't know the meaning of the word. What's that?

Loren Splashing, see.

Maureen Where?

Loren Someone in the water, Maureen.

Maureen God save me.

Loren Someone swimming is all.

Maureen Light's in my eyes.

Loren Ducked under now.

Maureen Is it him? Is it? Loren?

Loren There. There. See.

Hosgood walks slowly through the willows, stands watching a Southern soldier, Rowatt, who sits with his back against a tree whittling at a stick with a knife. Crutches lie at his side. There's a flash of sunlight. He looks up. So does Hosgood. Diamonds of sparkling water are caught in the air just for a moment as the girl splashes in the water.

Hosgood Nothing like beauty, is there?

Beat. Rowatt turns. Their eyes catch and hold, summing each other up. Then Rowatt turns back to the view.

Rowatt That's a – what d'you call it – a chemise she has on there. (*He drags the word out.*) Che – mise. Now. I have seen my mother in a chemise. And my sister I have seen in a chemise many, many times. Course that's not my sister swimming there. Different thing, a chemise, when it's not your sister wearing it.

Hosgood Think she knows we're here?

Rowatt I don't think she'd be so free. You going to shoot me?

Hosgood If I was?

Rowatt I'd say my prayers.

Hosgood No gun, see. You?

Rowatt Wouldn't like to spoil a quiet day.

Hosgood Sharp knife you got there.

Rowatt For use on sticks only. I leave knife-work to butchers.

Beat.

Hosgood Where'd you get yours?

Rowatt grins at him. Just pats his injured leg.

I mean the battle you got hurt in, that's what I'm enquiring about.

Rowatt Gettysburg.

Hosgood Where were you?

Rowatt Peach Orchard. You?

Hosgood Little Round Top. Healing alright, is it?

Rowatt Doing nicely. Thank you kindly for enquiring.

Hosgood How'd you get here?

Rowatt My daddy brought me home. Where might your home be?

Hosgood Far away. Too far.

Beat.

Bad luck you coming back here to this.

Rowatt Focuses the mind, certainly.

Hosgood The wind blows where I come from. Tang of salt in the air. Mind if I . . .

Rowatt You alright?

Hosgood sits down next to Rowatt.

Hosgood General Grant whittles like you. Chips away at a piece of wood till there's nothing left of it. Doesn't make anything. That water's good and clear.

Rowatt Swim if you like, feel free.

Hosgood Might disturb her. Wouldn't want to do that.

Rowatt Is that blood?

Hosgood No.

Rowatt Looks like it to me.

Hosgood Had a piece of bacon.

Rowatt You a Devil come to tempt me?

Hosgood Held it against me. Stain is all.

Rowatt If you say so.

Hosgood Gave the bacon away, of course.

Rowatt Why would you do that?

Hosgood Met a man whose need was greater.

Rowatt Can't remember when I last saw bacon.

Hosgood Good bacon.

Rowatt You tell me where it is, maybe I'll take my knife and go get me a piece of it.

Hosgood Not worth losing your life over.

Rowatt I go much longer without any, I might argue that point. I might argue my life will be lost from hunger anyway. Right now my stomach's telling me that my throat must be cut.

Hosgood You got blueberries, though.

Rowatt Help yourself.

Hosgood Maybe I will at that.

Rowatt Fine blueberries. Fine. I am here to tell you, however, that man cannot live by blueberries alone.

A bird cries.
  Water ripples.
  Light sparkles.
  Hosgood and Rowatt watch the girl swim.

Hosgood Wouldn't be so bad, would it?

  Beat.

Dying, I mean. Wouldn't be so bad if Heaven was like this.

Rowatt There's a hotel in Washington DC, my daddy
told me. Tobacco spit's thick on the carpet. Senators
stay there. Congressmen. Carpet's damp with spit. My
daddy never held with the chewing of tobacco. My
daddy is a fastidious man. Said to me that for him
from then on that foyer was the entrance to Hell. And
though you might linger in that foyer for all eternity
you would never get to Heaven through it.

Hosgood Hell's no hotel foyer. Not as far as I'm concerned.
When we mined under you. When we blew your lines
of defence sky high. When we sent our troops into the
crater. When you shot them. When you massacred
them. My brother was down there. That was Hell.

Rowatt I'm sorry for your brother.

Hosgood Lot of good men.

Rowatt I could tend to that wound for you.

Hosgood I'm watching, I tell you.

Rowatt Sniper's bullet, was it?

Hosgood You know something about snipers?

Rowatt Man has a choice he wouldn't be a sniper.

Hosgood Injured man has no choice, that what you're
telling me?

Beat.

Rowatt I could try at least to take care of it.

Hosgood Finish the job?

Rowatt Make you more comfortable.

Hosgood Quiet while I'm watching.

*Loren's picking from a laden bush, putting some in the
straw hat, stuffing some in her mouth.*

Maureen Don't you gorge, Loren Maeve. Don't you
gorge on these, they'll go straight through you.

Loren Never seen so many.

Maureen Don't say I didn't warn you. She's got short hair.

Loren See these, Maureen.

Maureen Look at her with her short hair.

Loren Spoonfuls of honey and blueberries. That'll build his strength, won't it? Spoonfuls of honey will. And pie.

Maureen Loren, pay attention.

Loren Maybe she had the fever and they cut off her hair.

On the river bank.

Hosgood You don't look like a fighting man.

Rowatt Come in all sorts these days, fighting men.

Hosgood I grant you that.

Rowatt Right you are, though. A life of quiet and gentle contemplation of the beauties this earth has to offer is what I would choose if I had a choice, but you have brought trouble to my doorstep.

Hosgood You made the trouble.

Rowatt You're in my land. I am not in yours.

Hosgood That the only reason you fight?

Rowatt See. The way I see it. Leaving aside the question of all men being created equal for those better qualified than I am to argue, there's no viability to slavery in the South. It's run out of it's viability. A man works to better his life, his and his family's. Else why would he work? Slave's life doesn't get any better, no matter how hard he works. So he does as little as possible, eats as much as he can. Same as you or me would do in his position. He's not stupid, your slave. Low output, high maintenance. Doesn't make sense.

So I'm not fighting for slavery – to keep slavery in the South – I'm not fighting for that. You dictate to us though. Righteously. Then you come here. You don't just fight. You burn and you steal. Unarmed women and children, you pull their homes down round them. And I don't see by what right you do that and so . . .

Hosgood You fight?

Rowatt Need every man we've got.

Hosgood Still fight, hurt like you are.

Rowatt I don't use my legs to shoot with.

Hosgood Good shot, are you?

Rowatt Hunter has to be a good shot 'less he likes to see suffering.

Hosgood You hunt?

Rowatt Been known to.

Hosgood Though I am your enemy . . .

Rowatt I would relieve your suffering. If you were armed in front of me threatening me and mine I would shoot you.

Hosgood knows he's talking to the sniper. Nods his head.

Hosgood She's coming out the water. See. Walking out the water.

Maureen fans herself in the shade.

Maureen You ever get an intuition?

Loren Don't feel the need.

Maureen You never had one?

Loren Intuitions make a person give up.

Maureen I'm having one now, Loren.

Loren We need to go make a pie.

Maureen I got something to say to you.

Loren I need to get home. Right now I need to.

Maureen You see her?

Loren That chemise is practically transparent.

Maureen There she is with her short hair. There is this bundle of soldier's clothes and no soldier.

Loren Don't stare at her like that.

Maureen She can't see me.

Maureen lifts the clothes and hides them in the middle of a bush. Loren watches.

Loren I need to get these home.

Maureen I am going to put something to you.

Loren My brother, Maureen. My brother.

Maureen You go, then. Go on. Go.

Loren Aren't you coming?

Maureen There is a girl with short hair. Here is a bundle of clothes here in the middle of this bush. Suppose the two belonged together.

Loren She's a girl, Maureen.

Maureen I know that.

Loren Those are men's clothes.

Maureen Get down, Loren. Get in here 'fore she sees you.

Maureen grabs Loren. The blueberries spill.

Loren They've gone all over the place.

She gathers them up.

Maureen There's plenty left.

Loren I don't want them dirty.

Maureen Get down, Loren.

She grabs Loren's arm and pulls her down.

Loren You're hurting me.

Maureen You watch. Watch her. Watch her now. What she does.

The girl from the water walks to the place on the bank where the uniform had been.

Maureen Lookin' for her clothes, see.
Loren So what then? So what?
Maureen Jem Matthenson said there were women fighting for the Yankees. Disguising themselves as men.
Loren I'm sick of Jem Matthenson.
Maureen I'm talking about women soldiers marching and shooting and fighting like men.
Loren Take a brave woman.
Maureen She's a Yankee.
Loren Doesn't mean she isn't brave.
Maureen See. See.

The girl from the pool sits at the water's edge, shivers, wraps her arms round herself, bows her head.

Rowatt gets to his feet.

Rowatt You going to let me see that wound?
Hosgood She's cold, see.
Rowatt You let me see that wound.
Hosgood You a doctor all of a sudden?
Rowatt Sun'll warm her.
Hosgood She needs help.
Rowatt Your brother died, right?
Hosgood Men left in the crater injured, they didn't make a good death.
Rowatt You got any more brothers?
Hosgood No.
Rowatt Sisters even?
Hosgood I have no siblings.
Rowatt Think of your mother and let me help you.

Beat.

Hosgood Thing I despise most is a sniper.

Beat.

Rowatt Thing I despise most is a fool.

Hosgood gets to his feet. It hurts him to do it.

The fire flares.

Stewart It is a fact that a man with a wound on the losing side in a battle, he dies. Man with the same wound on the winning side lives. Older man with a wound lives, boy with the same wound dies. In the first place the winning side has hope. Hope gives life. In the second place man's been through a lot, knows you can live through pain, so he does, he lives. Boy doesn't know enough to live through pain so he dies.

Hancock Man with a dream lives too, that your point?

Stewart What keeps you alive, Hancock?

Hancock Mealtimes. I look forward to them. You know?

Stewart It's coming. You pass that drink now.

Hancock I don't want to halt any progress towards this feast.

Stewart This stuff's too weak to halt anything.

Hancock I'm not forcing you to partake.

Stewart No offence meant.

Hancock passes his flask.

Maureen whispers, crouched low.

Maureen If she's a soldier, right, we might just kill her.
One less of them to worry about.

Loren I don't know how to kill anybody.

Maureen You must be the only one for miles around here
that doesn't.

Loren She's not that much older than us, Maureen.

Maureen What's age got to do with it?

Loren No.

Maureen Don't you want to do something for the Cause?

Beat.

You and me, we're in this just like everyone else. We've
got to do our bit. That's what's expected.

Loren No one knows we're out here.

Maureen We know.

Loren We haven't got a gun.

Maureen I've got string.

Loren You can't kill someone with a piece of string.

Maureen I never come out without string. It's good and
strong, my string.

Loren What d'you use it for?

Maureen Rats. You don't think they walk into the
cooking pot do you? Leap up onto the stove and beg
to be cooked? Well they don't, Loren Maeve. You have
to work to catch your rat and you never know where
you might come upon a fruitful spot. If you'd caught
rats, your brother might not be failing now.

Loren Are you going to choke her?

Beat.

She's lying down now in the sunlight. She's drying off in
the sunlight. You can't kill someone like that. Lying in
their chemise in the sun.

Maureen We got to.

45

Loren No.

Maureen For the Cause.

Loren I don't know what the Cause is. I never have.

Maureen Course you do.

Loren I don't.

Maureen We have the right to keep slaves that no one can ever take from us.

Loren We've never owned slaves. Neither have you.

Maureen Doesn't mean we shouldn't have the right. No one can tell me what to do. They take one right away from us what other rights they going to deprive us of? They take our human property away from us, what other property they going to take from us? They going to take the dresses off our backs just because they think they're stronger than we are? Stand there and order us to strip ourselves in the street?

Loren We're talking about depriving a person of life, of breath itself.

Maureen A Yankee. I do not know why you are so reluctant.

Loren She's a girl in a chemise, she's not a soldier.

Maureen I say she is. Those are soldier's clothes we put in the bushes there, or am I having a sainted vision?

Loren They're soldier's clothes.

Maureen Does she or does she not have short hair?

Loren Yes, but we said . . .

The girl by the water starts to cough, rolls over on her side.

There. There. See. Fever. Fever passed, but fever all the same.

Maureen A soldier can't have fever, then?

Loren I just want to save my baby brother's life.

Maureen I will never be your friend again if you don't do this.

Loren Alright.

46

Maureen What?
Loren Don't be my friend. I can get along without you.
Maureen I always thought you were the bold one. Of the two of us. It was you was bold.

Beat.

I will tell the whole town about you. I will tell them you're a traitor.

Beat.

Loren? With you or without you, Loren?

Willow branches blow in the breeze. Shadows and sunlight. Maureen creeps up on the girl in the chemise, dozing by the pool. Gets the string round her neck and pulls. The girl fights, scratches, spits and chokes. Maureen holds on. The girl's stronger than she is.

Maureen Loren. I need you. Loren Maeve. You get over here now.

The girl starts to get the better of Maureen. Loren jumps on her back.

You haul on that string. You haul on it now.

Maureen and Loren fight the girl. They are trying to kill her. And the girl begins to fail.

Hosgood blunders through the undergrowth. Rowatt's behind on his crutches. Hosgood hauls Loren off the girl's back. It's not easy for him. Rowatt hits Maureen with his crutch. She passes out.

Loren What have you done? You've killed her.

The Southern soldier tends to the girl in the chemise.

Loren She's a soldier.
Rowatt She's just a girl.

Loren She's still a soldier.
Rowatt I don't kill women.
Loren You're a traitor.

*Hosgood can't hold Loren any more. She rushes to
Maureen's side.*

Rowatt Loren Maeve, isn't it?
Loren She's hardly breathing.
Rowatt Your mother know you're out here?
Loren (*to Hosgood*) What're you lookin' at? (*to Rowatt*)
Tell your Yankee friend to take his eyes off of me.

Hosgood sinks down.

Loren What's wrong with him?
Rowatt (*to the girl*) You alright?
Bridh I reckon.
Rowatt What's your name?
Bridh Bridh.
Rowatt Irish?
Bridh What's that to you? Get off me.

Beat.

Get your filthy stinking hands off me.
Rowatt I saved your life.
Bridh Am I supposed to say thank you?
Rowatt Might ease the path.
Bridh Why would I want to do that?
Rowatt You have me there.
Bridh You want to look to your friend over there. I can
take care of myself. Been doin' it long enough.
Rowatt Pardon me.

He stands and bows to her.

Bridh Very graceful.
Loren Are you a soldier?
Bridh You move away from me.

Loren You'll run away if I do.

Bridh I want room to breath is all.

Loren Maureen says you're a soldier.

Bridh That Maureen?

Loren What of it?

Bridh Look where thinking got her.

Loren She says you're a soldier.

Bridh She says shite, then.

Loren Who's side are you on?

Bridh Who's on my side?

Loren Everyone's on a side.

Bridh Not me. Get some water for your hellfire friend there. Wet her forehead.

Loren Who are you, then?

Bridh That's a man with a bullet in him.

Rowatt He says not.

Bridh I've seen them deny it before now. Doesn't stop it killing them.

Loren You were wearing soldier's clothes.

Bridh Where are they?

Loren Wasn't my idea, killing you.

Bridh That makes me feel a whole lot better.

Loren If you're not a soldier . . .

Bridh I borrowed the clothes. The man I borrowed them from's asleep in my bed.

Beat.

Tell them.

Beat.

You.

Rowatt Beg pardon, ma'am.

Bridh 'Beg pardon, ma'am.' Name's Bridh. Him that calls me 'ma'am', he's mocking me.

Rowatt No offence.

Bridh Way I see it.

Loren Bridh?

Rowatt Beautiful name.

Loren Bridh what?

Bridh I don't think my mammy ever knew that. Or if she did, she didn't tell me.

Loren It's slaves don't have last names.

Bridh That's about placed me then. I'm a slave alright. A wage slave.

Loren What's that?

Bridh Means I have to eat. Means no one feeds me but me. Means I have to work how I can wherever I can or I don't eat. Means it isn't certain that I will eat. Means every day eating's all I think about.

Loren What's your work?

Bridh He knows. His lordship over there. He's the sort I work for.

Loren He's a Confederate.

Bridh He's a man.

Loren I don't understand.

Bridh I'm Irish. I'm a woman. The piece of stupidity this war is, think I'd take one side or the other? Whatever side survives, that's the side I'm on. I'm an independent.

Loren Is that why your hair's short?

Bridh It's long to how it used to be.

Loren Why'd you cut it?

Bridh I saw a fashion plate in a French magazine. Thought I'd be upsides with the French.

Loren Is that the truth you're telling me?

Bridh You calling me a liar?

Loren Did you have a fever?

Bridh I didn't.

Loren Why's it short, then, your hair?

Bridh Some folk don't like a soul to be too independent.

Beat.

Loren Somebody did that to you?

50

Bridh Take care they don't do it to you.
Loren Why would they?
Bridh You're consorting with the enemy now. They'll think you're a spy.
Loren For talking to you?
Bridh It's him I'm thinking of.
Loren He hasn't said anything.
Bridh You should go home.

Beat.

Give me my clothes and go home.
Loren What am I supposed to do with Maureen?
Bridh Carry her.
Loren She's quite heavy. She says I've got thick ankles, but she's the heavy one really.
Bridh Why don't you give me my clothes?

Loren goes to get the clothes from the brambles.

Loren Maureen might be angry with me.
Bridh You've got to be your own person. Much as you can be. Slaves, soldiers and whores, course they're not their own people.
Loren Is that what you are?
Bridh A slave like I told you.
Loren A whore?
Bridh Don't like that word.
Loren You said it first.
Bridh So I did.
Loren Are you, then?
Bridh Are you going to give me my clothes?

Loren passes them to her.

Loren My little brother's hungry. He might die he's so hungry. And when we give him things to eat, he can't hold them down. He has pains in his stomach. Like he's been shot he has pains.

Hosgood pulls himself up. Shivers.

Bridh Cold creeping up on you?

Hosgood Don't put them on.

Bridh This is my day off. My day off I do what I want. I don't do what any man tells me.

Loren You are a whore.

Bridh Not today. I'm bathed and I'm washed clean I'm a new woman today. Good as you are.

Hosgood You're beautiful.

Bridh Don't you look at me with those soft eyes.

Rowatt Group of women I heard of. They got this girl. She was earning her living. Women didn't like it. Tied her to a post and shaved off her hair.

Beat.

One thing I hate worse than I hate some men. Some women.

Beat.

You need to get that boy's jacket off. Cut that bullet out of him.

Hosgood No.

Bridh What's your name?

Hosgood Hosgood.

Bridh Kind of name's that?

Hosgood Family came from Devon, England, long time ago.

Bridh Family's going to die out if that bullet's left in you.

Loren He's got a pink froth on his lips.

Hosgood wipes his mouth.

Rowatt Bullet's in his lung.

Bridh I have a proposition for you, Hosgood. You want to hear it?

Hosgood Sure. Yes.

Bridh You let . . . what's your name?
Rowatt Rowatt.

She looks at Loren.

Loren I'm Loren, ma'am. Loren Maeve.
Bridh Rowatt and Loren Maeve here, they're going to
ease you out of that jacket of yours, then I'm going to
tell you my proposition.

Hosgood starts to laugh.

As well you can laugh.
Hosgood Better be a good one.
Bridh It's a good one. Do we have a deal?
Hosgood Haul away.

Maureen starts to come to. Bridh sits on her.

Bridh You carry on.

*Loren and Rowatt take the jacket off as gently as they
can.*

Maureen Get off me. Get off. Get off.
Bridh I've seen people die from a bump on the head.
Maureen You have not.
Bridh Moving around too much after, that's what they
die of.

Maureen spits at her.

Bridh Well, look at you. Big and brave, aren't you? Your
mammy taught you well.
Maureen Get up. Get off.
Bridh Lay him down.
Maureen (*struggling*) What're you doing? He's a Fed.
You can't help him.

*Bridh reaches out and grabs the string, twists it round
Maureen's ankles and wrists.*

53

Maureen Are you going to let her tie me up?

Rowatt Are you going to keep out of the way if she doesn't?

Maureen Take them prisoner, go on.

Rowatt Man on crutches, think I'd win, do you?

Maureen Loren'll help you.

Rowatt You stay right where you are, Loren.

Bridh You keep very still, Maureen. For the honour of the Confederacy.

Maureen I don't like your tone.

Bridh Well, you know just what you can do, don't you?

Beat.

Hosgood?

Hosgood I'm alright. You had a proposition for me.

Maureen tries to roll.

Bridh Loren, you come over here and keep this friend of yours away from us.

Maureen My wrists are getting cut so they are.

Hosgood What's your proposition if I let you cut this bullet out?

Maureen My circulation's stopped. I could get gangrene from this.

Bridh walks over. Crouches down by him. Smooths the hair away from his forehead. Rowatt's sharpening his knife on a stone.

Bridh You want to know what it is?

She's very gentle with him.

Hosgood Tell me.

Bridh You really want to know? Will you give us some room here, Rowatt. I'm going to give this man a reason to cling on to his life. I am going to put something to him and I want privacy to do it. In a minute I'll need you.

Rowatt moves away. Turns and watches Hosgood and Bridh.

Bridh whispers in Hosgood's ear. There's a silence broken only by the lapping of water, the distant cry of a bird and the pale quiet rustle of Bridh's whispering in the sunlight.

Stewart's sharpening his knife on a stone. The bacon sits proud and intact on another stone. The bread's cooking. Hancock's holding out his hand to the flames.

Hancock See the veins in that. See the blood flowing through the veins in that.

He takes his hand away.

Won't be quiet tomorrow. Can't ask for that. Be back to normal tomorrow.

Stewart saws the bacon into thick slices.

Hardly rashers these. More like chops.
Stewart Turn the bread over.
Hancock Least we'll die with our bellies full.

Spark of sunlight.

Bridh You accept my proposition?
Hosgood It is more than generous.
Bridh It's a once-in-a-lifetime. So I won't have you insulting me by turning it down.
Hosgood I would think the less of myself if I did any such thing, ma'am. Bridh.

She touches his shoulder. His cheek. He catches her hand, kisses it. Holds on to it.

Do what you have to. Whatever it takes.

Beat.

Bridh I've got the sun in my eyes.

Rowatt Take my hat.

Bridh You ready, Hosgood?

Hosgood First name's Edwin.

Bridh I like Hosgood better.

Hosgood I'm ready.

Bridh Wait. Wait, wait, wait. Wait. Where's my clothes? You take anything out the pocket of my clothes?

Maureen We're not thieves.

Bridh You bring my clothes to me.

Maureen Don't you.

Rowatt holds her in place with his foot. Loren runs to get the clothes.

Bridh Don't get all pricked by those thorns, will you?

Maureen What do you care?

Bridh I am so sick and tired of your mouth.

Loren What have you got?

Bridh There's a bottle in that pocket. Give it to Rowatt.

Loren hands Rowatt a medicine bottle.

You see, you get a customer from the medical tents. Sometimes. The medicine doesn't always go to the sick.

Loren What is that?

Bridh Might help him. I don't know. Worth a try. I seen men dreaming on this stuff.

Rowatt holds Hosgood's head. Lets him drink.

Nothing wrong with dreaming. Better than pain.

Bacon frying.

Stewart They ain't singing over there. I like it when they sing.

Hancock Think they're planning something?

Stewart Think we are?

Hancock Guess they'll tell us soon enough. Good smell. You can feel that smell right in the pores of you.

Stewart You hear them talking sometimes over there.
  Night air carries the sound. Yarns they spin.
Hancock I like a good story.
Stewart Can't ever remember them, I can't. I hear them
  and they're gone from my head.
Hancock Don't remember ever smelling better bacon
  than this.
Stewart I used to have a good memory.

  *Beat. Hancock stretches his hand out to the fire. It's
  shaking again. He closes his fist.*
    Loren's crouching by Maureen.

Maureen What're they doing now?
Loren Cutting into him.
Maureen I'm going to be sick.
Loren Don't look, then.

  Beat.

Maureen Are they not done yet?
Loren There's cloth from his shirt in where the bullet
  went.
Maureen He's going to die, isn't he?
Loren Maybe.
Maureen I don't care if he does.
Loren He talks different to us. He don't look any different.
Maureen Will you take this string off of me?
Loren I don't want him to die and Rowatt doesn't.
Maureen Take the string off. He ought to look different
  to us. That would be a whole lot easier.
Loren Why would it?
Maureen You know.
Loren I don't.
Maureen I want to hate him.
Loren I don't want to hate anyone.
Maureen Not even Becky Jennison?

Beat.

Loren I despise her and I will do all my life long.

Firelight.

Stewart I call this cooked now. It's cooked. Might as well eat.

Sunlight on the girls.

Maureen Would you touch a man like that?
Loren With a knife, you mean?
Maureen You are so stupid sometimes.
Loren She's cutting into his flesh with a knife.
Maureen She's touching him with her very heart.
Loren How is she?
Maureen Well, if you can't see that, Loren Maeve, you must be blind.
Loren Of course you know everything.
Maureen I know about touching. A little bit I know. Untie me.
Loren Say please.
Maureen I won't help you make the pie. So your brother will die after all.
Loren Why is 'please' so hard to say?

Beat.

Maureen I don't need you to sound like my mother.
Loren You're just plain stubborn, Maureen.

She starts to untie the string.

Maureen You know when I had this round her neck, her over there?
Loren What about it?
Maureen I did it because . . . that's what you're supposed to do, isn't it? Kill your enemies, I mean.
Loren You wouldn't have killed her really.

Maureen What if I had, though?

Beat.

See how gentle she is.
Loren She's done with the knife now.
Maureen We're friends still, aren't we?
Loren The way she's looking at him.
Maureen Loren?
Loren I suppose we'll always be friends.
Maureen Even if . . .
Loren What?
Maureen What'll happen to us when they win, Loren?

Beat. Rowatt picks up his crutch.

Rowatt I'm taking you two back.
Maureen Did you get the bullet out?

Beat.

Rowatt You pick up your blueberries.
Loren It was in too deep, wasn't it?
Rowatt What you got in that sack? Is that flour in that
  sack?
Loren And honey we've got.
Rowatt You're rich.
Loren How will they get back, the two of them?
Rowatt She'll find her way.
Loren And him, will he?
Rowatt Come on now. Come on.

*They go, leaving Bridh sitting with Hosgood's head
in her lap.*

Hosgood Afternoon's leaving us.
Bridh Well, it would.
Hosgood About that proposition.
Bridh What about it?
Hosgood I won't be taking you up on it, will I?

Bridh I want you to drink all of this you can.

Hosgood Marry me.

Bridh Just like that.

Hosgood It's a good offer.

Bridh What do I get out of it?

Hosgood You won't have to put up with any of my bad habits, I can promise you that.

Bridh I don't see a preacher.

Hosgood I see a cathedral of green, what do we need a preacher for?

Bridh What about a ring?

Hosgood Take that signet off my finger.

Bridh No, Hosgood.

Hosgood Take it off my finger.

Bridh They'd say I stole it.

Hosgood I'm cold.

Bridh I know.

Hosgood Take my ring.

She eases the ring off his finger. Slips it onto her wedding finger.

Bridh That what you want?

Hosgood You take that home for me. Will you?

Bridh Your home?

Hosgood A long way north from here.

Bridh It's too big for me.

Hosgood Wear it on a chain round your neck.

Bridh I don't have a chain.

Hosgood Find one. Take it home. They'll like to know you at home. They'll like to hear you were with me. They'll take care of you.

Beat.

I feel like I've known you all my life.

Bridh Here.

She pulls out a stem of grass. Twists it round his finger.

That makes it right. Now you're my husband.

He puts a hand up to touch her hair.

Hosgood I like your hair.
Bridh I'm glad someone does.
Hosgood By the time my folks see you, it'll be real fine.
Bridh A long way north then.
Hosgood Salt spray and a breeze always blowing.
Bridh Hold tight to my hand.

Beat.

Hosgood You could kiss me.
Bridh Now?
Hosgood I would be obliged.

She kisses him. A long kiss. Then she sits very still as the sun sets. Just sits there with his head cushioned in her lap.

Bridh Sweet dreams.

Firelight.

Stewart and Hancock wipe their plates with the flat bread.

Stewart See. Fat's solidifying.
Hancock No loss, then.
Stewart No loss.

Away from the river now. Loren, Maureen and Rowatt are walking back to the town. Loren stops.

Maureen I'm tired, Loren Maeve. Come on.
Loren You smell that?
Maureen Come on home, Loren Maeve. Right now.
Rowatt I can smell it.
Maureen It is not right to have secrets from me. It is not kind.
Rowatt Someone's cooking bacon.

Late afternoon sunlight shines on enemy lines. It hits Stewart and Hancock by the fire.

Maureen Yankees.
Loren They've stolen it. They've stolen it from my little brother.
Maureen Let's go get it, then, before they eat it all up.

Rowatt slides the wrapping off his crutch.

Rowatt You stay right where you are.

The crutch laid bare is a rifle. Rowatt raises it to his shoulder.

Loren I think they've finished the bacon. I think they've finished it anyway.

Maureen follows his eyeline.

Maureen Difficult shot.
Rowatt Long is all. Squeeze the trigger, that's what my daddy taught me. Don't pull it, squeeze. And what you have in your sights, human or animal, respect it enough to shoot it dead.

BROKEN HALLELUJAH

The two girls watch Rowatt. Stewart's in the sunlight.
  Rowatt shoots.
  A flash of light.
  Blackout.

The End.

The Pity of War

Sharman Macdonald interviewed by Jim Mulligan

It's not someone who's seen the light
It's a cold and it's a broken hallelujah.

So sings Leonard Cohen ('Hallelujah' on *Various Positions*, 1985), and in her play Sharman Macdonald takes up the theme of how friendships are formed and break apart because of the violence of war, and how some believe in the unbroken Hallelujah and others reject their God.

Broken Hallelujah is set in Petersburg during the American Civil War. In the lull between fighting, two scenes are acted out. There is the sordid dugout beyond the outer defences of a besieged town where Yankee soldiers cook some top-quality bacon they have acquired. Away from the dugout, the action moves from a yard in the town to the river, bringing together two girls who are also looking for bacon with Hosgood, the Confederate sniper Rowatt and a down-the-line prostitute.

> I started writing my play because I thought it behoves us to know something about modern America and they say modern America was forged in the Civil War. I don't think there is a parallel to that war anywhere else. The play cannot be presented as if it were not in that specific time and place, but I hope it transcends the specific. It has to work on its own terms, so if an audience thinks it's only about the American Civil War that's fine by me. If they care to think about Iraq, for example, then that's also fine. However, any production has to be faithful to the words on the page.

In the dugout Hosgood is nonchalant about snipers. 'Gone, see. No Southern trash planter slave-owning son-of-a-whoring-bitch sniper there. Gone.' Sadly, he speaks too soon. Before the first scene is over he has acted out of a mixture of bravado and boredom and put his head over the parapet to be shot by a sniper.

When we return to the trench the dynamics have changed. Hosgood has gone and Stewart is cooking the bacon watched by Hancock. The talk meanders along, touching on the changes in society, the loss of faith, the progress of the war, the emancipation of women, death and, above all, food.

There are clear parallels between the two soldiers and the two girls. Stewart has rejected God. Goodness doesn't mean anything to him. When a man's dead, he's dead. This Hancock counts as blasphemy. Loren, for her part, isn't the least scared of the Almighty. She does not see the Almighty making her sick brother better and she refuses to pray. Maureen, on the other hand, believes the rebel cause is sacred to God.

> I decided to choose a time in the siege when nothing is happening. It's boredom that leads soldiers into danger. It can lead to annihilation. It leads to two deaths in this play. The girls are thirteen and fourteen and the soldiers are not much older. That was the awful thing. They were so young. Some of the drummer boys were only twelve when they died.

There are many echoes of Leonard Cohen's song from the moment Bridh is seen swimming, with cropped hair and wearing a lace-trimmed chemise.

> *Your faith was strong but you needed proof,*
> *You saw her bathing on the roof.*

This is probably the first time the characters have come face to face with the enemy. There is confusion about whether prisoners should be taken or a temporary truce declared. The situation is complicated by two things: Hosgood is dying and Rowatt is the sniper who has shot him. Rowatt is rational and single-minded. He knows the war is not about the right to own slaves. There is no viability in slavery. He is fighting out of a sense of injustice. 'You dictate to us . . . You don't just fight. You burn and you steal . . . I don't see by what right you do that.' He is a contradiction in that he is prepared to help Hosgood as he is dying, yet he has no qualms at all about shooting another Yankee soldier.

> I love Rowatt. He's a strong man, the wisest in the play and the one who commits the greatest sin. I use that word in a non-religious context. He's a sniper. It's the only thing he can do and he knows it's a sin. He is a good man, and I am fascinated by how a good man can do an awful act, how he can be diverted from the path along the way. Rowatt is one of those – very intelligent and able to express himself beautifully, but a killer.

Rowatt is a killer, but he will not kill a woman even though Bridh is a Yankee and a prostitute. It is doubtful if Maureen and Lauren know what Bridh is doing there. They are inexperienced, although Maureen has ventured down the path with Jem Matthenson. She is no longer lilywhite. She has let Jem kiss her and touch her, but she has no regrets and no guilt. 'It was a sweet moment, Loren Maeve, and I'm not going to indulge in the kind of gossip that will sour its memory.' Perhaps it is this fleeting pleasure that makes her fear the war will end when there are only women left.

Hancock sees womankind as wantons. A woman has an appetite that has to be sated. Maybe. But the wanton in the play, Bridh, is very secure in her sexuality and self-belief. She knows that slaves, soldiers and whores are not their own people. But on this day she is bathed and washed clean, a new woman, as good as anyone, and she whispers a proposition to the dying Hosgood. Maureen can see that Bridh may be cutting Hosgood with a knife but she is also touching him with her very heart.

In a cathedral of green, without the blessing of a preacher and with a ring made of grass, Bridh pledges herself to Hosgood. She kisses him and sits there with his head cushioned on her lap. 'Sweet dreams,' she murmurs. She hears a shot. That is the pity of war.

Production Notes

The title derives from the Leonard Cohen song 'Hallelujah' and focuses in particular on the line, 'It's a cold and it's a broken hallelujah.'

Interested in the American Civil War, Sharman is also concerned with the more recent British alliance with the US, in particular the war in Iraq. Sharman took Petersburg for the landscape, and set the play at a point when war could have been stopped but wasn't. Being a Celt, she doesn't find writing English terribly easy, so most of her work is Welsh or Scots. She also loves the musicality of the Virginian tongue.

SOUND AND MUSIC

Use sound from which to create a palette. Find music that sets the right tone – though Civil War music (particularly the fiddle) can sound quite clichéd. There are places where music can help scene breaks or suggest passages of time. But don't over-use music, and avoid underscoring the whole play, since that's more of a cinematic approach.

Of the forty-seven available cover versions of the song 'Hallelujah', I suggest you listen to those by Leonard Cohen, k. d. lang and Jeff Buckley. k. d. lang's version – in fact the whole album *Hymns on the 49th Parallel* – captures a similar world to that of *Broken Hallelujah*. You could use the last stanza when Hosgood goes over the top. Joshua Bell and Edgar Meyer's album *Short Trip Home* is another option.

Listen to 'The Night Came On' from Leonard Cohen's album *Various Positions*. Music by Joan Baez and Bob Dylan relating to the Vietnam War could also be helpful.

Remember the two gunshots.

The birdsong could be sparrows, robins or crows. It should be a sweet sound evocative of Virginia.

No one knows what a rebel yell sounded like since it is unrecorded, so you'll have to make it up.

PRONUNCIATION

Lop off the endings when saying *-ing*.
Soften 't' midway through words.
'Neither' is pronounced *nyther*.
'Against' is pronounced *agenst*.
'The' is pronounced *thah*.

Working in dialect is challenging for actors. Emphasise the importance of clarity, and clarity of ideas. This play is particularly good for exploring North and South dialects, and a bit of Irish (Bridh). Dialect can activate character work, but it isn't essential. Take time to find the life of the characters. Ask the characters to write a letter to somebody, not necessarily someone in the play. Letters are useful when exploring the backstory of the characters.

THE BACKGROUND

Glory, *Cold Mountain* and *Gone With the Wind* are good movies to see to get a sense of dialect and a taste of the time (*Glory* depicts the story of Colonel Robert Shaw and the 54th Massachusetts, the first black regiment).

The Master, by Colm Toibin, who writes as if he were Henry James, is good from a female perspective.

Lots of Southern soldiers deserted (they didn't have leave) to return to their families. They were often shot as a result. • The Confederates and Yankee soldiers would have been aged between fifteen and nineteen. • The North was named by its rivers, the South by its villages.

Some four hundred women were scattered through the North and South as soldiers. Many of them went to war because they didn't want to leave their husbands or brothers, so accompanied them dressed as men.

The siege is both real and metaphorical: it is a siege of the heart, land, body, thoughts, in all the places in which they are trying to exist.

Establish what's specific about the day on which *Broken Hallelujah* happens.

The young people in this play have little control over what they do or say. Death could take them in a flash of sunlight. They are waiting for that call. The length of the siege emphasises the stasis. They are soldiers and citizens alike.

CHARACTERS

There are seven brilliant parts and their status differs remarkably. The decision about seeing STEWART's death will depend on your staging. Positioning will dictate a lot. Which character gets shot? Do you *want* to clarify that Stewart gets shot? It is a great shame that Stewart gets the bacon and then gets killed. Stewart is a survivor, noble and respectful of women (His mother has influenced his relationships with others.) He's too good to last?

HANCOCK is a wannabe. He wants his own ideas and talking points. He's had sexual experience, but no other kind. He puts his foot in his mouth and gets dirt back.

LOREN and MAUREEN can't get out of town. They overhear a lot. There is great importance in rumours and parental orders, demands and opinions. Maureen is just entering womanhood. Loren is still adolescent. Women changed their style of clothes, wore corsets and put their hair up once they reached puberty. Maureen is more socially conscious; she thinks of the future and wants to be seen as an adult.

BRIDH comes from an area of New York that a few years back was thrown into crime. The Irish were on both sides in the war – Bridh escaped street prostitution by going into the war. It's interesting that she should not have anyone in her life.

ROWATT is a well-bred Southerner. He brings charm and wants to help the girls. He has a measured countenance. Play his status.

HOT-SEATING

The actors at the Bath retreat were 'hot-seated'. Here are their answers to questions posed by the directors. Your actors will come up with variations; but make sure all the off-text responses asked of the actors in character are based on what they have either found in or deduced from the script.

HOSGOOD • Aged sixteen. • Has never been in love. • Has been in service for about a year. • Grew up in New York with his family. Brother went to war and he joined the same regiment. • His mother wasn't happy about him joining; father didn't have much to say. • Had a close relationship with his brother, so it was hard when he went to war. He was three years older. He has no other siblings. • He doesn't know where his brother is buried and is angry that he died.

It's boring in the trenches. He was once scavenging when he found a yard, tripped on a rock, found a hole and a piece of bacon in it, then ran away with it. • He used to have to work. He was a fishmonger, then took over his brother's job. They were based in the Lower East Side of New York; his family was not wealthy. • He didn't consider his mother's feelings; he had to see his brother, who was angry that he showed up. • Didn't have much schooling, just through his father.

It was a game to go over the lines. He didn't disguise himself. • Uniforms are difficult to distinguish.

He didn't want to believe he was shot. He was dazed afterwards and had a lazy adrenalin running through him. He needed to do things, but couldn't. It was freezing, but he was burning inside.

It would be interesting if Hosgood never got things right with his brother. Was his brother a friend or colleague of Stewart's?

The stasis of being quiet is intolerable. Stewart does the cooking; Hancock shakes and talks a lot. Hosgood can't do that. • There's an interesting moment of serendipity between Bridh and Hosgood. • Sharman visualised Hosgood's home as Maine; but New York does work.

MAUREEN • Aged fifteen. • Father is dead: God took him away. • Her favourite possession is a really nice peach – what? – dress? made by her mother. She has had it a long time, but it fits because she has shrunk a lot! • She gets what she wants – mostly.

Jem Matthenson is very special for her. He lives a few houses away. He isn't old enough to be in the war. • Loren lives next door. Their mothers are friends. She's thirteen, Maureen has known her since she was born. • Her ma is clever and taught her to draw, play the piano and gave her general knowledge.

She sometimes does chores. • She teaches Loren a lot. They're very close. • She once went to another town to buy pretty things, but it wasn't very far away.

She is going to get married, have three kids and a big house. • Ma doesn't know about Jem, she doesn't need to know. Maureen wasn't ladylike. • She has never fired a gun, but it would help in case she was in front of a Yankee. • She gets rats for mother and brother, and has learnt how to kill them herself. Had a shoelace and strangled one in the cellar. She shut her eyes to do it. • Mother peppers the rat – don't think about the taste.

Confederates are right, we should stand up for our rights and fight. • We should have the right to a slave. Her family doesn't, but she will when she is married.

STEWART • Doesn't have a surname, doesn't want to be associated with past life. • Left home because of his mother's choice, and wants to move on. • In the future, he wants to marry a nice girl, live in the countryside and be a farmer, somewhere quiet. • Doesn't know if he believed in God before, doesn't now.

His mother was religious; he was asked to believe but now he is in the war he can't see that God is doing anything for him. • It's hard to explain what he has seen: it is horrible. He has seen many friends come and go. • His mother shaped who he is. He went to war so they could have money, but it was her choice. She taught him independence and life lessons. • He has never stolen or profited from other people's suffering. Got the boots from a friend who shared similar experiences. He said Stewart could have them. He was still alive.

Has been stationed everywhere. He was in Petersburg, but not for long. • He was friendly with Hosgood's brother and took it upon himself to look after Hosgood after his brother died. • He wants to sustain his life until after the war. He wants to care for Hosgood, although he is sometimes annoying. Theirs is like a relationship between siblings. • He is fighting a war. At first he believed in a cause, now he just fights.

His mother said there was a prepayment from the army, so he felt there was a need to go – her need. (There are several situations similar to his, where the rich pay for the poor to go to war instead of their sons. The payment would have been about $300.) • His mother wouldn't say if she believed in the cause. She read *Uncle Tom's Cabin*.

He feels like a slave. Someone bought him. But he doesn't like slavery. • If someone asked his advice, he'd tell recruits to cope in their own way.

Stewart is nineteen or twenty. It was a four-year war, and this play is set near its end. • The fight scene is complex and must be carefully worked out: it needs to be scary.

JOHN HANCOCK is sixteen years old. He is losing track of many things, including his birthday. • Comes from a small town in California. • Joined up at the start of the war, and was a drummer boy at first. • Has been to Cold Harbor, Antietam. • Used to have a photo of his parents, but lost it. • To relieve the boredom, he talks, listens to people, looks for food.

Loves Stewart, although he has only known him since he got the bacon. • Joined up with friends from town, who are now all gone. • He needed to fight, and believes in stopping the South. His father wanted him to sign up. • He had a brother (who died) and a sister (who is still with their mother). • He had a basic education in reading and writing, but it wasn't very good. • Has one letter that keeps him going, from his mother.

He used to swing on a tree by the waterhole, his sister still plays there. That thought keeps him on track. After the war, he hopes to go home to the tree and to the sun.

Tries not to look at men's faces when he is about to kill them. He just aims and fires. There's so much confusion, he doesn't always know whether he has hit the man.

Had one girlfriend, but she decided to scratch around with someone else. Hasn't been with anyone since he joined. • He doesn't really sleep, as he fears something might happen to him. So he doesn't dream. But he thinks of his parents; they are precious memories. • The bacon tastes horrid: it's like eating string.

BRIDH • Seventeen years old. She doesn't have a last name: she was never given one. • She has been in America for four and a half years, and was from Northern Ireland originally. • She started here as a cleaner, then turned into a 'slave', working for men in various ways. • She travelled with the armies to Virginia. She can't stay in one place for very long. • Her hair was cut four months ago. A man's girlfriend found out about them and a group of women tied her to a post and cut her hair in revenge.

She is independent in this war, and doesn't take sides. • She tries not to create relationships with people – it's too hard. • Her only priority is to get food. • She would like to take time off when she can, sitting peacefully alone and relaxing.

Sometimes she is paid in money, sometimes food – depends what the men have. But it is agreed beforehand. • She took her uniform from a man she was with. He took her clothes – she doesn't know why!

She learnt to swim in Ireland. • Used to believe in God but her prayers weren't answered. • Thinks of her mother to keep her peaceful and safe – but not when she is working. • Would like to return to Ireland eventually.

She has seen healers, but isn't a healer; no professional medical history as such. • She hasn't been emotionally close to a man. • She would like to be attached to Hosgood but can't: he might die. She has to keep surviving. Wanting to survive keeps her going. There has to be something better.

She has met other girls who do the same job. • She used to go around camps to get business. Word would get round about her. It's more difficult now that her hair is short.

LOREN-MAEVE • Aged thirteen, from Petersburg. • Her home is quite small; she lives with her mother and brother. It's a small community. • Father is at war, she doesn't know where. He is alive.

Best friend is Maureen. They like similar things. They are like sisters. They fight, but always make up. She's changing and talks about things Loren doesn't care about, including the war. She can be annoying!

Loren cares about her brother. He's ill. They don't have much food. Their father would care for them when they were ill. She will do anything to make her brother well.

She doesn't fear the Yankees. She doesn't believe in the Cause, because it took Father away. It has changed their lives. But she thinks they'll win and hopes the war ends soon.

She doesn't get angry, she takes it out on Maureen, who is closer to her than her mother at the moment. • She could confide in Maureen, but doesn't believe you should talk about feelings.

A friend's family has a slave. They're not allowed to speak to her. Her life must be hard. Loren wants to talk to her.

They play with a few younger boys in the community. Maureen has a friend called Jem. He's quite arrogant. He touched her once, but Loren isn't jealous. • She wants to marry someone she can talk to, confide in and who sees her as an equal. • She doesn't pray any more. Her prayers don't get answered. Religious beliefs have changed since the war.

Ma Tyler doesn't have children. The stealing is calming down, but it's still desperate. She's not sure what will happen if she gets caught. Ma Tyler will be angry and she might hit Loren for it.

ROWATT • Is proud of his father. • He was shot at Gettysburg and called a sharp-shooter. He can't believe he has been shot in the leg. • He got home of his own accord and met a couple of people along the way. Didn't have permission to leave. • Hasn't seen his family in a long time. • It is a brutal war, but everyone who can, should fight. • 'They' continue to burn our villages, plunder, loot. • He fights because they fight. To defend the side. To stop them. They're trespassing on our land. In an ideal world people should come to an agreement and realise they've done wrong.

He doesn't despise Abraham Lincoln as much as others. But Rowatt is a Confederate, so cannot admire Lincoln. He admires Jefferson Davis as a man of stature.

Loren Maeve is a bit of a liability. • There's no one special in his life, but he keeps trying. Bridh is a beautiful name, and she's a nice lady. Sure of herself.

If he wasn't crippled, he wouldn't shoot people. But he is, so he doesn't have a choice. Any way of fighting is honourable. He doesn't feel ashamed. • He has killed fifteen people and never saved anyone's life. • He knows how to relieve the pain of being shot and once tried, but the bullet was too deep. He got to know the wounded man, found they were alike and felt obliged to help. The next day, he saw two other Yankees, but didn't feel any compunction about shooting at them.

COSTUME

Aim for authenticity. Re-enactment groups are useful both to watch and for sharing information with actors.

See the Southern Skirmish Association: www.soskan.co.uk.

The soldiers' uniforms were worn out, and they couldn't easily distinguish each other. They would pick clothing up as they moved along, stealing boots, etc.

They would have worn forage caps, and officers had brimmed hats, but these would have gone by the time the play is set. *Remember, hats on stage cast shadows on and can sometimes obscure actors' faces*. Rowatt's status should be reflected in his slightly better clothes. As a sniper in the trees, he wouldn't be so much in the mud.

STAGING

Dugout. • Yard. • Some place that is not the dugout, nor the town, but near water. • Place nearby, where

Bridh is discovered. • Place where girls forage for berries and observe Bridh.

The writing is precise, but the staging is not prescriptive.

Possible complications

Small spaces (being able to have observation points, suggest a sense of distance).

Rowatt and the girls needing to see across to the dugout.

Not having actors seated at all times in the dugout, but still maintaining the threat when Hosgood stands up.

Movement between locations.

Finding a life between Maureen and Loren in the long scenes.

Once you've decided upon settings, explore the characters' responses to them, including what it is like to trespass in the yard.

Sharman recommends finding a sense of heat in the yard. A yard is a garden with a barn, rolling lawns edged with garden, wide open spaces.

The girls need to walk for ages and then suddenly find the trap door. There's a lot of crawling, low on the floor.

Navigating the architecture is interesting. It's a challenge to pick berries and eat them onstage.

Cast someone who can fit into a hole!

For staging the water, there is a builders' material called tuffspot (or tough spot), which is two metres wide and has a six-inch deep tray, used for cement mixing. This could be filled with water. Or you could use shallow pondliners with a rope around them. For either of these options, you could use stage lights to bounce the reflection of the water onto a backcloth in order to give a sense of expanse.

ACTIONING

The words are the action. Pinpoint what you are trying to make the other person feel. This can change midway: it's not fixed; you can experiment along the way.

Actioning helps to find a momentum, particularly in long scenes. It usually starts with bland dialogue. • Two people greet each other. • Then use movement to give each person an objective. • Play out the dialogue. • Give each line an intention (I need you; I avoid you). • Act it out physically, saying the intention before the line:

'Hi' (I need you).

'Hi' (I avoid you).

'How are you?' (I urge you).

'Fine' (I escape you).

'Good' (I drink you).

'See you later' (I crush you).

Then stop saying the intention, but play the scene feeling it. Apply this exercise to a scene in the play.

Get off book as early as possible.

Judge your lines according to what you get back from the other person.

Try a rehearsal over the telephone. You can't see whether or not the lines are landing.

SUGGESTED RESOURCE MATERIAL

Shelby Foote's *The Civil War*.

Colm Toibin's *The Master*.

Knoxville's *Diary*, includes colour plates relating to his job, and maps.

Explore images of camp cooking and costuming.

Find Kenneth Burns' documentary series. It shows thousands of plates from the period, with voice-overs from American actors, and outlines the effects of the war.

Mary Chestnut's diary, *A Diary from Dixie*.

See also http://sunsite.utk.edu/civil-war/warweb.html

The Widow of the South, a novel by Robert Hicks, is set around a cemetery for Confederate soldiers killed at the Battle of Franklin.

American Brutus: John Wilkes Booth and the Lincoln Conspiracies, a book by Michael Kauffman that illustrates life in the United States and the assassination of Lincoln.

Workshop facilitated by Craig Slaight
with notes taken by Emma Thirwell

FEATHER BOY: THE MUSICAL

Nicky Singer and Peter Tabern

with lyrics by Don Black
and music by Debbie Wiseman

Nicky Singer has written four adult novels and two books of non-fiction. Her first novel for children *Feather Boy* won the Blue Peter Book of the Year Award and the TV adaptation won a BAFTA for Best Drama. Her second book *Doll* was nominated for the Booktrust Teenage Prize and she recently published *The Innocent's Story*. She co-founded, and for ten years co-directed Performing Arts Labs, a charity dedicated to training writers for screen, theatre and opera. She's also worked in TV, notably as presenter of the BBC2 series *Labours of Eve*.

Peter Tabern's TV credits include *Streetwise* and *Eye of the Storm* (UK Writers' Guild Award for Children's Drama), a thirteen-part science fiction drama, *Life Force*, and film adaptations of *Children of the New Forest* (as co-author) and *Stig of the Dump*, which earned him his second BAFTA and the 2002 International EMMY Award for Children's Drama (directed by John Hay). In 2003 he adapted *Feather Boy* for the BBC, which won a BAFTA for Best Children's Drama, 2004 (directed by Dermot Boyd). He recently adapted Terry Pratchett's novel *Johnny and the Bomb*, and is currently working on the second series of *Hex*.

Don Black has won two Tonys for *Sunset Boulevard*, an Oscar for his song 'Born Free', five Academy Award nominations, three Tony nominations, five Ivor Novello Awards, a Golden Globe and many platinum, gold and silver discs. He has written over a hundred songs for motion pictures, a quintet of James Bond theme songs and two US number one hits. Recent musicals are *Dracula* (with Christopher Hampton) and *Bombay Dreams*. A biography, *Wrestling With Elephants*, was published last year. He is working on a Shanghai musical and a new version of *Bar Mitzvah Boy*. He was awarded an OBE in the Queen's Birthday Honours list.

Debbie Wiseman has composed and conducted over 150 scores for film and TV, including the BAFTA award-winning TV series of *Feather Boy*. Her album to accompany Oscar Wilde's fairy stories was nominated for a Grammy Award and made into a trilogy of animated films, *Wilde Stories*. She has won and been nominated for two Ivor Novello Awards, a TRIC Award, and two RTS Awards. In 2004 she was awarded an MBE for services to the music industry.

Characters

Robert

Kate

Niker

Wesley

Lucy

Deggsy

Robert's Mum

Robert's Dad

Edith

Ernest

Albert

Mavis

Matron

Orderly

Catherine

Headmaster

Head of Pastoral Care

Photographer

Act One

SCENE ONE

Catherine (*offstage, but voice filling the auditorium*)
In a time that is yesterday and tomorrow and
eternally present, there lived a man who dreamed of
firebirds . . .

*Niker is at centre stage with a huge piece of paper
on an easel, sketching an incredible mythical bird.
Robert, downstage, is watching admiringly.*

Robert What are you doing, Niker?
Niker What does it look like I'm doing, Norbert?
Robert Is it one of Miss Raynham's stories? Is it for Miss
    Raynham?
Niker No, it is not for Miss Raynham.
Robert It's good, it looks like a Firebird.
Niker Does it? Pass me the red.

*Robert obediently passed a pot of red paint and a
brush. Niker begins making elaborate fill-in brush
strokes.*

Robert Who's it for?
Niker You really don't get it, do you?
Robert What? Get what?
Niker Life. Mainly. It's not for anyone, it's for me.
Robert I wish I could draw like you.

Cue song: 'Fly Away'.

Niker Yeah. Dream on.

*So Robert does.
Lighting change. This is Robert's imagination:*

Niker's bird back-projects, bigger and bigger – a huge outline red bird, filling the stage, lights obliterating Niker. It's only the bird Robert and the audience see.

FLY AWAY

Robert (*sings*)
    Each time I make a wish, I wish I could have wings.
    There are days when I stare up at the sky
    And wonder what I would do if I could fly . . .

    Fly away
    With the world below me.
    Fly away
    Above the tallest trees
    Far away.
    One day I'll just take off,
    I'll simply fly away with the breeze.

SCENE TWO

The classroom.
    Kids enter carrying a few tables and chairs: Kate, Wesley, Robert, Lucy and Deggsy, plus six or more others, come sprawling onto the stage. Only Niker remains aloof. Robert addresses the audience.

Robert Welcome to Class 7R, my class, Miss Raynham's class. You'll get to meet them all, from Jonathan Niker, the coolest of the dudes . . .

Robert indicates Niker, who lounges on a chair set out by someone else with his feet up on a table.

To the divine Kate Barber . . .

Indicates Kate, who's reading a magazine.

To Robert Nobel, the nerdiest of the nerds.

He is about to point to someone else, but the finger lands on him.

That's me. You can call me 'Norbert', everyone else does. Isn't that right, Kate?

Kate *(nose still in magazine)* What?
Robert *(to audience)* Isn't she wonderful?
Wesley Norbert No-Chance!
Deggsy Norbert No-Chance-at-All!

With the exception of Kate and Niker, the kids form a circle round Robert. He tries to escape, but Deggsy pushes him, causing him to crash into Wesley. Kate continues to read her magazine – after all, this is nothing new, it happens pretty much every day.

Wesley Oi!

Cue song: 'Wanna Make Something of It?'
    Wesley begins the song, first two lines, and then passes the 'baton' (which is the song and Robert) around the ring and the classroom. Initially Niker doesn't sing, just sits with his feet up watching, but gradually the kids take Robert nearer and nearer to Niker and eventually they push Robert into him. The danger level immediately escalates as Niker takes over the song.

WANNA MAKE SOMETHING OF IT?

Kids *(spoken)* Wimp . . . Nerd . . .
Wesley *(sings)*
    Wanna make something of it?
    Do ya? Do ya?
Deggsy
    Fancy your chances?
    Do ya? Do ya?
All
    Ask yourself why

You're the one we pick on.
Why you'd be the one
We'd choose to be sick on
It's because you
Haven't got a clue,
You're brainless and stupid and wimpy and short-
    sighted too!

(*Spoken.*) Thick . . . Creep . . .

All
Wanna make something of it?
Dare ya . . . Dare ya.
I'd like to see it.
Dare ya . . . Dare ya.

Niker
I don't know the meaning of surrender,
I am the one who sets the class agenda.
Niker don't give in,
I was born to win.
Looking at you I'd say we're lucky you ain't got a twin!

Kids (*spoken*) Wimp . . . Nerd . . .

Wesley
Norbert No-Bottle,
No chance, you're pathetic.

Niker
We shouldn't blame him really
It's probably genetic.

Kate *and* **Girls**
Niker is sexy, it's hard to stop lusting,
It's fun to flirt with Niker,
It doesn't feel disgusting.

All
Wanna make something of it?
Thought not . . . thought not.
You got a problem?
Thought not . . . thought not.

If we had to choose a boy to throttle,
All of us would choose Norbert No-Bottle.
He's got nothing to say – not a word.

Niker
He just sits there like a turd.

All
Maybe Norbert No-Bottle was born to be a nerd.

(*Spoken.*) Freak . . . Creep . . .

The teacher, Catherine Raynham, enters, saving Robert from further humiliation.

Catherine Come on now, settle down, settle down. Right. Now then, someone once said, 'When an old person dies, a library goes up in flames.' What do you think they meant by that? Wesley?

Wesley Er . . . old people smoke in bed, Miss?

Catherine No, I don't think so.

Lucy Yes, they do, Miss. My grandad smokes in bed, he smokes everywhere . . .

Catherine I think they were talking about the stories old people have inside them. (*Taps her head.*) Locked away in here. When they die, the stories die with them.

Niker Oh no, not stories again! What is it with you and stories, Miss Raynham?

Catherine Do I take it, Jonathan Niker, that you think this class is too grown up for stories?

Niker Yes. Except – (*scanning other pupils*) maybe Norbert there.

Catherine Personally, I think one never grows out of stories. In fact I think stories may be the most important form of communication we as human beings have. (*Pause.*) What do you think of that, Jonathan?

Niker Niker, just Niker.

Kate I'm not sure Niker *is* a human being, Miss.

Robert (*adoring*) Beautiful and so witty!

Catherine Right. That's quite sufficient. I have planned an exciting new project. I'm calling it the Elders' Project and I hope you'll all want to take part. We're going to visit the Wayfield and do some work with the residents there. Now, does anyone know the Wayfield?

Lights down and immediate transfer to:

SCENE THREE

Wayfield entrance hall. Lights up on a huge painting or wall-hanging – 'The Firebird'. Class 7R enter, led by Catherine Raynham.

Catherine Here we are, welcome to the Wayfield Care Home.

A wheelchair pushed by an Orderly and transporting one of the residents crosses the stage. The children watch in silence; the resident stares right back at them.

Wesley Don't you mean the barmy bin, Miss?

Catherine No, Wesley, I don't. And I'll thank you to treat the residents here with respect. Now, I need to find Matron, so if you'll all just wait here a moment . . .

Catherine begins to exit – immediate hubbub.

. . . quietly!

Catherine exits.

Niker This is a project too far. This is really taking the mick.

Kate (*mimicking Catherine*) On the contrary, Jonathan Niker, together we will unlock the wisdom of the old. We will learn something.

Cue song: 'Old People'.

Niker Yeah, like the importance of dying young.
Robert At least we get time off school.
Niker Go crawl back in your hole, Norbie.

*In the song Niker is clearly the leader of the gang, and
the kids mimic the old people dribbling and shaking,
not being able to keep awake, etc. And, when we meet
the elders in the following scene, some of them are
dribbling and shaking and falling asleep . . . Robert
does not take part in this song, but meanders about,
and finally comes to rest in front of the 'Firebird'
picture, where he stands staring.*

OLD PEOPLE

Niker
    Old people dribble and shake,
    They can't stay awake,
    And you can hardly hear 'em.
    Old people cannot stand noise
    Or digital toys
    And they smell when you're near 'em.
Wesley *and* **Deggsy**
    Old people can't kick a ball
    Or climb a wall,
    When they dance they go dizzy.
Niker
    Old people never drive fast.
Kate *and* **Lucy**
    They live in the past,
    None of their drinks are fizzy.
Niker
    They're always talking about the old days and the war.
    They keep on saying, 'They don't write good songs any
        more.'
    They're not into rap music, iPods leave them cold.
    I hope Fifty Cent never grows old!

Wesley
My grandpa is grumpy and stoops,
Eats lots of soups
And moans about his pension.

Kate
My grandma takes lots of pills
For very strange ills –

(*Spoken.*) What *is* water retention?

Niker
Old people always walk slow
And they don't know their inches from their metres.
Old people's hands are like ice,
Say everything twice
And like to sit near heaters.
They're nice to be around for a minute or two,
Wouldn't want to hang around much longer . . .

All
Would you? Would you? Would you?

At this final 'Would you?' all the kids, who have been totally ignoring Robert, crowd round him and use the final words as an aggressive, startling 'Boo'. Robert is not much startled – he's used to it.

Robert (*emerging from his daydream and pointing at the picture*) Look. Kate – look! It's the story, it's Miss Raynham's story.

Niker It's a picture, Norbert.

Robert It's the Firebird!

Catherine enters.

Catherine Come on now, Matron says we can all go to the lounge. This way.

Robert (*indicating the picture*) Miss Raynham . . .

Catherine Not now, Robert. Come along everyone.

SCENE FOUR

Wayfield residents' lounge.
Lights up on the Wayfield residents. Albert, Mavis and six or more other old people in waiting-room chairs, in wheelchairs. Those who are able stand do so as the children enter with Catherine and form a nervous huddle.

Catherine Here we are then. (*to old people*) Thank you for letting us be here . . .
Mavis Who is it?

Cue song: 'Young People'.

Albert It's the young people. Can't you see them?
Mavis I can hear them. Noisy beggars. Why do they have to be like that?

After Catherine's spoken intervention, this song works like a kind of ironic dance with the old and young people singing against each other at the same time as nodding and smiling (grimacing) and gradually pairing off. Mavis ends up with Niker, Robert with Albert.

YOUNG PEOPLE

Mavis (*sings*)
Young people, swagger and swear,
Don't care what they wear
And they stick pins in their belly.
Young people are always rude . . .
Elder 1
Love being tattooed . . .
Elder 2
They wouldn't know Gene Kelly!
Catherine (*spoken*) Now everyone, just space out, find yourselves a partner.

She puts Mavis' hand in Wesley's.

Mavis (*shaking free of Wesley*)
Young people get in your way.

Elder 3
Expect you to play.

Elder 4
Even with diabetes.

Mavis
My grandson's dopey and dim,
I should've drowned him
When he was just a foetus.

All Kids
Old people get out of breath,
Talk about death,
Don't understand our humour.
Old people keep winding clocks,
Love watching the box
While eating a satsuma.

Niker
They're nice to be around for a minute or two.

Mavis
Wouldn't want to hang around much longer . . .

All Kids *and* **Elders**
Would you? Would you? Would you?

Mavis (*to Niker*) Two of my family died in this place.

Albert No they didn't, you daft brush. (*He extends a hand to Robert.*) I'm Albert.

Robert Robert.

Albert Robert and Albert. Bert and Bert. Do they call you Bert?

Robert No.

Albert They should, you look like a Bert.

Catherine So, now we're ready to begin. I thought we might start with a story. There was once a man who dreamed of Firebirds . . .

*Enter Edith in her wheelchair. She raps on the floor
with her stick. Everyone falls silent as she takes centre
stage and looks around.*

Albert Eh up, now we're for it.
Catherine Welcome, we were just beginning, Mrs . . .
Edith Miss. Miss Sorrel. What's all this noise?
Catherine It's the project, didn't they tell you? I'm sure
    we can find you a partner . . . Kate?
Edith No. I don't want a girl. I want a boy.
Catherine Jonathan perhaps . . . ?

Niker steps forward.

Edith In fact I want . . . (*She scans the entire room and
finally points at Robert.*) . . . that boy.

Cue song: 'Magic Moment'.
    *'That boy' is not an obvious geographical choice.
As though her pointing finger were a wand, the whole
group of elders and kids part like the Red Sea for her
to see him properly.*

Robert (*looking around as though he's misheard*) Me?
Wesley Sick!
Niker (*shakes his head*) Old people.
Robert I don't believe it. She chose me!

*Robert makes his way through the Red Sea path to
Edith.*
    *Lights down on all but Robert and Edith. Robert
extends a hand.*

I'm Robert, Miss Sorrel.
Edith Edith. You may call me Edith. And you may take
    me out of here.

SCENE FIVE

Wayfield Garden.
  Lights down on the residents as we follow Robert,
pushing the wheelchair downstage, away from the others.

Edith So what is it we're supposed to be doing, Robert?

Robert Just talking, I think. Like I'm supposed to tell
  you a bit about me, only there isn't much to tell, and
  then I have to ask you stuff like if you were married
  or had children . . .

Edith No and no.

Robert Oh. Okay. And, well then, you're supposed to tell
  me your wisdoms.

Edith Wisdoms – what wisdoms?

Robert Stuff you've learnt over the years.

Edith What if I've learnt nothing?

Robert Well, just something important, then. The most
  important thing in your life.

Edith (*no pause*) Top Floor Flat. Chance House. 26 St
  Aubyn's. (*Pause.*) You can go there. Walk. It's not far.

Robert (*humouring*) O–kay.

Edith You can do it. I knew it as soon as I saw you.
  You're an extraordinary boy, a remarkable boy.

Robert (*startled and disbelieving*) Me?

Edith Of course. And you're young, you can do anything
  you want. (*Pause.*) Look. (*Scrabbles in her handbag,
  extracts a mirror.*) Look here. What do you see,
  Robert?

Robert A lady.

Edith Liar. You see a hag, an old hag. Funny, every time
  I look I expect to see the girl I was when I was twenty
  with hair and skin like yours. Then I look and there's
  the old hag.

Cue song: 'It's Still Me in Here'.

98

Lights up on the elders and the kids, still on stage in the Wayfield residents' lounge. Albert is now paired with Kate and Mavis with Niker. The elders sing individually to their child. Robert and Edith are probably still lit. Edith is stiff and unyielding: these are her sentiments but she couldn't possibly let go enough to express them.

Mavis Do you understand what I'm saying?
Niker Not really.

IT'S STILL ME IN HERE

Mavis (*sings*)
My eyes are not as bright, my skin is not as tight,
But it's still me in here.
My knees hurt me a lot, my mem'ry's gone to pot,
But it's still me in here.

Elder 1
On the outside I may look a little worse for wear,
Forget my face, ignore my hands, you shouldn't be
    looking there.

Elder 2
I may be old and lame but part of me's stayed the same,
How do I make it clear that it's still me in here?

All Elders
I've learned that you can't judge a book by its cover,
You have to read the pages.
I've also learned that a loving heart never ages.

Mavis
Though I am not as strong and the future's not as long
Some things don't disappear, yes it's still me in here,
Yes it's still me in here.

Lights down on elders and kids.

Edith So you will go, won't you? To Chance House. You
must go, promise me?

Robert Why do you want me to go? What do you expect
me to find there?

Edith I don't know . . . I don't remember.

Robert (*pause*) Do you want to go back inside?

He tries to turn the chair but she stops him.

Edith No. I don't want to go back in there.

Robert Why not?

Edith (*pause*) They have . . . 'sing-songs'.

Robert can't help smiling.

Robert Oh. Is that so terrible?

Edith I don't sing. I never sing. I haven't sung in thirty
years.

Robert So what *do* you want?

Edith I want you to go to Chance House. You will go,
you must go, promise me?

SCENE SIX

Robert's house. Later that day. Robert enters.

Robert Mum. Mum – guess what?

No answer. It's clear there's no one at home.

Oh.

*He depresses an ansaphone button . . . Lights up on
Mum, Annie Nobel, in nurse's uniform.*

Mum Robert, it's Mum. I'm really sorry love, but there's
been an accident. Motorway pile-up. And the hospital's
really short-staffed, so I'm going to have to stay on.
I can't say how long for. Can you do yourself a pizza?
Bye love, God bless.

Robert Same old, same old.

Ansaphone beep. Second message. Lights up on Dad, Nigel Nobel, in suit.

Dad Hello, Robert. It's me. Dad. I need to speak to your mother. She seems to be in one of her not-returning-my-calls modes. Do you think you could get her to ring me? Thanks. Great. Well . . . speak to you another time. Obviously. Not this weekend though. Jo and I are away. Bye.

Robert Hi, Dad. Love you too. (*He moves downstage to computer, sits. Addressing computer*) Just you and me again, friend. (*Switches it on.*) Do you want to know what happened in my day? (*Mimicking computer, robotic voice.*) 'Of course I do.' (*As himself.*) You do? Really? (*Computer.*) 'I said so, didn't I?' (*As himself.*) Okay. It was like this. I got chosen.

Cue song: 'Bold and Fearless Dot Com'.

You know, me, Robert Nobel, the one who never gets chosen. Okay, I only got chosen by some batty old woman who wants me to go some old house. But hey – it's a start.

Robert is still quite insular when the song starts, communing with his computer, but by the time he gets to 'Bold and Fearless Dot Com' he's up on his feet, and when gets to 'Hit the web' he's really begun to get into it, playing the part of the strutting Big Celeb.

BOLD AND FEARLESS DOT COM

Robert (*sings*)
Wouldn't it be great to sit at my computer
And with one click of my mouse
Become a hero in my house?
I'd find me a site, to change me overnight.
I'd be as good as any Harry, Dick or Tom

By clicking Bold and Fearless
Dot Com.
Bold and Fearless Dot Com.

Wouldn't it be cool to turn into a leader
That the other kids respect
And just for once start to connect?
When I hit the web I feel like a big celeb,
I would strut around the classroom with aplomb,
Thanks to Bold and Fearless . . .
Dot Com.

At the repeat of this 'Bold and Fearless Dot Com', all the kids from the class, led by Kate, Niker and Wesley, come on stage and form a vaguely threatening semi-circle around Robert. They are wearing fancy dress, the boys in top hats and carrying canes.

Kids (*spoken*) You're joking, aren't you?

Beat. A held moment when Robert realises it could all go horribly wrong.

Robert No. I can see it all.

Now the kids start a big show routine with Robert as their leader – Niker and company actually singing 'Norbert the nerd, that's the stupidest thing we ever heard. He's got self-esteem' etc., and Kate swooning in his arms. They end up all kneeling to their god – Robert.

Kids (*sings*)
Norbert No-Bottle! Norbert the nerd!
That's the stupidest thing that we've ever heard!
He's got self-esteem,
Living a dream
And soaring like a bird.
Robert
I would hold my ground.

Kids
> He would hold his ground.

Robert
> I'd stand up for myself.

Kids
> He'd stand up for himself.

Robert
> I'd be certain and secure.

All
> Positive and sure.

Robert
> Then who knows, maybe
> (*Kids sing aahs*) Lovely Kate would notice me.
> There won't be anyone that Robert's running from
> When I find . . .

All
> Bold and fearless,
> Confident and tearless,
> Bold and Fearless . . .
> Dot Com.
> Bold and Fearless Dot Com.

The kids break, dust themselves down and form a new semicircle, vaguely threatening. They are larger-than-life characters now and there is a Clockwork Orange *feel to their costumes.*

Niker Only it's not quite true, is it, Norbie? Because you have been chosen before. Last summer, remember?

Robert No, not that.

Niker Yes, that! You remember, don't you, Kate? He got chosen then.

Kate Oh yeah, I remember.

Niker So tell it.

Robert No.

Niker I said, 'Tell it.'

Cue song: 'Wanna Make Something of It?' underscore.
As Robert tells the story, we see it acted out.

Robert It was last summer. Seems like yesterday. They
invited me to join them, and I went. I even felt
honoured. There was to be a little test. A join-the-gang
test. Nothing difficult. Nothing they hadn't all done.
Even Kate. My princess. How could I refuse? They
took me to . . . to . . .
Niker A cellar. A deep, dark cellar.
Kids We locked him in. We stamped him down. (*He
stamps on hatch.*) We left him there, all alone in the
dark. He screamed and he screamed . . .

They scream.

. . . but no one came.
Niker Kate didn't come.
Kate Nobody came.
Wesley Morning came!
Kate But only after quite a long night.
Niker We pulled him out into the daylight. He was
blinking. Helpless.
Kids Blinking helpless!
Niker Kate was there *then*. She saw it.
Kate Look, he's pissed himself.
Robert And I had.

Punches himself. Underscore stops.

(*to kids*) Shove off! Leave me alone!

Cue song: 'Fly Away'.
*Huge, gracious waves from the kids. They all exit
except Niker.*

Niker Welcome to the first day of the rest of your life.
Don't get any big ideas, little Norbie. (*Little wave.*) Fly
away, why don't you?

He goes, leaving Robert in a heap.

Robert Why don't I?

FLY AWAY

Robert (*sings*)
Each time I make a wish
I wish I could have wings.
There are days when I stare up at the sky
And wonder what I would do if I could fly . . .

Fly away with the world below me,
Fly away where no one knows my name.
Far away from my school and parents
Where every rotten day is the same.

Fly away, I would take Kate with me,
Fly away and do fantastic things.
Fly away . . . no, it just can't happen.
You just can't fly away without wings.

SCENE SEVEN

Outside Chance House. A flight of steps and a boarded-up door, above which, in gold letters, are the words:
CHANCE HOUSE, 26 ST AUBYN'S. *Enter Robert with schoolbag, mooching. He starts forward, then jumps a mile as Niker and Wesley leap out from nowhere.*

Wesley You weren't thinking of going in there, were you?
Robert No. Why would I?
Niker Good, because you know that deep, dark little cellar you kipped in one night?
Wesley Nothing compared with big, tall Chancey Housie.
Robert What do you mean? What are you talking about?
Wesley Chance House. Way, way bad. Bad house. Bad karma.

Robert Tell me.

Niker Everyone knows and he doesn't! Shall we tell him?

Wesley A boy died in that house.

Robert What boy? Who?

Niker Just a boy, Norbie. Pasty little thing. Little fluffy hair, little glasses . . . bit like you, as it happens.

Wesley Sort of stupid, useless.

Niker But his mum couldn't see it, could she? He was her little angel. Told him he was wonderful. So wonderful he could fly. So what does the little angel do?

Wesley He gives it a go.

Niker He opens the window and gives it a go. Top-floor flat . . .

Robert Top-floor flat? Are you sure?

Wesley Higher the window, more the strawberry jam, and there was plenty of jam for this boy.

Cue song: 'Wanna Make Something of It?' reprise.

Niker (*to Robert*) Landed about where you're standing now. You feeling alright, Norbert? You've gone a bit pale, pasty-looking . . .

Robert runs off. They shout at his back.

Niker *and* **Wesley** (*sing*)
Norbert No-Bottle, no chance, you're pathetic.
We shouldn't blame him really, it's probably genetic.

SCENE EIGHT

Wayfield. Edith in bed asleep. Ernest sitting at the bottom of the bed in an outdoor coat. Enter Robert.

Robert (*taken aback*) Who are you?

Ernest I might ask the same of you!

Robert Me, I'm no one . . . I'm Robert. I'm on the project.

Ernest Ah, the project. Ernest Sorrel. Edith's husband.
  (*Pause.*) How old are you, Robert?

Robert Twelve.

Ernest His age. His height.

Robert Whose age. Whose height?

Ernest What have you been talking about with Edith?
  What's she been saying?

Robert Nothing. She just mentioned Chance House.

Ernest Chance House? No. She couldn't just mention
  Chance House. It's over thirty years since she could
  even say the name.

Robert She asked me to go there. Top-floor flat.

Ernest Well, don't. Do you hear me? Edith is ill, very ill.
  And I don't want her hurt any more.

Robert Miss Sorrel said she didn't have a husband. No
  husband. No child.

Ernest No child? Well, we all remember things, Robert . . .
  and forget them.

  Cue song: 'Snapshots'.

Sometimes you have to forget, or you couldn't go on. And
  sometimes you have to remember, for the same reason.

*Blackout on Robert and lights on Ernest and Edith only,
as Ernest sings the first two verses of this song. He's
singing it as a love song to Edith, lost in his memories,
excluding Robert totally. Then lights on Robert alone
as his memory triggers and he sings his own verse to
the exclusion of Ernest. The final verse should be sung
in unison but not to each other: Ernest and Robert are
still locked in their own isolated memories.*

SNAPSHOTS

Ernest (*sings*)
  Snapshots.
  I close my eyes and see

Snapshots
Of how life used to be.
And what fantastic snapshots I see.

Edith singing our boy to sleep,
Her voice was sweet and true
As she sang the song 'Ev'rything About You'.

Robert
Ev'ry meal in the Nobel house
Was a meal for three.
Dad was always there
And he bought me the coolest clothes to wear.

Robert *and* **Ernest**
Snapshots.
I close my eyes and see
Snapshots
Of how life used to be.
And what fantastic snapshots I see.

Edith stirs in the bed. Ernest immediately makes an exit.

Robert Your husband was here.

Edith Impossible, I haven't got a husband. Did you go? Did you go to Chance House. To the top-floor flat?

Robert I looked at it. It's all boarded up.

Edith Looked at it? What use is that?

Robert It's not a nice place. It might be dangerous.

Edith Nonsense, I've told you, you can do anything you want to. Now pass me my stick. And my dressing gown.

Cue song: 'Fly Away' underscore.
Edith gets out of bed and into her wheelchair, then gestures Robert to wheel her upstage. Lights up on the 'Firebird' picture. They both stare up at it.

Edith I could have been a singer. I had a beautiful voice. Everyone said so. But he put a stop to that.

Robert Right. Um, who put a stop to it?

Edith Ernest, of course, my husband.

Robert I thought you said you didn't have a husband.

Edith I don't. Not any more. He said it wasn't a suitable occupation for a lady. Music hall. I wasn't to sing, wasn't to train. (*Defiant.*) But I did. (*She deflates.*) For a time anyway. So you'll go back – to Chance House? To the very top, the top-floor flat?

Robert I told you, it's all boarded up.

Edith Surely there's a way you could get in.

Robert It doesn't feel right, you know. It feels . . . scary.

Edith Robert, you must not be afraid. You're a wonderful boy. An extraordinary boy. You can do anything you want. You can fly.

Robert What!

Edith You're the sort of boy who can fly.

Robert backs away.

Oh, don't do that. Say you'll go for me!

Catherine (*offstage voice*) Come on everyone, let's finish with a song.

Cue song: 'One Man Went to Mow'.
    And the immediate response of the elders and kids:

Elders *and* **Kids**
    One man went to mow, went to mow a meadow.

Edith Oh no, I can't bear it. They do it on purpose.

Robert Does it hurt?

Edith No . . . Yes! Yes, it hurts. It hurts! Please, Robert, make it stop!

She begins to sob. Robert is very uncomfortable.

Robert Okay. If it means that much to you, I'll go.

She stops crying, smiles.

SCENE NINE

The graveyard.
    Cue song: 'Fly Away' underscore.
    It is the end of the school day. Kate and Robert are on separate parts of the stage, book-bags over their shoulders.

Kate (*seeing him and calling*) Robert!
Robert Robert? (*Looks over his shoulder.*) Is there another Robert here? (*There isn't.*) Oh joy.
Kate I've got something to show you.
Robert Something to show me?
Kate You don't have to repeat everything I say, Robert. You just have to follow me!
Robert Follow you?
Kate Come on!

    Cue song: 'Fly Away' reprise.

Robert Don't worry, I'm right behind you!

FLY AWAY

(*Sings.*)
    Fly away, I would take Kate with me,
    Fly away and do fantastic things.
    Fly away, one day it will happen,
    I'll just fly away, I'll have wings.

    She leads him to the centre of the graveyard.

This is it? A graveyard?
Kate No, look.

    She points out a gravestone inscribed: TO OUR
    BELOVED SON, DAVID SORREL, AGED TWELVE.
    There are fresh flowers on the grave.

It's him, isn't it? Your old Mrs Sorrel's son. The one who jumped out of the top window of Chance House.

Robert Oh.

He kneels at the grave, traces the name with his finger as he reads . . .

'To our beloved son, David Sorrel, aged twelve.' (*Pause.*) She asked me to go, Kate. To the house. To the top-floor flat.

Kate That's mad.

Robert Yes. But I'm going to do it.

Niker erupts from behind the tomb of Claud Mosen. He's obviously been listening in.

Niker Oooh, do not go there, Norbert No-Bottle. I am the ghost of the strawberry-jam boy . . .

Kate Don't you ever give up?

Niker No. It's not in the job description. (*to Robert*) And who are you kidding? You're not going inside Chance House, you haven't got the bottle. You, my little Norbie, are a bottle-free zone.

Robert You're wrong, Niker. I am going. I promised Mrs Sorrel.

Niker Mrs Sorrel is half-blind, half-deaf and about three-quarters dead. She ain't going to know if you've been or not, is she?

Robert She'll know. *I'll* know.

Niker Ah, but *we* won't know, will we, Kate?

Kate (*shrugs*) So? I don't want to know.

Niker Oh, that's not very nice. Norbie's big adventure? Tell you what, Norbert, why don't I come too? Even better, why don't we make a night of it? You and me, alone in spooky old Chance House. Go on, I dare you.

Robert says nothing.

Kate (*to Robert*) You don't have to, you know.

Robert's eyes swing from Niker to Kate, then back to Niker.

Robert Okay – I'll do it.
Niker Great. Sleeping-bags at dusk.

He grabs Robert by the shirt-front. Robert's glasses fly off.

And if you don't show, I'll kill you.

He releases Robert and turns to go.

Kate And if you don't show, maybe he'll kill *you*.
Niker Ooh, scary!

Niker exits.

Kate (*handing Robert his glasses*) You don't have to be quite so pathetic.

Cue song: 'Fly Away' underscore.

SCENE TEN

Chance House. Dusk. Enter Robert, being followed by kids from the bully group, except for Wesley, Kate and Niker, dressed in ethereal grey as Fears of the Night Kids. Robert can't see them. Niker is sitting on the steps with a drawstring sleeping-bag. Robert has a rucksack.

Robert (*to himself*) I am not afraid. I am not being followed.

Cue song: 'A Full Moon and a Dripping Tap'.
    The kids follow Robert, stop when he stops. There is nothing there. Except the Fears of the Night.

Niker (*appearing*) What kept yer?
Robert Niker?
Niker Yes, Norbert?
Robert Do you ever feel like . . .

*The Fears of the Night Kids all crowd round Niker
and shriek 'Boo'. He doesn't move a muscle.*

Niker Scared? Nope.

*They enter the house, Robert first. All the noises of the
house are made by the Fears of the Night Kids. The
noise of branches scraping against windows. The drip,
drip of water. It's dark, Robert is moving very slowly.
The Fears of the Night Kids sing.*

A FULL MOON AND A DRIPPING TAP

Fears of the Night Kids (*sing*)
   A full moon and a dripping tap
   Will scare you half to death,
   It's hard to catch your breath.
   (*Whisper.*) Was that a ghost you saw?
Niker Can we up the speed rate here?

*Robert is jostled by Fears of the Night Kids, but holds
his ground, continuing slowly.*

Fears of the Night Kids (*sing*)
   A dark house and a creaky stair
   Will stand your hair on end,
   Could drive you round the bend.
   (*Whisper.*) What was that on the floor?
Niker Oh, for God's sake.

*He pushes past Robert. It suddenly turns considerably
darker. Even the Fears of the Night Kids stop.*

You got anything useful in that bag of yours?
Robert Like what?
Niker Like a torch, for instance.
Robert Yes, yes I have.

He rummages and finds it.

Niker Give it here.

Niker snatches it, switches it on – a very pale beam.

This got any other setting than dim? No, don't answer that, Norbert.

A loud creak made by the Fears of the Night Kids.

Fears of the Night Kids (*sing*)
What is real and what's imagination?
Who can tell at times like these?
When your heart's in your mouth
And your teeth won't stay still
And you can't control your knees.

Another loud creak.

Niker What's that?
Robert Just the sound of the house.
Niker Houses don't have sounds.
Robert Yes, they do. The one you locked me in, the one with the cellar, that had sounds.
Niker Shut up, Norbert. Keep your brain on the job. All the way to the top, right? That little doorway up there.

They ascend the staircase, the Fears of the Night Kids between Niker and Robert. Robert is in front, Niker pushed backwards by one of the Kids.

Fears of the Night Kids (*sing*)
A full moon and a dripping tap
Will make your jaw go slack,
Give you a heart attack.
(*Whisper.*) What is that behind the door?

One kid snatches the torch and turns it off. Sudden total darkness and an appalled silence.

Niker You jerk. You stupid brainless jerk. How could you bring a torch with dud batteries, you . . . gerbil!
Fears of the Night Kids (*sing*)
The cobwebs, the shadows,

You could die from fright.
You'd give everything you own
For someone to switch on a light.

*At the very top of the stairs, a door swings open,
shedding some light . . .*

Niker (*whisper*) That's the room, the strawberry-jam
boy, it's his room. There's a light on.

Robert Just a street light. Probably.

Niker Street light! What planet are you on, Norbert?

Robert Or moonlight. When you're somewhere strange,
especially when you're locked in, your eyes play tricks.
Your mind plays tricks. Or that's what I found anyway.
When you locked me in.

Niker Shut up. This isn't about you.

Robert Isn't it?

Cue song: 'A Full Moon and a Dripping Tap' reprise.

Niker You're enjoying this.

Robert You think?

Niker Come on, we've done enough, let's go.

Robert No, I'm going all the way. That's what we said.

Niker We've done it. It's between you and me. Nobody
else. Who cares?

Robert I care.

Niker Well, I'm going.

Robert So go.

Niker (*pause*) You want me to say sorry, is that it?

Robert Do you want to say sorry?

Niker No.

Robert Okay then. Go.

Niker I will. I'm going. I'm really going. Sorry, Robert.

*He turns and goes, clawing and stumbling through the
darkness, the Fears of the Night Kids in close and
tripping pursuit . . .*

Fears of the Night Kids (*sing*)
The cobwebs, the shadows,
You could die from fright.
You'd give everything you own
For someone to switch on a light!

*Niker exits and so do the Fears of the Night Kids,
slamming the front door behind them. For the first
time in the scene there is a total and appalling silence.
Robert looks back where Niker has disappeared –
and up to where the light is, as if caught between the
urge to flee and the urge to go on.*

Cue song: 'Fly Away' underscore.

*Robert begins to ascend the final stairs. As he
reaches the fateful door to the room where the boy
died, it swings open to greet him. Robert walks into
the light . . .*

Blackout.

End of Act One.

Act Two

SCENE ONE

Wayfield Rest Home.
   Lights up on a gaggle of children arriving, among them Niker, Kate and Robert, as if for an elders' session.

Wesley And you stayed all night in spooky old Chance House?
Niker Yeah. So what?
Kate And you didn't go crazy?
Wesley And start, like, foaming at the mouth?
Niker Nah! Most of the time I was asleep, dreaming my happy dreams. Isn't that right, Norbert?

   Without waiting for a reply, Niker and the kids walk on. Robert stops and so, at some distance from him, does Kate.

Kate Is that what really happened?
Robert (*shrugs*) If he says so, I guess it must be true.

   Kate exits, following the others. Robert turns towards Mrs Sorrel's room. Matron appears . . .

Matron Robert, I need to talk to you . . .
Robert I'm supposed to be with Mrs Sorrel . . .
Matron It's Mrs Sorrel I want to talk about.
Robert (*suddenly worried*) What's the matter with her?
Matron She's ill, Robert . . . Mrs Sorrel is *very* ill, very ill indeed. She has cancer.
Robert Is she going to die?
Matron Yes, I'm afraid she is. (*Pause.*) But then we're all going to die one day, aren't we?
Robert Can I see her?

117

Matron No, that's the point. I don't think it would be a good idea, not at the moment – perhaps in a day or two, if she's feeling better.

Lights down as Matron exits, leaving Robert alone. Lights up on Edith apparently asleep in bed. After a few moments Robert enters and takes three white feathers from his pocket.

Robert Mrs Sorrel, it's me, Robert. Matron says I can't talk to you. Can I talk to you, Mrs Sorrel?

Edith's eyes remain closed. After a few moments Robert gently lays the feathers on the bed beside her hand and turns sadly away.

Edith (*eyes still closed*) I don't much like Matron.

Robert turns back smiling.

Robert Neither do I.
Edith That's that then. Lift me up.

Robert dithers.

Come on! Pillows! (*As he comes closer she stares at him.*) You're different. (*Pause.*) You've got bigger.
Robert Maybe you've got smaller.
Edith No, I can see it in your eyes. Chance House, top-floor flat! You've done it, haven't you?
Robert There was nothing there. At first I thought there was, but there was nothing, just these.

He shows her the feathers.
Cue song: 'Fly Away' underscore.
Edith takes the feathers as if in a trance.

Edith Once there was a man who dreamed of Firebirds. And one day as he rested from his labours, a Firebird came down from the sky. It was hot and needing to bathe. The Firebird slipped off her coat of golden feathers, and there stood the most beautiful woman the man had ever seen. And as she swam, the man took the coat of feathers and hid it in the forest . . . When the Firebird left the water, she wept for her missing coat but the man said nothing. He took her to his house, and there she stayed, until in time she forgot she was a Firebird and that she'd once been able to fly . . .

She snaps out of trance. End of 'Fly Away' underscore.

You could make me a coat of feathers.

Robert What?

Edith Pass me that jacket. There on the chair . . .

Robert hands it to her.

Edith (*quietly*) I want you to make me a coat of feathers.

Robert almost laughs out loud – can she be serious?

Robert *How?*

Edith (*impatient*) Find feathers, sew them on, you can do it!

She presses the jacket and the Chance House feathers into his hands.

Robert (*it's ridiculous*) No, I can't! I can't sew!

Edith A boy who can go to the top of Chance House can do *anything* if he wants to enough!

Robert Except sew!

Edith Just do it, David!

Robert David? You called me David. I'm Robert. David's your son. Your dead son.

Edith (*stricken*) Dead? David's dead? Who says my baby is dead?

Robert No, not now! Years ago. Thirty years ago. He died when he was twelve – yes?

Edith begins to sob. Enter Matron with an Orderly. Matron carries pills in a small plastic pot.

Matron (*to Robert*) How dare you, you sneaky little . . .

Edith (*roaring upright in the bed*) Don't you speak to my boy like that!

Matron strides to the bedside, pulls Robert to his feet.

Leave him!

Matron (*to Robert*) Out, right now!

Edith Do it, David! Do it for me!

Matron and the Orderly bundle Robert out of the room. Edith sinks back on her pillows.

Edith (*almost to herself*) He's going to make me a coat of feathers.

Lights down.

SCENE TWO

Robert's house.
  Lights up on Mum, rootling around in the dirty laundry basket, and Robert, who is sitting on his bed with the pink jacket and a sewing kit, trying with increasing exasperation to thread a needle.

Mum Whatcha doing?

Robert (*serious*) I'm not sure.

Mum What?

Robert Mainly trying to thread this needle!

Mum But what's it for, what are you making?

Robert A coat of feathers.

Mum A coat of feathers.

Robert For the project. Mum, how long does it take to die if you've got cancer?

Mum Whoa – big question. Well, for a start it doesn't mean you're going to die just 'cos you've got cancer. It depends on the type of illness, it depends on the person.

Robert What about, you know, when you get better for no apparent reason?

Mum Spontaneous remission? It happens. Not as often as one would like. Are we talking Mrs Sorrel here?

Robert nods.

I'm sorry.

Robert Don't be. She's not dead yet. (*Huge exasperation about the needle.*) How do you do this!

Mum Here. (*She takes the thread and licks the end.*) Lick it. Makes it easier.

She hands the threaded needle back to Robert.

Robert Thanks. (*Pause.*) You know, I don't think Mrs Sorrel's very happy.

Mum Robert, I know you want to help her, but maybe you can't. Maybe no one can.

Robert She says you can do anything if you want to enough.

Mum Not always, love. Here, give me that.

She indicates the coat and the feathers – Robert gives them to her.

You need a good knot, too. (*She makes one.*) Believe me, 'wanting' isn't always enough.

Cue song: 'What You Gonna Do?'

Some things just happen, good things, bad things.

During this song Mum is totally involved in her memories, Robert totally involved in the coat as he interjects the spoken lines, telling how and where to position the feathers.

WHAT YOU GONNA DO?

Mum
I wanted your dad and me

121

To live 'happy ever after'.
But we didn't,
No we didn't.

Robert (*spoken*) No – put it on the front.

Mum

We wanted our house to be
Filled with love and laughter.
But it wasn't,
No it wasn't.

Robert (*spoken*) Other way up.

Mum

If I made a list of all I wished for that didn't come true
I'd soon run out of paper,
But that's life – what you gonna do?

Robert (*spoken*) How do you do that stitch?

Mum

When I was a little girl
I was gonna be an ice skater.
But I wasn't,
No I wasn't.

Robert (*spoken*) That's good.

Mum

And then I wanted to be a Dolly Parton impersonator.
But I couldn't,
I just couldn't!

Robert (*spoken*) Thanks, can I have it now?

Mum

Bad things happen all the time to people who love you,
Some things you never find out.
Guess that's life – what you gonna do?
Yes that's life – what you gonna do?

(*Spoken, finally giving back coat*) What I'm saying is –
you don't have to do this, you know that, don't you?

Robert You're wrong, Mum, I *do* have to do this. I *totally*
have to do this.

Mum In any case, you've only got three feathers. You'd need thousands . . .

Robert Right.

Robert steps out of this scene, and goes downstage with his plastic bag, where he finds Ernest Sorrel clearing a debris of feathers from David's grave. Ernest has laid down a bunch of flowers he's been carrying.

Robert Mr Sorrel.

Ernest (*jumps*) Oh, Robert.

Robert What is it?

Ernest A pigeon. Or it was a pigeon. Urban foxes, I'm afraid.

As they talk Robert collects feathers from around the grave.

Edith's dying, you do know that, don't you?

Robert (*fiercely*) No, she's not! She's going to get better. I'm going to make her better.

Ernest (*not wanting to disillusion him*) You do make her better.

Robert No, *really*. I'm going to make her a coat of feathers. It's what she wants, like in the Firebird story . . .

Ernest Oh, the Firebird. You know it was me, I suppose? The man who took away her coat?

Robert You stopped her singing.

Ernest (*still musing, as if he hasn't heard Robert*) The one who trapped her, so she couldn't fly . . . And now it's too late.

He gives Robert the last of the feathers and walks sadly away.

Robert (*calling after him*) It's not too late! You can do anything if you want to enough!

Ernest No, Robert, it *is* too late. Years too late.

As Ernest disappears into the darkness, Robert wanders back to the bedroom. He puts his bag on the bed. Mum peers into it.

Mum They don't look that clean.
Robert But I washed them!
Mum (*nose in bag, sniffing*) Not with my Rose Geranium soap!
Robert Sorry, Mum.
Mum This is getting out of hand.
Robert It's not.
Mum It's a ridiculous task.
Robert It's a matter of life and death. Can you show me that knot again?

Lights down on Robert and Mum.

SCENE THREE

Robert's bedroom. Robert, still sitting sewing. When Mum enters he stuffs the coat into the bag and pretends to be reading. He has the book upside down.

Mum They've called me in for the eight o'clock shift. I'm sorry, love. Will you be alright?
Robert (*not looking up*) Of course.
Mum And no more sewing. Late-night sewing ruins your eyes. (*Turns book the right way up.*) And your brain.
Robert Yes, Mum.

Mum exits. Robert grabs the Sainsbury's bag with the coat and an outdoor jacket and walks around as –
    Lights up on Edith, asleep in bed.

Mrs Sorrel.

No response.

Mrs Sorrel, it's me.

Edith (*from a long way out*) Mmm?
Robert Robert. Robert Nobel.
Edith Mmm.
Robert I've done the coat. Well, started it . . . It's here.
    I've brought it.

He puts it up for her to touch. She runs her hands in it.

Edith You're such a good boy. (*She opens her eyes.*) It's
    beautiful.
Robert It's not finished.
Edith When will it be finished?
Robert Soon. I work on it day and night.
Edith God bless you, Robert Nobel. (*She smiles and then
    looks away from him.*) Is it dark?
Robert Sorry?
Edith Outside, is it dark, is it night?
Robert Yes.
Edith And are there stars?
Robert I think so . . . Yes.
Edith Then take me out.

Robert dithers.

Please.

*He wheels up her chair. She lifts her bedclothes. She's
in a thin cotton nightdress.*

Robert It's cold.

He stops. Edith smiles.

Edith (*gently*) There are rugs.

He tucks her in.

(*impatient*) Come on, come on. We need to go left.
    Through the fire door. It's not alarmed.

He wheels her outside.

And there it is, an extraordinarily dark sky with any number of brilliant stars. In the chair Edith seems to grow taller, reaching up towards the stars, breathing them in.

Not long now. Once there was a man who dreamed of Firebirds . . . You remember?

Cue song: 'You're Not Going Anywhere'.

The one who hid the Firebird's coat of feathers? He was not a wicked man – in time the Firebird even grew to love him and then a child was born, a boy, a remarkable boy who grew up strong and brave. The Firebird's child roamed far and wide and one day he found the coat of feathers, deep in the forest where his father had hidden it. The boy ran home and showed it to his mother who held the coat softly in her hands and wept when she remembered that she was a Firebird who had once been able to fly . . .

Robert (*puts his hand on hers*) Mrs Sorrel?
Edith I love you, Robert Nobel.

YOU'RE NOT GOING ANYWHERE

Robert
> You're not going anywhere,
> Don't make any plans.
> There'll be lots of years before
> We stop holding hands.

> I'll never run out of ways to keep you here.
> That's how it must be.
> You're not going anywhere
> Without me.

> We have so much
> More to do,
> Every day I
> Learn so much from you.

You're not going anywhere,
Put your bags away.
I would hate it on my own
So you better stay.

I'll never run out of ways to make you smile,
That's how it must be.
You're not going anywhere
Without me.

That's how it must be.
You're not going anywhere
Without me.

Alarm bells cut into the final note of the song – torch beams criss-cross the stage. Matron appears with her trusty Orderly.

Matron Edith! There you are, we were so worried!

Then she sees Robert.

You again! You have no right to be here!
Edith He makes me better!
Matron Go home, Robert!

She and the Orderly wheel Edith away.

Edith He makes me better!
Robert I'll finish the coat, I promise!
Edith Come soon, Robert Nobel, come soon . . .
Robert (*to himself*) I *will* make you better!

Robert is alone on stage, then we see that Ernest Sorrel has appeared from the shadows.

Ernest (*sadly*) Too late, Robert. Years too late . . .
Robert It isn't finished yet! You'll see!

He runs off. Ernest slowly follows Edith.

SCENE FOUR

School Art Room.

Catherine (*voice off*) Come along, everyone, I need the
rest of the Mayfield work in the Art Room now. It all
has to be glued today.

*Lights up on Robert in the Art Room. He's examining
the triptych of work made by the old people and the
kids. The left-hand panel is earth colours – hand-prints
and animals and quotes: 'If you can't do a good turn,
don't do a bad one.' The central panel is more fairytale
coloured – silver and blue – and there is a large space
at the top, in the shape of a bird, or a coat of feathers.
The right-hand panel has a picture of a man, a beautiful
woman and young boy. There's a ring of observers
and, in copperplate script, 'The Firebird Story.' Robert
goes up to the panels and begins to mumble-read.*

Robert 'The boy ran home and showed the coat of
feathers to his mother, who held it softly in her hands
and wept when she remembered that she was a
Firebird who had once been able to fly . . . And with
her coat restored, what should she do, stay with her
boy or fly away?'

*Behind Robert, the noise of someone entering. He
whips round. It's Kate – he yells at her.*

What happens?

Kate looks blank.

The Firebird story! How does it end?

Kate (*shrugs*) She flies away. She flies away, she leaves
her boy and she flies away.

*She sees the look on Robert's face and knows it's not
the answer he wanted.*

128

(*apologetic*) That's how Miss Raynham told it . . . Sorry.

Robert takes the coat of feathers from its bag.

Wow, amazing! What is it?
Robert It's for Mrs Sorrel, she asked me to make it.

Kate runs her hand over the feathers, which now cover the front of the jacket. They ripple softly, magically.

Kate It's like it's alive.

Catherine arrives with Niker. She has a roll of artwork.

Catherine Kate, Robert . . . what do you think?

She unrolls Niker's painting for them.

It's brilliant, isn't it?

Robert is already putting his coat of feathers back in the bag, but Kate stops him.

Kate Look at this, Miss Raynham, see what Robert's done.
Catherine Show me.
Robert It's nothing, it's not finished . . .

But Catherine won't be put off. Setting the Firebird picture aside, she takes the coat of feathers and holds it up.

Catherine What an incredible idea! Did you do this?

Robert nods.

(*to Niker*) Isn't it remarkable?
Niker (*shrugs*) What is it?
Catherine Oh, come on! It's a really original take on the Firebird story.
Niker No it's not, it's some crappy feathers stuck on an old jumper.
Catherine Jonathan! Tell you what, why don't we display

them both, side by side. Your picture and Robert's
more . . . organic approach. What do you think?

Niker grabs a squeezy bottle of adhesive from a desk.

Niker Why not? Good idea. I'll stick it down for him . . .
Robert No way! (*He grabs the coat from Catherine.*)
Niker (*advances flourishing the glue*) Chick, chick, chick,
chick, chickie . . .
Kate Leave it, Niker.

*Niker lunges for Robert, who jumps backwards,
clutching the coat.*

Niker Give it here – Feather Boy!

Cue song: 'Wanna Make Something of It?' underscore.

Robert Never!

*Enter the class kids led by Wesley, who senses the
drama immediately. A threatening ring yelling 'Fight!
Fight!' forms round Robert and Niker.*

Catherine Boys! Boys! Stop it at once!

*Niker lunges again. This time Robert is not quick
enough – Niker gets his hands on the coat and begins
to pull. Robert holds on like grim death, but Niker
is pulling, pulling, his hands are around a couple of
large feathers. One final pull and they tear free. Niker
waves them triumphantly.*

Robert I'll kill you!

*Robert lets rip. At first Niker fights back, but Robert
completely overwhelms him. The ring breaks, other
kids rush in to help Catherine separate them, but it's
no use. Niker just shields himself from the punches
raining down. Soon he isn't even resisting, and then he
isn't even moving – and Robert has to be dragged off,
still fighting, by the other kids.*

At last he stands there, white-faced, chest heaving,
staring down at Niker, who is unmoving, bruised and
bloody. Catherine moves into Robert's line of vision as
offstage an ambulance siren approaches.

Catherine Robert! Robert, look at me!

End underscore 'Wanna Make Something of It?'

Whatever explanation you have, I warn you, it's not going
to be good enough.

She takes away the coat of feathers.

SCENE FIVE

Robert's kitchen. Robert is sitting at the table, staring
forward, twiddling his thumbs. Behind him in a
semicircle are the Headmaster, Head of Pastoral Care,
Catherine and Mum. They speak slightly fast, like a
maniacal tape fast-forwarding.
Cue song: 'Fly Away' underscore.

Headmaster In the light of the severity of the offence . . .
Head of Pastoral Care A first offence, Headmaster . . .
Catherine (*to the back of Robert's head*) Do you feel any
    remorse, Robert?
Headmaster The boy had to go to casualty, have stitches.
Head of Pastoral Care Counselling should definitely be
    considered . . .
Headmaster Not to mention the damage to school
    property . . .
Mum (*very much slower, a moment of stillness in the*
    maelstrom. They all turn to look at her) It's not
    Robert's fault. It's mine. And his father's. I don't think
    we've been paying attention.
Headmaster (*resuming normal maniacal business and*
    herding everyone but Mum off the stage by the end

of his speech) I have no option but to exclude Robert Nobel from school for a period of one week. Thank you all for coming.

End 'Fly Away' underscore.
    They all exit, leaving Mum alone. She walks forward and joins Robert in the kitchen.

Mum Which means you have to stay in the house.
Robert But I've got things to do!
Mum You certainly have. And you can start by telling me what happened.
Robert He had something of mine . . .
Mum And? What was that?
Robert Mrs Sorrel's coat of feathers.
Mum That wretched jacket!
Robert He was messing it up! He was going to wreck it!
Mum Robert, listen to yourself! You very nearly put a boy in hospital over an old cardigan and some feathers . . .
Robert But it's important! You don't understand. If I don't finish it, Mrs Sorrel's going to die!

Mum looks – 'He really believes it!' She takes him by the shoulders.

Mum No, she isn't!
Robert You don't know!
Mum You're right, I don't know. I don't know if she's going to die but I *do* know the jacket won't make any difference, whatever you think, and it sure as hell isn't worth fighting over. (*Pause.*) Right, well, believe it or not I have to go to work. You stay put, young man. I've left lunch out. (*She turns to go, turns back.*) And by the way, I love you, Robert Nobel.

She goes. Robert sits, paces, lifts the phone, dithering. The doorbell rings. It's Kate.

Kate Can I come in?

Robert (*adoring repetition, as per Act One*) Come in?

Kate Don't start.

Robert Sorry.

She comes in, bearing a plastic bag.

Kate I brought you something. (*Gets out the coat.*)

Robert Brilliant! You don't know what this means!

Kate Must be something big if it made you fight Niker.

Robert It's Mrs Sorrel's life . . .

Kate looks – is this another piece of Robert's weirdness? Robert changes the subject.

Robert Why didn't he hit me back?

Kate He tried to. Don't you remember? You were too much for him. It was like you grew, right in front of our eyes. How weird is that?

But Robert has begun to check the coat – his fingers increasingly frantic.

Robert I don't believe it!

Kate What?

Robert The feathers Niker pulled off. They're the ones from Chance House. I have to get them back, they're special, you don't understand!

Kate Hey – chill. Relax. What do they look like?

Robert Grey.

Kate Grey.

Robert They were grey!

Kate Okay. Okay. We'll get them back.

Robert And I'll need more, tons more.

Kate Right, I'm on to it. (*She gets out her mobile phone.*)

Robert You are?

Kate And Robert – I apologise.

Kate dials a number, lights up on the other side of the stage where the phone rings in Niker's right hand.

In his left hand are the feathers. Niker picks up.

Kate Niker, I've something really important to ask you.
Niker Go ahead, doll.
Kate The feathers, the ones from yesterday, have you still
   got them?
Niker Who wants to know?
Kate I do.
Niker (*twirling feathers*) No, I don't keep trash.
Kate Niker . . .
Niker No, sorry, not at home.

He clicks off. Lights down on Niker.

Robert He's got them, hasn't he?
Kate No – maybe . . . I don't know. Don't worry, I'll get
   others. I'll get you thousands. You'll be able to finish
   the coat, I promise.

Kate dials another number. Lights up on Wesley.

It's me. I need your help. It's a matter of life and death.

*Cue song: 'Feathers'. A frenetic chorus piece, a chain
of ring-tones and Robert's doorbell, beginning with
Kate and then (second verse) lines and half-lines being
sung by individual kids or groups of kids. Lights up,
lights down, all kids heaving to, answering phones,
looking for feathers, ringing Robert's doorbell,
bringing him contributions, and all the while Robert
is not singing, just sewing, sewing, sewing. Final light
on Robert and the finished coat.*

FEATHERS

Kate
   We gotta get some feathers,
   Don't ask any questions,
   Any kind of feathers,
   Here are some suggestions –

Try the local duck pond,
That's where you should be heading,
There's bound to be some feathers,
Ducks are always shedding.

Group of Kids 1
Feathers we must get feathers.

Group of Kids 2
Don't ask why.

Group of Kids 3
We can get them from anything that can fly.

Group of Kids 1
An ostrich.

Group of Kids 2
A vulture.

Group of Kids 3
A flamingo.

Group of Kids 1
A hen.

Group of Kids 2
My cousin's got a parrot.

Group of Kids 3
And so's my Uncle Ken.

All
Undo all your pillows, get the feathers to Kate.
Hurry up! It's urgent!
We might be too late.

Kate
Rip your parents' duvets,
Don't look at me like that –
Get 'em from a peacock
Or your grandma's hat.
Try a park, a farm, a zoo –

All
Just come back with a fistful of feathers
Or I'll tar and feather you.

Robert Thank you, Kate. Thank you for ever!

SCENE SIX

Mayfield Rest Home. Old people and kids are gathered, the triptych finished now, with Niker's 'Firebird' picture glued in the middle space, and the 'end of the story' space filled with a beautiful flying bird under a rainbow: sunshine, but also rain. Niker and Mavis are standing in front of the artwork, and downstage from them is a kneeling photographer.

Photographer Heads a bit closer, Mavis – is her name Mavis? Bit closer in Mavis, love.

No response, no movement.

Is she deaf?

Niker Yes.

Photographer (*screaming*) Mavis love, could you move in a little, love?

Mavis (*still not moving*) It'll all come to no good, mark my words.

Niker (*lifting his arm to embrace Mavis*) Mavis . . .

Mavis moves in, the camera whirrs and clicks. During this Robert has entered, carrying the coat bag and moving surreptitiously, around the day room in the direction of Edith's room. Lights up on Edith, lying in bed and breathing heavily. Ernest is sitting by her side.

Robert Mrs Sorrel, it's me, Robert.

No response.

I've finished the coat. It's finished.

No response.

Mrs Sorrel – (*Takes coat from bag.*) – feel this!

No response. Ernest shakes his head. Robert is panicked now.

Mrs Sorrel!

He takes her hand and plunges it into the coat.

Edith Aa–ah.
Ernest Edith?
Robert Do you want it on? Do you want to put the coat
on?

There's a small flutter of Edith's hands.

Ernest I'll lift her. Edith . . .
Edith (*as if seeing him for the first time*) Ernest, you
came back.
Ernest My love, I never went away. We're going to help
you with the coat.

Robert and Ernest help her gently into the coat.

Robert Does it hurt?
Edith No. (*She opens her eyes.*) Not at all.

Pause.
Cue song: 'Everything About You'.

Edith Hold me. I'm going . . .
Ernest No, oh, please no . . .
Edith . . . to sing.

*Only when she begins Edith – and the music – stutters
hopelessly. She clears her throat, tries to begin again,
Ernest takes her hand, clutches it, she begins again,
and again until the song comes. At 'Off I go', she peels
back her cover, begins to get out of bed. Ernest, as if
it's the most natural thing in the world, slips an arm
about her and lifts her to the floor, where they begin to
dance and sing together as they might have done when
young and in love. Robert is very still, an observer on
the scene, as if this is another of his visions, the
culmination of everything he's worked for, because*

she's living, isn't she, dancing? But in the last verse she begins to falter, her steps all wrong. Ernest supports her, stumbling, lifts her back to bed and reality. She comes to the last line of the song, gets stuck on 'heart', repeats and repeats, like a stuck record, like a heart breaking, and then finally moves on to 'sing' which should be a pure clear note held until the last of her earthly breath.

EVERYTHING ABOUT YOU

Edith

Everything a . . .
Everything a . . .
Everything about you
Makes me see
Just how rosy this world can be.
I see your face and I start to glow,
I hear your voice and off I go.

Everything about you
Makes me shine.
Am I dreaming? Are you all mine?
I pinch myself but I'm still awake,
It's all too much for one heart to take

Ernest *and* **Edith**

I feel I'm in a world of make-believe –
What other tricks have you got up your sleeve?
Everything about you
Thrills me so
Ever since we first said hello.

Edith

You look at me, winter turns to spring.
Promise me you won't change a thing
'Cos everything about you,
Everything about you,
Everything about you makes my heart . . .

138

Heart . . .
Heart sing.

When the note and Edith finally die, Ernest lays his head on Edith's breast.

Ernest Oh my darling girl. Oh my sweet angel.

There is no place for Robert at the bedside. He touches Edith perhaps one last time and then stumbles from the room. Niker is walking towards the room.

Robert Don't say a thing.

Niker doesn't. He lets Robert pass, looks after him.

Catherine (*storytelling to the assembled elders and kids*) 'And others say that when the boy awoke the following morning he was so sad that he lost his voice and . . .'

She and the others catch sight of Robert: his body language brings her to silence. No one says a word as they watch Robert walk – very alone – across the front of the stage. After a painfully long time Kate finally crosses over to him and puts her arms around him.

SCENE SEVEN

The steps of Chance House. There's a new board up, a builder's board – NEW DEVELOPMENT: PROPOSED YOUTH AND UNEMPLOYMENT CENTRE. *Robert is staring up, past the board to the top-floor window. Ernest is staring at Robert.*

Ernest Penny for them?

Robert I was thinking about your son. David. About why he jumped from that window.

Ernest Jump? David never jumped. Who told you that nonsense? He was born with a heart defect. He could have died at any time, but it happened to be here. This

is where Edith left him when she went to her secret
singing lessons. Only Edith couldn't accept that. She
thought that if she hadn't gone for a lesson that day,
if she'd have been with him, she could have saved him.

Robert (*quietly*) And if I'd finished the coat sooner I could
have saved *her*!

Ernest takes him by the shoulders.

Ernest Don't you dare say that! Don't even think such a
thing! Edith had cancer. It happens. People die and it's
no one's fault. Don't go through life blaming yourself,
please, Robert. You gave her everything.

Robert She gave me stuff too. She said I was the sort of
boy who could fly.

Ernest I should have let her fly. That's what love is –
letting your loved ones fly.

Enter Kate and Niker. Kate is calling.

Kate Robert! Robert! Oh, hello, Mr Sorrel. (*to Robert*)
He did have them. The feathers – he grabbed them as
he fell. Show him, Jonathan.

*Niker reaches inside his jacket and brings out the three
Chance House feathers. Robert takes the feathers.*

Ernest 'Some say that when the Firebird flew, the boy
was so sad that he lost his voice and became silent.
Others say that the next day he found three shining
golden feathers on his pillow, and these feathers
brought him courage, love and luck for all of his life.'
Good luck, Robert Nobel.

Cue song: 'You're Not Going Anywhere' reprise.
*   The others watch as Robert moves away downstage
on his own, holding the feathers. He speaks directly to
the audience.*

Robert Courage – I plan to learn more of that. Love –
I think maybe, for now, I have enough. And luck –

well, if Mrs Sorrel taught me anything she taught me
you make your own luck.

YOU'RE NOT GOING ANYWHERE

You will be my guiding star,
I feel you're still here.
All those demons in my head
I no longer fear.

I believe you'll always keep an eye on me
Whatever I do.
I'm not going anywhere
Without you.

(*Spoken.*) As for the rest of my life – did Niker become
my new best friend? No. Mr Sorrel my new best
grandad? No. How about – Mum and Dad got
together again? Fat chance. And Kate? Well, nothing's
quite that simple, is it? But you know what?

He holds up the feathers.
    Cue song: 'Bold and Fearless Dot Com' reprise.

For a boy who's been to the top of Chance House, nothing
can ever be quite the same again. So who knows?
Maybe one day . . .

Cast pour onstage for bows and final reprise of:

BOLD AND FEARLESS DOT COM

Robert
    I'll know who I am
    And I'll be glad to know me,
    Got no reason to be shy –
    How many boys know they can fly?
    If you want to soar
    Come knocking at my door –
    I'm the man you should be taking lessons from.
    Stop clicking Bold and Fearless Dot Com.

All

> Norbert No-Bottle,
> Norbert the Nerd,
> That's the stupidest thing that we've ever heard.
> He's got self-esteem,
> Living a dream
> And soaring like a bird.

Robert

> Look at me, I'm cool.

All

> Look at him, he's cool.

Robert

> I've turned into a leader.

All

> He's turned into a leader –

Robert

> That the other kids respect.
> With every sentence I connect,
> Positive and sure.

All

> Positive and sure.

Robert

> Always certain and secure –

All

> Certain and secure.

Robert

> See me strut around the classroom with aplomb –

All

> Mister Bold and Fearless,
> Confident and Tearless,
> Bold and Fearless Dot Com,
> Bold and Fearless
> Dot Com!

The End.

Letting Your Loved Ones Fly

Interviews by Jim Mulligan

Feather Boy opens with Robert watching Niker paint a picture of a Firebird, creating something beautiful for its own sake, not the action you would expect from someone who goes on to bully and humiliate Robert. All Robert wants to do is fly away, to dream, to escape from being the nerdiest of nerds. He does this through the power of storytelling but the setting for his escape is not promising.

A group of teenagers, undertaking a school project in a care home for senior citizens, are mimicking old people dribbling and shaking and not being able to keep awake. The song they are singing is scarcely complimentary: they can't stand noise or digital toys; they smell; they're not into rap music; they are bothered by water retention; they don't know their inches from their metres. Robert does not take part in the song. He meanders about, finally coming to rest in front of the Firebird picture. At the end of the song the singers crowd round Robert in an aggressive way.

The opening scenes of *Feather Boy: the Musical* encapsulate the elements that have been transferred from the novel by Nicky Singer to the book by Singer and Peter Tabern, to the lyrics by Don Black, and to the music by Debbie Wiseman. We have the relationship between young people and their elders, a mystical story and a young boy who is isolated and bullied. By the end of the musical, young and old have collaborated on a multi-media project, Robert has thrashed Niker both psychologically and physically, and everyone has grown in awareness.

NICKY SINGER When we started I was quite frightened about what might happen. I knew that in a musical the original material is gutted; Don Black talks about raping a book, but I think we have kept the essence of the story and the characters. The original novel is primarily about storytelling, but also about bullying and empowerment. Robert describes himself as an outsider, but by the end he is telling his own story in his own words.

DON BLACK My job as a lyric writer is to find a matching voice. On the stage you are listening to Nicky's dialogue, and when the lyric comes along the transition should be seamless. Usually a song comes in a musical when the emotions become so great that the words are not enough. Usually the big points, the signposts, are the songs.

DEBBIE WISEMAN When I was writing the music I was picking up on those moods. So 'Fly Away' is a little bit mystical just as the Firebird is a mystical story. 'Bold and Fearless Dot Com', however, is an inspirational, uplifting song, in the sense that Robert has aspirations not to be a nerd or a geek but to be respected by his friends.

The interior journey Robert makes is with one of the elders, Edith Sorrel, who was frozen emotionally when her son died. She blames herself for sneaking off for singing lessons and is convinced that if she had been with her son he would not have died. Legend has it that her son had fallen from the upstairs window of Chance House, whereas in reality he had been born with a heart defect and could have died at any time. There are similarities between her son and Robert – both are the same age, both are somewhat neglected by their mothers, both vulnerable. As their friendship grows, Robert comes to believe that if only he can create the magical coat of feathers like the one in the Firebird legend, he will be able to save Edith. Of course he cannot do that, because she is dying of cancer, but he is able to give her a moment of greatness and healing. She puts on the coat of feathers and, for the first time since her son dies, she sings: 'Everything about you makes my heart sing.' It is a moment of sorrow and redemption and love. Her voice becomes stuck on the word 'heart', which she repeats and repeats like a stuck record, like a heart breaking, and then finally she moves on to 'sing', a pure clear note that she holds till the last of her earthly breath.

NICKY SINGER I wanted Robert to be a boy who had an empowering relationship with Edith. We decided that the bullying incident would have him locked for a night in a cellar. Then, in response to Edith's demand, he goes to the top of the spooky house at night. Niker, the bully, is scared and runs off, but our hero has already been there. He has done his time, he is able to rise above the fear. In other words, the bullying has made him stronger. I didn't want Robert to be a total loser as a victim. He is self-deprecating, comical and nice. Nor did I want Niker to be a conventional bully. He is creative, sexy and good fun. He is the flip side of Robert. He is the person Robert would like to be.

In the end things go on pretty much as normal. Maybe Robert gets the girl and he and Kate live happily ever after. Maybe not. Niker does not become Robert's friend and Mr Sorrel does not become a surrogate grandad. Robert's mum and dad do not get back together. But, 'For a boy who's been to the top of Chance House, nothing can everbe quite the same again.'

DEBBIE WISEMAN I wasn't conscious of restricting the range because we were writing for young people. I wanted it to be a challenge. These songs can be sung by anyone, but I had to make sure the range of notes was not too wide – although I was tempted at times and the end of 'Full Moon' is very high. We have given the companies a piano score and the vocal lines and they can have just a piano or they can dream up their own orchestration. It could be a school band or a chamber orchestra or two or three players. They will put their own stamp on it.

DON BLACK I've never written lyrics for old people, so this was very appealing. My favourite song is 'It's Still Me in Here'. Anyone can relate to that. The song says, 'Don't look at my face and hands. I am still me.' Old people are the same inside as they have always been. They don't feel old. That is true and very touching.

Production Notes

Nicky Singer originally set her story in Brighton, but there are no specific allusions so it could be set anywhere.

You could orchestrate the score with various instruments or just with piano keyboard for accompaniment. The lyrics should always be clearly sung. Avoid choosing an actor whose voice is breaking to play Robert (it would be a bit clichéd if Niker had a broken voice and Robert didn't). Robert's voice has to be reliable as there is a lot resting on his character.

You'll need to decide whether to use amplification or to go acoustic. This will depend on the size of your space in relation to the size of the voices. In a large auditorium it would be best to have amplification, as it is irritating for an audience not to be able to hear the lyrics. But clarity is as important as volume, and talent is irrelevant if the actor cannot be understood. Doing exercises before the show, like having the actor speak lines to the back of the auditorium, is useful. So are warm-up songs.

STAGING

Read the play out loud with your designer. Read it to each other to discover the atmosphere, tone, colour, flow and rhythm. Consider such practicalities as whether it will be in-the-round, how to get furniture on and off, etc.

Ask if you need a set at all – always begin with this question. You do need two bedrooms – but you can make

minor changes to suggest two very different locations.
You could use the same bed for both Robert and Edith.
Do everything with just props, chairs and blankets.
You don't need an actual flight of stairs – they can be
physicalised/acted out. Likewise, you don't need to have
a building – someone could just hold a sign.

Give a sense of being in a classroom, but don't make it
too literal. Any chairs, soft furnishings and so on can be
recycled for the care home. The kitchen could be suggested
by Robert sitting with a bowl of cereal.

The graveyard can be achieved with just a tombstone or a
cross. A stylised approach should be encouraged.

Introduce costume elements such as slippers, padding and
wigs into rehearsals early on, especially with the elders
and the characters who need to age up. The costume
requirements are not too demanding, as there aren't
many changes. Avoid cliché, though. Question whether
the costumes would be best if they look lived in. Also if
there is some relationship to the set design.

Keep scene changes fluid through the use of lighting and
keeping characters on stage. Avoid having your crew
moving sets/props across stage as it interrupts the action
of the play. Have the actors make the scene changes if
they can and if it makes sense.

Take time to choreograph the fight between Niker and
Robert. The dynamics of the music should parallel the
action of the fight sequences.

The Fears of the Night Kids are imagined. They are also
the natural sounds of a house. Only Robert sees them at
first, not Niker – they are in his imagination. But towards
the end the Fears are transferred from Robert to Niker.

The light in the house could be the ghost of the boy. The
energy of the house is located here. It creates a supernatural

experience – later we find out the boy didn't die from the fall, but we don't want the audience to know this yet. The light can go on as a physical/external occurrence. It could be a street light – the door swings open and it's there.

You might choose to play it so that the fears are *all* in Robert's imagination.

Arrange for the actors to have a CD to sing along to at home – they will learn it by listening. Before a performance run a song that involves the full company, as this will serve as a good warm-up and will help with focus.

When the lines have been learned, it is vital that the actors listen to each other so that their reactions are played truthfully – it's as much about the other person on stage as the character who is speaking.

This first song establishes the relationship between Robert and the audience because it's very personal and enables them to hear his inner thoughts and aspirations.

Niker should be a lead actor, sexy and cool but also vulnerable.

When Edith dies, Robert and Ernest are with her. It's a dramatic moment, but if you want to keep it truthful then it's not a big number. She just dies on the note . . . it's not a melodramatic death. Her death note should be the most beautiful note she has ever sung.

EXERCISE

Look at Act One, Scene Ten. Mark up the floor, creating a square – this could be the house with steps. Niker is sitting at front with rucksack – have the steps centre stage.

For the sake of this exercise, imagine the Fears of the Night Kids are just in Robert's imagination. Tell him there is a path that he must take – have him circle the house twice, ignoring Niker. Have the imaginary Fears of the Nights Kids follow Robert and do all that he does – when he stops they stop and freeze.

Repeat the exercise. This time they can acknowledge each other and poke and taunt Robert while he walks. Have them whisper Niker's name to Niker before he answers whether he's scared. He shouldn't show his fear at this point. Robert should have problems seeing him in the dark. Place the kids in front of Niker to create more of a visual awareness.

Hold the music until Robert and Niker step into the house. When they do, the Fears of the Night Kids should scatter and crouch down on their knees. Robert and Niker should wait until they have settled to enter. There might be a dead energy between the Kids settling and the music beginning – the Kids can make house sounds (creaking, etc.) until the intro ends.

As Robert walks around the house, the kids can grab, poke, make physical contact with him (but not Niker) and may even make eye-contact with him.

Don't let things get under-energised – don't drop the inflection at the end of sentences. It should be like passing a baton to the other to keep the energy going.

Before taking the stairs, take a deep breath together before 'ascending'.

When Niker says 'That little doorway up there', all should look up to create a focus.

When Niker leaves, he has to bound down the stairs, following the same path as before. One by one, the Fears of the Night Kids should follow him, responding with the same actions as Niker – running, stopping, etc.

When Robert steps forward (and Niker and the Kids have left), he should step into the light, over the threshold, and fall forward. To create the mystery of what happens, go to instant blackout.

It's more interesting to see a frontal view of the actors' faces rather than the sides.

Robert should have more of an imaginative commitment to stepping through the door.

The fall should happen before the last note of music.

WARM-UP EXERCISE

Hum to begin. • Change to sirens. • Use the teeth and the tongue, the lips and the teeth. • Run the Rs the Es and all of the vowels. • Go up the scale. • Go down the scale. • (Actors tend to be flat in the morning – this can be fixed by smiling.)

Different spaces will demand different projection – have the actors walk around – this also relaxes them more. • Have them think that they are singing out of the top of their head. • Pull the nape of the head up (Alexander technique). • Pretend that you are a puppet and someone is pulling up the strings. • Imagine that the audience is above you and looking down. • Get in a circle and do massages. • Get them to massage their jaws. • Have them hum the same note – then you will know who may have pitch-matching problems. • Make sure that the mouths are open for all vowels.

Get into an exercise routine.

Do shoulder rolls, back then forward. • Pant (don't hyperventilate) – ha ha ha ha – make sure that it's open, as if you are biting an apple. • Yawning emulates the best singing – it's like having an entire apple to bite. • Don't drop the jaw – but do have an open mouth. • Lie on the ground, head on each other's diaphragms, feel the deep breathing from low down.

Humming – put fingers on top lips – if there isn't a vibration, then you aren't doing it properly. • If you don't feel it, then it's probably too low – the teeth should have a slightly open gap. • Do long hums on each note – after four or five, open to 'ah'. • Do a cut-off for the last.

Do eight tone scales down, then go up – encouraging more chesty/belly sound – work on mid-register, don't take it too much – it must be nasal and open in order to keep the voice safe – it will sound more gritty and not so beautiful.

If your jaw is tense, then your tongue is also probably tense, impeding high notes.

Rub hands together, then rub them down the sides of your neck. • Rub sides of fists together, rub down the side of the jaw and hum a siren sound.

Vowel exercise – a-e-i-o-u, all of the same tone. • The changes should be felt in in the back of the mouth, not the front. They should all be in the same place – do about an octave.

Sing the song 'The Grand Old Duke of York', marching throughout and emphasising the consonants. • To challenge the actors, take out a word such as 'up' or switch the words up and down.

Workshop facilitated by Lindsay Posner
with notes taken by Amy Schier

LIAR
This High School Movie Is a Play

Gregory Burke

Gregory Burke's previous work includes *Gagarin Way* (Traverse/NT Studio/Arts) and *The Straits* (Paines Plough). He gained the Most Promising Playwright award in February 2002, Best New Play at the TMA Barclays Awards and shared the Meyer-Whitworth Award for *Gagarin Way*. Other work includes *The Party* (part of *Citizone*, the Glasgow Live Millennium Soap Opera) and *Occy Eyes* (BBC Radio 3).

Characters

Ronnie
a right good-looking liar

Eck
a namesake of a famous man

Beefy
a chunky, fearless chap

Katie
a bit of a goddess with a brain

Kylie
ditto

Kelly
ditto, but sans brain

Chanelle
a stunna

Montana
another stunna

Tam
a Ned

Shug
a Ned

Willie
a Ned

Kellie-Marie
a Femned

Mary-Anne
another Femned

Li'l Tim
a ginger Fifty Cent

Krystal
Li'l Tim's bitch

Halfmast
a nerd whose trousers don't quite reach his feet

Brett
tiny Marilyn Manson lookalike, scourge of Neds

Several Heathers
a group of angry indie-rock chicks

Assorted youth tribe extras and partygoers

SCENE ONE

A hint of video shop. Ronnie, a good-looking lad of about sixteen, spies a girl, Katie, looking at the films. He watches her at a distance before passing her, scoping the wall to see what film she has picked. He smirks. Pauses. Walks back.

Ronnie Excuse me.

Katie moves and simultaneously notices him. He studies the back of the DVD case. Shakes his head.

Whatever happened to him?
Katie (*looks up*) Sorry.
Ronnie Whatever happened to him?
Katie Eh . . . yeah.
Ronnie I suppose the tricky, transitional journey from child star to serious actor is all the more hazardous when you're being royally bummed by the king of pop. (*Beat.*) That's not gonna do anyone any good, is it?
Katie No it isn't.
Ronnie (*picks up another case*) Now, *American History X*. That's a film.
Katie You enjoy prison movies, do you?
Ronnie Yeah.
Katie (*nods and smiles*) Yeah?

Pause.

Ronnie What?
Katie Nothing.

Pause.

All the weight training?
Ronnie Eh . . .
Katie The shower scenes? (*Beat.*) Is that what you like?

Pause.

Ronnie I'm not gay.
Katie No one said you were gay.
Ronnie It's not a gay film.
Katie Oh come on, neo-Nazis are intrinsically gay.
Ronnie Are they?
Katie Is it your favourite film?
Ronnie No. (*Puts it back on the shelf.*) I'm just saying it's good.

Pause. He puts out his hand.

I'm Donnie.
Katie Oh. Okay. (*She shakes his hand.*) Donnie.

Pause.

Ronnie What's your name?
Katie My name?
Ronnie In some cultures it's a custom that when someone introduces themselves to someone else the other person tells them their name too. (*Beat.*) I've never been there. I saw it . . . in a film.

Pause.

Katie Katie.
Ronnie Hi, Katie.

Pause.

So what's your favourite film?
Katie Well, it's quite weird.
Ronnie Weird?
Katie Not weird, but . . . it's . . . funny.
Ronnie A comedy.

Katie No, I mean it's funny that your name is Donnie and my favourite film is . . .

Ronnie *Donnie Darko?*

Katie Yeah.

Ronnie Really?

Katie Yeah.

Ronnie That's mad.

Katie I know.

Ronnie But then I suppose it's a lot of people's favourite film.

Katie It's still weird that you're called Donnie.

Ronnie I think my mum liked the Osmonds.

Katie The who?

Ronnie The Osmonds. They were a very naff band when she was growing up.

Katie Well, Donnie is a cool name. (*Beat.*) Sounds like a superhero.

Ronnie What makes you think I'm not?

Katie (*laughs*) You know you're Donnie Darko.

Ronnie Yeah. (*Beat.*) Don't get me wrong, I'm not one of those people who's obsessed with it or anything. I mean, I think a quick glance at the stuff in *The Philosophy of Time Travel* shows you it's all a lot of rubbish, but it does make some good points about soap. (*Beat.*) And in this crazy mixed-up world we're living in, that's always a good thing.

Pause.

Katie I don't agree that soap's the most important invention.

Ronnie You don't?

Katie I'd say it was spectacles. (*Beat.*) Lenses.

Ronnie Interesting.

Katie Doubled the working life of people at a stroke.

Ronnie Very interesting. (*Beat.*) As you don't even wear glasses.

Katie You don't have to use something to appreciate its
value. (*Beat.*) I'm sure you're the same with soap.
Ronnie (*laughs*) Very good.
Katie It's called humour.
Ronnie It's funny.
Katie Thank you.

Pause.

Ronnie Do you do anything else?
Katie All sorts of things.
Ronnie Really?
Katie Oh yeah, I'm a regular entertainer.
Ronnie So entertain me.
Katie It's my day off. (*Beat.*) Even entertainers need a
day off.
Ronnie I suppose.

Pause.

Well, seein' as it's your day off, do you want to go and
get a coffee or something?
Katie No.
Ronnie Oh, okay.
Katie I mean, I don't even know you.

Pause.

You could be anything.
Ronnie Or even something.

Pause.

And isn't that the point of the coffee? To get to know me?

Pause.

Katie I don't really like coffee.
Ronnie So what do you like?

Pause.

Tea?

Pause.

Tonic wine?

Pause.

Whatever it is you like, we can go and get it, now.

Pause.

Katie What school do you go to?
Ronnie I'm not at school.
Katie No?
Ronnie No.

Pause.

I mean, do I look like I'm at school?
Katie Well, yeah, you do a bit.

Pause.

So what do you do?
Ronnie I'm a . . . well, I'm not yet, obviously, but I'm
    gonna be a . . . footballer.
Katie Really?
Ronnie Eh . . . yeah.

Pause.

Katie That's a shame.
Ronnie A shame.
Katie They're usually idiots, aren't they?
Ronnie They're not all idiots.

Pause.

Katie I don't know anything about football.
Ronnie (*smiles*) Good.
Katie Good?
Ronnie Well, no, not good, just, you know, you wouldn't,
    would you?

Pause.

Katie So, who are you going to be a footballer for?
Ronnie Who?
Katie Yes.
Ronnie Who am I going to play for?
Katie Yes.
Ronnie Which team?
Katie Yes.

Pause.

Ronnie Norwich City.
Katie Norwich City?
Ronnie Yeah.
Katie How did you end up playing for them?
Ronnie It's . . . it's a long story.

Pause.

Katie I've got an auntie in Norwich.
Ronnie Have you?
Katie Yes. My uncle supports Norwich.
Ronnie Oh . . .
Katie Never misses a game.
Ronnie Great.
Katie Will he know who you are?
Ronnie Probably not. I've . . .
Katie I'll ask him . . .
Ronnie I haven't played for the first team or anything.

Pause.

Listen, why don't you give me your number?
Katie My number?
Ronnie Your phone number?
Katie And why would you want that?
Ronnie To phone you. Or text you or something.

Pause.

Katie I would, but I don't have a phone.

Ronnie You don't have a phone?

Katie Not on me.

Ronnie But you must know the number?

Katie It's new, I forget.

Ronnie So you don't drink coffee and you don't have a phone. (*Beat.*) What do you do?

A phone starts ringing. It is obviously in her bag. Katie begins to leave the shop.

Katie I am sometimes in here. Quite a lot actually. I like films. You should just come in occasionally. You might just get lucky.

She exits. Ronnie smiles.

SCENE TWO

Eck and Beefy, two lads of about sixteen, are sitting in a school playground. Eck is spitting as only a teenage boy can spit, at an almost professional level.

Eck They chased us all the way through the centre. Through the bus station, into the multi-storey.

Beefy Shug said he got hit with a brick.

Eck He had to run into Boots and hide in the photo bit.

Beefy Yeah.

Eck I hid under a car.

Beefy Yeah.

Eck There were about forty or fifty of them.

Beefy Fifty!

Eck Easy, maybe more. It was difficult to tell with all the shoppers.

Beefy Tam said about ten.

Eck There was at least thirty.

Beefy Willie said about twenty.

Eck Willie. He was that far in front he never saw nothing.

Pause.

I ruined my jacket.
Beefy Which one?
Eck The one with the hood, the green one.
Beefy Good.
Eck What?
Beefy That's a horrible jacket.
Eck No it's not.
Beefy You should be happy.

Pause.

Eck If I see that boy that looks like Marilyn Manson up the town again I'm gonna . . .

Pause.

. . . think about doin' something.

Pause.

Beefy Who'd have thought it, Neds routed by Goths.
Eck They've got some hard lads these days.
Beefy Yeah?
Eck Yeah.

Pause.

These were like Super Goths.
Beefy Super Goths?
Eck Yeah. Like devil-worshipping ones and all that stuff. That one that looks like Marilyn Manson.
Beefy I heard he just got out of a young offenders'.
Eck I heard he sold one of his kidneys on the black market so he could buy new speakers.
Beefy Yeah?
Eck And someone else said they heard . . .
Beefy (*cuts in*) Have you decided about this weekend?

Eck No.

Beefy No you haven't decided, or no you're not having a
  party?

Eck I dunno.

Beefy You've got to have a party.

Eck I dunno.

Beefy How not?

Eck 'Cause everything'll get wrecked.

Beefy No it won't.

Eck It will.

Beefy Who's gonna wreck everything?

Eck Everybody.

Beefy Well, just a select few people then.

Eck No way.

Beefy Strictly vetted for suitability.

Eck That never works. (*Beat.*) Ever.

  Pause.

You remember the last time?

Beefy (*smiles*) Of course I remember.

Eck I can't go through that again.

  Pause. Looks at his watch.

Where's this new boy, then?

Beefy Dunno.

Eck You said lunchtime to him?

Beefy Yeah.

Eck Here?

Beefy Yeah.

Eck What does he look like?

Beefy Here he comes.

  Ronnie enters.

Ronnie (*to Beefy*) Alright.

Beefy Alright.

Ronnie (*to Eck*) Alright.

Eck Alright.
Ronnie (*to Eck*) Ronnie.
Eck (*to Ronnie*) Eck.
Ronnie Eck.
Eck This is Beefy.
Ronnie We already met.
Eck So you did.

Pause.

Ronnie So Eck?
Eck Yeah.
Ronnie That's short for . . .
Beefy (*cuts in*) Alexander.
Eck Shut up.

Pause.

Ronnie So why not Sandy?
Beefy Saaaaaaandy.
Eck That's why.

Pause.

Ronnie Must be crap having that name.
Eck How?
Beefy That's why people call him Eck.
Ronnie It's a tough name to live up to. Alexander. (*to Eck*) How old are you?
Eck Sixteen.
Ronnie 340 BC. He was sixteen. Won his first battle and founded a city, Alexandroupolis, named after himself. He was sixteen. His old man was away somewhere. Campaigning.

Pause.

What else are you gonna do when your parents are away?
Beefy Get your mates round, have a smoke.
Ronnie Win a battle, found a city, name it after yourself.

166

(*Beat.*) D'you like apples?

Eck Yeah.

Ronnie Well, how d'you like them apples?

Pause.

So what do people do round here for fun, then?

Eck The usual. We drink, we smoke, we get humiliated by girls. (*Beat.*) Sometimes all three on the same night.

Beefy In fact, Eck might be having a party this weekend.

Eck No I'm not.

Ronnie Why not?

Beefy He's too scared.

Ronnie Scared.

Eck I'm not scared.

Ronnie That's what I mean about being called Alexander.

Pause.

So are you gonna give me the tour?

Eck That we are, new boy.

Beefy (*opens his phone*) D'you want the virtual tour?

Eck Or the real one.

Ronnie Both.

They begin begin to walk through the school. As they do they pass various groups reflecting the social and cultural make-up of the school. Beefy films it with his phone and it is projected onto a screen behind the stage.

Eck It's like all schools, really.

They pass a group of girls, one or two of whom are entwined around their boyfriends.

Eck We've got your bog-standard, beautiful people. Which is a massive achievement in a town with a gene pool this size.

*Two particularly blonde and over made-up girls
appear on the screen.*

Beefy Hey, Chanelle. Hey, Montana.
Chanelle (*turning away in disgust*) Piss off.
Beefy Looking good.
Eck Unless they talk to you first, don't bother. But console
yourself that whilst at this moment in time she may be
the paragon of all that is beautiful in the female form,
ten years from now they're in a tower block somewhere
with four kids and a drunken hubby knocking them
about because he isn't any good at football any more.

*The screen shows a mixed group of glasses-wearing
eggheads.*

Eck There's your geeks.

Halfmast looks up from his computer magazine.

Beefy New glasses, Halfmast?
Halfmast For your information.

Pause.

No.

Halfmast looks back down at his computer magazine.

Beefy There's a dragon in his dungeon.

*A group of tracksuited, burberry-hatted Neds comes
on screen.*

Eck There's your Neds.
Neds (*to Eck*) A'right, wee man.
Eck Tam. (*Beat.*) Shug. (*Beat.*) Willie.
Ronnie That I'm used to.
Eck Ours are going through a bit of a crisis of confidence
at the moment having had a bit of a shopping centre
shoeing from our Marilyn Manson acolytes.

Beefy (*to Ronnie*) He was there.
Eck (*to Ronnie*) I'm merely affiliated.
Beefy Wannabe.
Eck You've gotta be if you want to walk through the town centre on a Saturday afternoon.

Then two girls, similarly dressed and both sporting numerous chains and a gold ring on every finger appear.

Eck You got your Femneds.
Ronnie Interesting.
Beefy New sov, Kellie-Marie?

They give him the gold-covered finger.

I don't know what those girls would do if Argos went bust.

They pass a group of male teens huddled around a very small Marilyn Manson lookalike.

Eck There's our Goths and Moshers . . .

The group are predominantly dressed in black and red. A lot of zips and silver jewellery. Baggy band T-shirts. Big boots and trainers.

Beefy That wee tiny guy's their leader.
Eck Brett.

The group let out a huge laugh.

Eck Oh yeah. They're celebrating now, but winning a battle isn't the same as the war.
Ronnie They'll get complacent.
Eck Oh yes.
Ronnie Their guard will drop.
Eck Time will dull their preparedness and then . . . (*He holds out his hand and points to the middle of his palm.*) Right there.

They pass a similarly dressed female group. Black nails and eyes. Fishnets and boots.

To the right, we have the female self-harmers. Affiliated with the Mansonite male version, but with a lot more focus on the dietetic dysfunctions. Full of rage. Very edgy. Don't make any sudden movements round them.

He makes a sudden movement and they hiss at him.

Beefy Every one of them is called Heather.
Eck Very little mixing among moshing sexes.
Ronnie I suppose if they went out with each other they'd have no reason to cut themselves.
Beefy Good point.
Eck You've got your Dizzee Rascals.

Several hooded boys with unfeasibly baggy trousers shuffle past.

Eck But white and stuck in a hillbilly town. Very sad.

They pass a couple leaning against the wall.

Beefy (*to Li'l Tim*) Dog.
Eck (*to Ronnie*) Li'l Tim.

Beefy knocks his fist together with Li'l Tim.

Beefy Tupac's still alive in here man. (*He hits his fist against his heart.*) He's still alive in here.
Eck (*to Ronnie*) Good for skunk, though.
Ronnie So where do you fit in all this?
Eck Well, we're kind of neither fish nor fowl. We're like the . . .
Beefy Unclassifieds . . .

Ronnie stops listening as Katie walks past with Kylie and Kelly.

Ronnie Shit.

Eck What?
Ronnie That girl.
Eck What girl?

Ronnie points at Katie.

Beefy Oh, that girl.

All three of them stand and look.

Eck She is. It has to be said. A girl.
Beefy I'd go as far as saying, she's some girl.
Eck Aye. (*to Ronnie*) But what you have there is the KKK.
Ronnie The Ku Klux Klan?
Beefy Katie, Kylie and Kelly.
Eck They maybe don't carry out any racially motivated, public lynchings but you should still take care not to offend.

Katie's face dominates the screen.

Ronnie Katie.

Eck and Beefy notice Ronnie is transfixed.

Beefy Very interesting.
Eck Indeed.

Pause.

(*to Ronnie*) Forget about that one, mate. (*Beat.*) She's got a brain, too.
Ronnie Yeah?
Eck Oh yeah. (*Beat.*) She's way out of your league.
Beefy I heard she met some footballer. (*Beat.*) He plays for Norwich.

Katie stops. Aware she is being stared at, she looks out of the screen.

Katie Donnie?

Ronnie Katie.
Beefy (*to Ronnie*) Donnie?
Eck (*to Kate*) Ronnie
Katie (*to Eck*) Ronnie?
Ronnie Katie.

Ronnie makes a run for it. We hear breaking glass.

SCENE THREE

Katie, Kylie and Kelly in the school toilets. Each of them looking into a mirror.

Katie Why would he say that?
Kelly I know.
Katie I mean, what was his point?
Kelly I guess he thought he was impressing you.
Kylie Are you impressed?
Katie No.
Kylie Sure?
Katie Positive.
Kylie Good.
Kelly What is it with boys and football?

Pause.

Katie To be fair, he didn't actually say he was a footballer.
Kylie I thought you said he did?
Katie No.
Kelly You did.
Katie I never. (*Beat.*) I said, he said, he was . . . going . . . to be a footballer. (*Beat.*) I think.
Kelly Same thing.
Katie It isn't the same thing at all.
Kelly It is.

Pause.

Kylie Of course the worst thing about it, is by extension –
Katie By extension?
Kylie Or is it implication?
Kelly Implication?
Kylie – he thinks that you look like a footballer's wife.
Katie No?
Kelly She's right, you know.
Katie No!
Kelly She's right.
Katie Shit.

   Pause.

I never thought of that.
Kylie (*to Katie*) But then maybe that's what you want?
Katie I don't.
Kylie Maybe you want to be a footballer's wife.
Katie I do not want to be a footballer's wife.
Kylie You sure?
Katie Of course I'm sure. (*Beat.*) I mean I haven't worn anything Burberry since I was eleven.

   Pause.

Kylie You could be the new Posh and Becks.
Katie Eeuugh.
Kelly Colleen and Wayne.
Katie Yuk.
Kylie Tweedy and Cole.

   Katie retches.

Kelly Why does the girl always go first? Namewise.
Kylie What?
Kelly Technically they're less famous, but they're first.
Katie What are you on about?

   Pause.

Kelly Nothing.

Pause.

(*to Katie*) Well at least he didn't try and pretend he was clever, that's the worst thing a guy can do.

SCENE FOUR

The school canteen. Beefy and Eck sit together, eating chips. Ronnie enters.

Beefy Alright, man.
Eck Sit down.

Ronnie sits.

Beefy So how was the hospital?
Ronnie I dunno. It was alright. I suppose.
Eck Alright?
Ronnie Aye.
Beefy I heard you ran through a glass door?
Ronnie (*rubs his head*) Maybe.
Beefy What did you tell her your name was Donnie for?
Ronnie I dunno.
Eck And why did you say you played for Norwich?
Ronnie It just jumped into my head.

Pause.

Girls, they all like that *Donnie Darko* film. They all fancy that guy.
Beefy That's true.
Ronnie I mean what's the chances of her going to the same school as me? (*Beat.*) And what's the chances of her havin' an auntie in Norwich?
Eck You need to show more imagination.
Ronnie I know.
Eck Footballer's too obvious.
Beefy Yeah.

Eck You need to act a bit tragic.

Beefy Yeah.

Eck Like the boy in the film.

Beefy Yeah.

Eck There needs to be some reason for you clinging to the belief that you can be a footballer.

Beefy Yeah.

Eck Maybe you got a bad injury and your dreams were shattered.

Beefy Yeah.

Eck My cousin, he couldn't play football again. (*Beat.*) And he said he never got more girls after him.

Ronnie What did he do?

Eck He broke his leg.

Beefy Badly.

Eck One girl, she signed his cast forty times.

Pause.

Ronnie (*to Eck*) If you were having a party I could invite her along?

Eck I'm not havin' one.

Ronnie Definitely?

Eck Definitely.

Beefy She wouldn't come with you anyway.

Ronnie You think?

Beefy (*pushes his plate towards Eck*) You've blown it. Girl like that isn't gonna be impressed by a footballer.

Ronnie No?

Beefy Only one thing's gonna impress a girl like that.

Pause.

Brains.

Pause.

Ronnie She's in my English class. I'm really good at English.

Pause.

What book do you do for English at this school?
Beefy *The Great Gatsby.*
Eck (*chokes on the chip*) Damn. (*Pushes the plate to Ronnie.*) Will somebody please tell me why I eat this shit.
Beefy Because you're an idiot.
Eck Oh yeah, that's it.
Ronnie (*shaking his head*) You two. (*He pushes the plate back to Eck.*) Great chips, but I'm going to have to get a move on if I want to read the study notes on this Gatsby fella.

SCENE FIVE

An English classroom. Katie sits at a desk with a book in front of her.

Ronnie Hi.

Katie ignores him.

Ronnie (*indicates the book*) The Gatsby.
Katie I'm sorry?
Ronnie The Gatsby chap.
Katie What about him?
Ronnie He was something else.
Katie You think?
Ronnie Oh yeah.
Katie You don't just think he thought he was something.
Ronnie No. (*Beat.*) He was some boy.
Katie Wasn't he just.

Pause.

Ronnie Bit of a shame and that. (*Beat.*) You know, what happened to him.

Pause.

Katie And what did happen to him?
Ronnie He got whacked.
Katie Whacked?
Ronnie Yeah. (*Beat.*) They whacked him.
Katie Whacked him?
Ronnie They killed him.
Katie Who killed him?
Ronnie The guy.
Katie Which guy?
Ronnie The guy from downtown.
Katie Who?
Ronnie The guy. (*Beat.*) The garage guy.

Pause.

Katie Have you even read this book?
Ronnie Of course I've read this book.
Katie You're sure you're not mixing it up with something else?
Ronnie Hey. (*Beat.*) I know this book.
Katie You don't even know your own name?

Pause.

Ronnie (*places his hand on the book*) This. (*Beat.*) This is one of my most favouritest books in the world.
Katie Really?
Ronnie Forget about it. (*Beat.*) Gatsby. He has it all. Messes it all up. He goes about with his mate because he likes his mate's wife. His mate has the mistress. He has the mistress for the mistress. They all get drunk. They crash their cars. They kill the mistress. The Gatsby gets whacked. (*Beat.*) What's not to like?
Katie Another novel written by another dead American male?
Ronnie You don't like it?

Katie Not really.

Pause.

Ronnie Well it does have its flaws.

Katie It does?

Ronnie Now that I think about it and stuff.

Katie So tell me what you think about its flaws?

Ronnie (*picks up the book and looks at it for a bit too long*) The way I see it is, this book is about the American dream. Gatsby, he achieves the material dream, but he doesn't get the girl. This is about the self-made man, who makes himself for the woman.

Pause.

Like *Scarface*, but without the cocaine. (*Beat.*) And not as good.

Katie What?

Ronnie *Scarface*. (*In a Cuban accent.*) 'In this country, you gotta make the money first. Then when you get the money, you get the power. Then when you get the power, then you get the woman.'

Pause.

Katie What on earth are you talking about?

Ronnie Al Pacino. (*Beat.*) In *Scarface*.

Katie So what are you saying? That the Great Gatsby would have been better off in the drugs trade?

Ronnie All I'm saying is that Tony Montana wouldn't have been shot dead in his own swimming pool by the guy that owned the garage down the road. And why? (*Beat.*) Because Tony Montana's swimming pool was in his living room and he could sit in it and see everybody coming up to his house on his CCTV.

Pause.

Katie Can I ask you something?

Ronnie Anything.

Katie Has it ever crossed your mind that you're too . . . thick for me?

Pause.

Ronnie I can see how you might think that, yeah.

Katie It's just . . . well, I have to make sure.

Ronnie Make sure of what?

Katie That you know what you're getting yourself into here.

Ronnie Oh, I know.

Katie Do you?

Ronnie nods slowly.

I'm going to have to make you look like an idiot.

Ronnie I'm willing to take that risk.

Katie There's no risk. It's going to happen.

Ronnie Okay.

Pause.

Now can I ask you a question?

Katie Ask away.

Ronnie Do you think we could ever become friends?

Katie No.

Ronnie No?

Katie Not a chance.

Pause.

Ronnie I suppose the truth is, at this stage, neither of us has the slightest idea where this relationship is going.

Katie This relationship?

Ronnie Yeah.

Katie We don't have a relationship.

Ronnie We know each other.

Katie Barely.

Ronnie We know that each other exists.

Katie I know that lots of people exist, it doesn't mean I have a relationship with them.

Ronnie We talk.

Katie You lie.

Ronnie We argue.

Katie You annoy me.

Ronnie And that isn't a relationship? (*Beat.*) That's the *Oxford English Dictionary* definition of a relationship, darling.

Pause.

Katie I just want to make sure we understand each other.

Ronnie I understand perfectly.

Pause.

You want to hug now?

Katie No.

Pause.

Ronnie You want to shake hands?

Katie puts out her hand and they shake hands across the desk. But they don't let go. They just look at each other.

Katie I'm glad we had this conversation.

Ronnie Me too.

Katie And I'm glad you're not a footballer.

Ronnie Why?

Katie You wouldn't still be at school and we wouldn't have had this conversation.

Ronnie Well, I'm glad I'm not a footballer too.

They finally let go of each other's hand. Pause.

Katie I hear you live quite near me?

Ronnie Yeah, I heard that too.

Pause.

Katie Wanna walk me home?

Pause.

Ronnie I do.

SCENE SIX

Katie, Kylie and Kelly in the school toilets. Each of them looking into a mirror.

Kylie And you said at least he didn't try to pretend he was clever.

Kelly I know.

Kylie I mean, what was his point?

Kelly (*to Katie*) I guess he thought he was impressing you.

Kylie Are you impressed?

Katie No.

Kylie Are you sure?

Katie Positive.

Kylie Good.

Pause.

Kelly What is it with boys and trying to be clever?

Pause.

Katie To be fair, he didn't actually say he was clever.

Kylie I thought you said he did?

Katie No.

Kelly You did.

Katie I never. (*Beat.*) I said, he said, he thought *Scarface* was *The Great Gatsby* with cocaine. (*Beat.*) I think.

Kelly Same thing.

Katie It isn't the same thing at all.

Kelly It is.

Pause.

Kylie Of course the worst thing about it, is by extension –
Katie By extension?
Kylie Yeah. (*Beat.*) Or is it implication?
Kelly Implication?
Kylie – he thinks that you look like some sort of nerdy
  bookworm girl who's impressed by a lazy critical link
  between a book he hasn't read and a film he's probably
  seen too much.
Katie No?
Kelly She's right, you know.
Katie No!
Kelly She's right.
Katie Shit.

Pause.

I never thought of that.

Kylie (*to Katie*) But then maybe that's what you want?
Katie I don't.
Kylie Maybe you want to be some intellectual's wife.
Katie I do not want to be an intellectual's wife.
Kylie You sure?
Katie Of course I'm sure. (*Beat.*) I mean, I haven't read
  any non-fiction since I was twelve.

Pause.

Kylie You could be the new Simone de Beauvoir and
  Jean-Paul Sartre.
Katie Eeuugh.
Kylie Marilyn and Arthur.
Katie Yuk.
Kelly Burchill and Parsons.

Pause.

Kelly I don't think Merlin was married to King Arthur.
Katie What?
Kelly Merlin and Arthur?
Kylie What are you on about?

Pause.

Kelly Nothing.

Pause.

(*to Katie*) Well at least he didn't try and pretend he was a
gangster, that's the worst thing a guy can do.

SCENE SEVEN

*Beefy and Eck sit together, idling and smoking a cigarette.
Ronnie enters.*

Beefy Alright, man.
Eck Sit down.

Ronnie sits.

Eck So how was English?
Ronnie I dunno. It was alright. I suppose.
Eck Alright?
Ronnie Yeah.
Beefy I heard you ranted about *Scarface* until even you
didn't know what you were saying.
Ronnie (*rubs his eyes*) Maybe.
Beefy What did you try and pretend you were clever for?
Ronnie I dunno.
Eck And why did you try and make out *Scarface* was the
Latino *Great Gatsby*?
Ronnie It just jumped into my head.

Pause.

Girls like that love a guy who can come up with a good
  theory about something.

Beefy That's true.

Ronnie I mean, what's the chances of her not being
  impressed by my Al Pacino impression?

Eck You need to be a bit more ingenious.

Ronnie I know.

Eck Being clever's too obvious.

Beefy Yeah.

Eck You need to make her think you've got a big secret.

Beefy Yeah.

Eck That you're hiding from something.

Beefy Yeah.

Eck That you're on the run.

Beefy Yeah.

Eck My cousin, he went on the run from a young
  offenders'. (*Beat.*) And he said he never got more girls
  after him.

Ronnie What did he do?

Eck He moved from house to house.

Beefy Yeah.

Eck One girl he knew hid him in her room for a week.

  Pause.

Ronnie (*to Eck*) If you were having a party I would
  never have said it.

Eck I'm not havin one.

Ronnie Definitely?

Eck Definitely.

Beefy She wouldn't come with you anyway.

Ronnie You think?

Beefy (*hands Eck the cigarette*) You've blown it. Girl like
  that's never gonna be impressed by a man without a
  brain.

Ronnie No?

Beefy Only one thing's gonna impress a girl like that.

Pause.

Gangsters.

Pause.

Ronnie I'm walking her home. I'm really good at walking girls home.

Pause.

What sort of gangsters have you got in this town?
Beefy Really crap ones.
Eck (*chokes on the cigarette*) Damn. (*Hands the cigarette to Ronnie.*) Will somebody please tell me why I smoke this shit?
Beefy Because you're an idiot.
Eck Oh yeah, that's it.
Ronnie (*shaking his head*) You two. (*He hands the cigarette back to Eck.*) Great fags, but I'm going to have to get a move on if I'm going to get this girl to think I'm on the run.

SCENE EIGHT

Ronnie and Katie walk.

Katie So . . . you just moved here?
Ronnie Yeah.
Katie Where from? Norwich?

Pause.

Sorry.

Pause.

Ronnie My parents got divorced. My dad had problems.
Katie What kind of problems?
Ronnie With his business.

Pause.

Katie Did he go bankrupt?
Ronnie No.

Pause.

He had . . . emotional problems.
Katie Right.
Ronnie He borrowed some money from a gangster, and
when he couldn't pay it back, they got all emotional
with him.
Katie I imagine they do. (*Beat.*) Get emotional. (*Beat.*)
About their money. (*Beat.*) Gangsters.
Ronnie He ran away. They still can't find him. The police
thought they might try and target my mum and me.
We had to change our names and stuff. I thought
Ronnie sounded kind of cool.

Pause.

Katie So, what, you're on witness protection?
Ronnie It's not so much a witness protection programme.
It's more we just have to be really careful. If someone
was to get to know who we were then . . . That's how
I had to lie to you, about my name. I'm not supposed
to tell too many people who I really am.
Katie I thought you lied to me because you thought that,
based on the fact that I'm a girl you could guess my
favourite film and then if you said you had the same
name as the lead character I would swoon.
Ronnie No.

Pause.

I was just being careful.

Pause.

And anyway, it wasn't too much of a lie. I only changed
one letter.

Pause.

Katie You're weird.
Ronnie I'm sorry.
Katie That was a compliment.
Ronnie Really?
Katie Yes.
Ronnie You're complimenting me now?
Katie Amazing, isn't it?
Ronnie Got any others for me?
Katie Don't push it.

Pause.

Ronnie So what about you?
Katie What about me?
Ronnie Tell me about you.
Katie What do you want to know?
Ronnie I don't know.
Katie Something boring?
Ronnie Something exciting.
Katie There's nothing exciting about me, I'm afraid.
Ronnie No?
Katie Well, nothing as exciting as you.
Ronnie There must be something.
Katie Nothing I can think of.
Ronnie Mum and Dad?
Katie Very together.
Ronnie Good.
Katie Three-bedroomed house. Two cars.
Ronnie Brothers and sisters?
Katie Younger sister, older brother. (*Beat.*) All healthy and well-adjusted.

Pause.

Or they look well-adjusted. (*Beat.*) They might just be pretending.

Pause.

Ronnie You're lucky.
Katie You think?
Ronnie Oh yeah. (*Beat.*) I would kill for normality.
Katie Some people think it's a curse.
Ronnie Do they?
Katie (*stops walking*) They think they have to invent stuff to make them special.
Ronnie That's just crazy.
Katie Isn't it?

Pause.

Well, this is me.
Ronnie Oh, okay.

Pause.

Katie I'll see you tomorrow.
Ronnie Yeah.

A car horn sounds. Katie looks round. The horn sounds again. Ronnie turns round. He looks horrified.

Katie Do you know them?
Ronnie No.
Katie They're waving.
Ronnie I don't think they are.
Katie Yes, they are.
Ronnie I don't think so.

The horn sounds again.

Katie I better go and see what they want.

We hear the noise of someone being slapped across the face.

SCENE NINE

Katie, Kylie and Kelly in the school toilets. Each of them looking into a mirror.

Kylie And you said at least he didn't say he was a gangster?

Kelly I know.

Kylie I mean, what was his point?

Kelly It beats me.

Kylie Why would anyone say their dad was on the run?

Kelly I guess he thought he was impressing you.

Kylie Are you impressed?

Katie No.

Kylie Are you sure?

Katie Positive.

Kylie Good.

Pause.

Kelly What is it with boys and gangsters?

Pause.

Katie To be fair, he didn't actually say he was a gangster.

Kylie I thought you said he did?

Katie No.

Kelly You did.

Katie I never. (*Beat.*) I said, he said that his dad was on the witness protection programme. (*Beat.*) I think.

Kelly Same thing.

Katie It isn't the same thing at all.

Kelly It is.

Pause.

Kylie Of course the worst thing about it, is by extension –

Katie By extension?

189

Kylie Yeah. (*Beat.*) Or is it implication?
Kelly Implication?
Kylie – he thinks that you look like a gangster's moll.
Katie No?
Kelly She's right you know.
Katie No!
Kelly She's right.
Katie Shit.

Pause.

I never thought of that.
Kylie (*to Katie*) But then maybe that's what you want?
Katie I don't.
Kylie Maybe you want to be a gangster's wife.
Katie I do not want to be a gangster's wife.
Kylie You sure?
Katie Of course I'm sure. (*Beat.*) I mean, I haven't worn anything Versace since I was thirteen.

Pause.

Kylie You could be the new Bonnie and Clyde.
Katie Eeeugh.
Kylie Ian and Myra.
Katie Yuk.
Kylie Fred and Rose West.

Pause.

Kelly We thought she was such a quiet girl. Kept herself to herself.
Katie What?
Kelly Then they dug up her back garden.
Kylie What are you on about?

Pause.

Kelly Nothing.

Pause.

(*to Katie*) Well, at least he didn't try and pretend he was
the one with the problems, that's the worst thing a guy
can do.

SCENE TEN

*Beefy and Eck sit together, idling and drinking a bottle
of Buckfast. Ronnie enters.*

Beefy Alright, man.
Eck Sit down.

Ronnie sits.

Beefy So what was the walk home like?
Ronnie I dunno. It was alright, I suppose.
Eck Alright?
Ronnie Aye.
Beefy I heard she slapped you across the face?
Ronnie (*puts his hand to his cheek*) Maybe.
Beefy What did you tell her you were on witness
protection for?
Ronnie I dunno.
Eck And why did you say your dad had disappeared?
Ronnie It just jumped into my head.

Pause.

Girls like that, they love a bit of tragedy.
Beefy That's true.
Ronnie I mean, what's the chances of him driving past
with my mum at that precise moment?
Eck You need to be a bit more inventive.
Ronnie I know.
Eck Tragedy's too obvious.
Beefy Yeah.

Eck You need to tell her you're mentally ill.

Beefy Yeah.

Eck That there's something wrong with your head.

Beefy Yeah.

Eck That you're mental.

Beefy Yeah.

Eck My cousin, he attempted suicide. (*Beat.*) And he said he never got more girls after him.

Ronnie What did he do?

Eck He cut his wrists.

Beefy Yeah.

Eck One girl, she cut her wrists when she heard he cut his wrists and ended up in the bed next to him in hospital.

Pause.

Ronnie (*to Eck*) If you were having a party, I could cut my wrists at it?

Eck I'm not havin' one.

Ronnie Definitely?

Eck Definitely.

Beefy She wouldn't come with you anyway.

Ronnie You think?

Beefy (*hands Eck the bottle*) You've blown it. Girl like that's never gonna be impressed by a guy with a dad.

Ronnie No?

Beefy Only one thing's gonna impress a girl like that.

Pause.

Self-harm.

Pause.

Ronnie I'm going to draw some scars on my arms. I'm good at drawing stuff.

Pause.

What sort of bandages do you have in this school?

Beefy The sick bay's on the first floor.

Eck (*chokes on the Bucky*) Damn. (*Hands the bottle to Ronnie.*) Will somebody please tell me why I drink this shit?

Beefy Because you're an idiot.

Eck Oh yeah, that's it.

Ronnie (*shaking his head*) You two. (*He hands the bottle back to Eck.*) Great Bucky, but I'm going to have to get a move on if I'm gonna give myself some scars for this girl.

SCENE ELEVEN

The school canteen. Katie is sitting at a table. Ronnie approaches.

Ronnie Do you mind if I sit here?

Katie Yes.

Ronnie puts down his tray and sits.

Katie Who cooked that for you?

Ronnie I don't know.

Katie Let me think? Was it Gordon Ramsay maybe?

Pause.

Or was it Delia Smith? She owns Norwich City, you must know her.

Ronnie I never said I played for Norwich.

Katie I know. I heard you not saying it.

Ronnie puts out his hand to touch her, she pulls away but not before she notices there's a bandage on his wrist. Ronnie pulls the sleeve down self-consciously.

Katie What happened to your arm?

Ronnie It's nothing.

Pause.

Katie Show me.

Ronnie No.

Katie Why not?

Ronnie It's embarrassing.

Pause.

Katie Do you do it a lot?

Ronnie (*shrugs*) Depends.

Pause.

I don't like to talk about it.

Katie Okay.

Pause.

You wanna see something. (*Pulls up her sleeve.*) I gave myself this when I was fourteen.

Ronnie Why?

Katie shrugs.

Nice lattice work.

Katie Thanks. I worked that in recently.

Ronnie Why?

Katie Don't know why. (*Beat.*) Exams, maybe.

Pause.

It's permanent.

Ronnie You wanna see something permanent?

Katie Okay.

Ronnie (*rolls up his sleeve*) New Year's Eve 2003. I'm totally drunk, and in the middle of it, as the clock strikes twelve and everyone else in the world is all celebrating and happy. (*He admires the scar.*) That's permanent.

Katie Okay. Okay. (*She pulls her top down over her shoulder.*) New Year's Eve 2000.

Ronnie Young?

Katie (*nods her head*) Eleven years old. Came out of nowhere. Just hit me, this feeling of . . . I don't know.

Ronnie You didn't go very deep though.

Katie I was eleven.

Ronnie I got that beat. I got that beat. (*He pulls up his top and points to his stomach.*)

Katie That's a beauty mark.

Ronnie A beauty mark?

Katie Yeah.

Ronnie How dare you. (*He looks at it.*) You might be right, though.

Katie I can beat that. (*Shakes her head. Pulls up her skirt, throws up her leg, banging it down on the table and points to her thigh.*) You see this.

Ronnie (*gulps*) Yeah.

Katie Eight months ago.

Pause.

That was the last one I did.

Ronnie I knew we would have stuff in common.

Pause.

You ever think about taking stuff like that further?

Pause.

Katie (*puts her leg down*) No.

Pause.

You?

Ronnie I have, yeah.

Pause.

I guess that's why I've been behaving so weird recently.

Pause.

In fact it was on Saturday. I had to get rushed to hospital.

Pause.

To Accident and Emergency.

Pause.

Katie Which hospital?
Ronnie Which hospital?
Katie Yes. (*Beat.*) Which hospital?

We hear the sound of a plaster being ripped painfully from an arm.

SCENE TWELVE

Katie, Kylie and Kelly in the school toilets. Each of them looking into a mirror.

Kylie And you said at least he didn't try and pretend he was mentally ill?
Kelly I know.
Kylie I mean, what was his point?
Kelly It beats me.
Kylie Why would anyone say they were?
Kelly I guess he thought he was impressing you.
Kylie Are you impressed?
Katie No.
Kylie Are you sure?
Katie Positive.
Kylie Good.

Pause.

Kelly What is it with boys and mental illness?

Pause.

Katie To be fair, he didn't actually say he was mentally ill.

Kylie I thought you said he did?

Katie No.

Kelly You did.

Katie I never. (*Beat.*) I said, he said he was pretending to self-harm. (*Beat.*) I think.

Kelly Same thing.

Katie It isn't the same thing at all.

Kelly It is.

Pause.

Kylie Of course the worst thing about it, is by extension –

Katie By extension?

Kylie Yeah. (*Beat.*) Or is it implication?

Kelly Implication?

Kylie He thinks that you look like you might be mentally ill too.

Katie No?

Kelly She's right, you know.

Katie No!

Kelly She's right.

Katie Shit.

Pause.

I never thought of that.

Kylie (*to Katie*) But then maybe that's what you want?

Katie I don't.

Kylie Maybe you want to go out in a tawdry, rock star-style suicide pact.

Katie I do not want to go out in a tawdry, rock star-style, suicide pact.

Kylie You sure?

Katie Of course I'm sure. (*Beat.*) I mean, I haven't listened to a Nirvana record since I was fourteen.

Pause.

Kylie You could be the new Kurt and Courtney.

Katie Eeuugh.
Kylie Sid and Nancy.
Katie Yuk.
Kylie Ronnie and Katie.

Pause.

Kelly Why do the guys' names come first?
Katie What?
Kelly Technically they're less alive, but they're first.
Kylie What are you on about?

Pause.

Kelly Nothing.

Pause.

(*to Katie*) Well at least he didn't try and say he was dying.
Katie No. (*Beat.*) And he better not.
Kelly That's the worst thing a guy can do.
Katie Because I'll be ready for him this time.

SCENE THIRTEEN

*Beefy and Eck sit together, idling and looking at a
computer screen. Ronnie enters.*

Beefy Alright, man.
Eck Sit down.

Ronnie sits.

Beefy So what was your lunch like?
Ronnie I dunno. It was alright, I suppose.
Eck Alright?
Ronnie Aye.
Beefy I heard she ripped the plaster off your arm?
Ronnie (*holds his wrist tenderly*) Maybe.

Beefy What did you not draw a scar under the plaster
  for?
Ronnie I dunno.
Eck And why did you say you attempted suicide and
  were rushed to hospital?
Ronnie It just jumped into my head.

  Pause.

Girls like that, they all love attempted suicides.
Beefy That's true.
Ronnie I mean what's the chances of her mum being a
  nurse and working in that Accident and Emergency?

  Pause.

Eck You need to show a bit less imagination.
Ronnie I know.
Eck You should just tell her you're ill.
Beefy Yeah.
Eck Properly ill.
Beefy Yeah.
Eck Terminal.
Beefy Yeah.
Eck My cousin, he died. (*Beat.*) And the girls went mad
  at his funeral.
Ronnie What did he die of?
Eck He crashed a stolen car.
Beefy Yeah.
Eck One girl still leaves a teddy bear on the wall he hit
  every year.

  Pause.

Beefy Now he's having a party you could invite her
  along and tell her you're dying?
Ronnie You're havin' a party?
Eck Yeah.
Ronnie Definitely?

Eck Definitely.

Beefy I'm going to make my special hooch for it an' everything.

Pause.

She won't come with you anyway.

Ronnie (*turns the monitor towards Eck*) You think?

Beefy You've blown it. Girl like that's not gonna be impressed by terminal illness.

Ronnie No?

Beefy Only one thing's gonna impress a girl like that.

Pause.

The truth.

Pause.

Ronnie I'm gonna tell her the truth. I'm good at telling the truth too.

Pause.

What d'you think I should tell her?

Beefy Just tell her you're you.

Eck (*chokes when he sees the screen*) Damn. (*Turns the monitor to Ronnie.*) Will somebody please tell me why I look at this shit?

Beefy Because you're an idiot.

Eck Oh yeah, that's it.

Ronnie (*shaking his head*) You two. (*He pushes the screen back towards Eck.*) Great porn, but I'm going to have to get a move on if I'm going to get my story straight and tell the truth to this girl.

SCENE FOURTEEN

Katie stands in the school corridor. Ronnie approaches.

Ronnie Hi.
Katie I don't think I want to speak to you.

She walks away. He follows.

Ronnie Listen, I've got something really important I need to tell you.
Katie I'm not interested.
Ronnie Look, I know I've been an idiot.
Katie You haven't been an idiot.
Ronnie I haven't?
Katie No. (*Beat.*) You've just been a liar.
Ronnie I have to lie.
Katie You think, therefore you lie?
Ronnie No.
Katie It makes up the core of your being? It's your essence? It defines you?

Pause.

Ronnie Sometimes you have to lie, because the truth is so . . .
Katie So what?
Ronnie So . . .
Katie No. I mean, so what? (*Beat.*) I don't care. (*Beat.*) Go and tell someone who gives a toss.

Pause.

Ronnie (*pathetically*) Okay. (*He doesn't walk away.*) I understand. (*He still doesn't go away.*) It would only cause you pain in the end anyway.

Pause.

Katie Okay, so what is it now?

Pause.

Some exotic tropical disease you haven't researched properly which is probably extinct?

Pause.

Cancer?

Pause.

Or is it that the only way you can stay alive is if you sleep with a girl's name beginning with K?

Ronnie How did you guess?

Pause.

Katie Why do you do it?

Pause.

Ronnie I dunno.

Katie Were you bullied?

Ronnie No.

Katie Did you have to wear a nappy till you were eight?

Ronnie No.

Katie Are you a bed-wetter?

Ronnie Only if I'm very drunk.

Katie Because there must be a reason. (*Beat.*) You aren't stupid.

Ronnie I'm not?

Katie No. (*Beat.*) You're not.

Ronnie Thank you.

Katie So why is it that you're such an idiot?

Ronnie Someone's got to do it. And, I mean, the pay's rubbish. But the hours are pretty good . . .

Katie So that's your real job? Village idiot?

Ronnie Listen, is a man's job the most important thing about them for you?

Katie I think you're jumping the gun describing yourself as a man.

Ronnie Okay, a boy then, a male. (*Beat.*) But I only said it because I . . .

Katie Because what?

Ronnie Because I'm new here and you're – you know . . . you're . . .

Katie I'm what.

Ronnie You're lovely.

Katie Lovely?

Ronnie Yeah. Lovely. Lovely. (*Beat.*) What's wrong with lovely?

Katie Nothing.

Pause.

And no, a man's job is not the most important thing. (*Beat.*) It's his salary. That's the most important thing.

Ronnie And after that?

Katie Savings.

Ronnie Bugger.

Katie You can't help there?

Ronnie No.

Katie Okay.

Pause.

So what do you go for in a woman?

Ronnie Well, I know it should be a sparkling personality, but I have to say, for me, it's how she looks in a bikini.

Katie Well, I guess you'll have to wait till summer.

Ronnie I'm willing to take a risk if you are.

Pause.

Katie The thing is . . . Donnie, Ronnie, I'm busy a lot of the time, what with my pressing advice sessions from my concerned friends.

Ronnie Give me a second chance.

Katie A second chance?

Ronnie I could maybe take you to places you've never been before. (*Beat.*) And back.

Katie Like where?

Ronnie I could take you to . . .

Katie A Spar shop somewhere?

Ronnie No.

Katie A park? (*Beat.*) A golf course?

Pause.

Do women scare you?

Ronnie No.

Katie So what is it about me that makes you act like this?

Ronnie Well, you're quite . . .

Katie Formidable?

Ronnie No. (*Beat.*) I was thinking more . . . annoying? (*Beat.*) Yeah, annoying. (*Beat.*) That's the term I'm thinking of.

Katie almost smiles.

Ronnie What was that? (*Beat.*) A smile?

Katie Maybe.

Ronnie Maybe?

Katie Maybe.

Ronnie Yeah, well, you maybe want to work on that a bit before you try it again.

Katie As always, thank you for your excellent input.

Ronnie It's my pleasure.

Pause.

Katie You know, I might be interested if I thought you had a personality. (*Beat.*) Do you have a personality?

Ronnie I dunno.

Pause.

I think I might.

Pause.

It's just . . . I haven't really needed one up to now. (*Beat.*)
I just relied on my cheeky smile. (*He smiles.*)

Pause.

But obviously that isn't enough any more.
Katie Well, maybe with some girls.
Ronnie I don't want 'some girls'.
Katie No?
Ronnie Just you.
Katie Me.
Ronnie Yeah. (*Beat.*) You.

Pause.

Look. I'm sorry. (*Beat.*) You know what it's like, if you
aren't something extraordinary nowadays, you're
nothing. If you're not good at something, or ill, or a
bad boy, you're nothing. (*Beat.*) There has to be
something that marks you out from the crowd.

Pause.

Katie But there is.
Ronnie What?
Katie You're the new guy.

Pause.

Ronnie And what if I don't have nothing else?

Pause.

Katie Sometimes nothing is a really cool hand to play.

SCENE FIFTEEN

Katie, Kylie and Kelly in the school toilets. Each of them looking into a mirror.

Kylie And you said at least he didn't try to pretend he was dying?

Kelly I know.

Kylie I mean, what was his point?

Kelly (*to Katie*) I guess he thought he was impressing you.

Kylie Are you impressed?

Katie No.

Kylie Are you sure?

Katie Positive.

Kylie Good.

    Pause.

Kelly What is it with boys and dying?

    Pause.

Katie To be fair, he didn't actually say he was dying.

Kylie I thought you said he did?

Katie No.

Kelly You did.

Katie I never. (*Beat.*) I said, I thought he was thinking about saying he was dying but I jumped in first. (*Beat.*) I think.

Kelly Same thing.

Katie It isn't the same thing at all.

Kelly It is.

    Pause.

Kylie Of course the worst thing about it is –

Katie By extension?

Kylie No.

Kelly Or is it implication?

Kylie – he thinks you look like the sort of girl who likes the truth.

Katie No?

Kelly She's right you know.

Katie No.

Kelly She's right.

Katie Shit.

Pause.

I never thought of that.

Pause.

Kylie (*to Katie*) But then maybe that's what you want?

Katie I don't.

Kylie Maybe you want to be some boring, truthful guy's wife.

Katie I do not want to be some boring truthful guy's wife.

Kylie You sure?

Katie Of course I'm sure. (*Beat.*) I mean I haven't been boring since I was . . . well . . . ever.

Pause.

Kelly We should go to their party.

Katie What?

Kelly They're having a party this weekend. We should go.

Kylie There is no way we're going to their party?

Kelly No?

Kylie No way. (*Beat.*) You remember the last one.

Kelly No.

Pause.

I collapsed, remember?

Katie Well, I'm going.

Kylie On your own?
Katie No.

SCENE SIXTEEN

Beefy and Eck sit together, idling and smoking a joint.
Ronnie enters.

Beefy Alright, man.
Eck Sit down.

> *Ronnie sits.*

Beefy So what was the heart-to-heart like?
Ronnie I dunno. It was alright, I suppose.
Eck Alright?
Ronnie Aye.
Beefy I heard you didn't even tell her you were ill?
Ronnie Maybe.
Eck Why didn't you just say you had cancer?
Ronnie I dunno.
Beefy And why did you say you were sorry?
Ronnie It just jumped into my head.

> *Pause.*

Girls like that, they love apologies.
Beefy That's true.
Ronnie I mean what's the chances of her knowing I was
   going to tell her I was terminally ill?
Eck You need to just keep telling her the truth, then.
Ronnie I know.
Eck You've got to now.
Beefy Yeah.
Eck It's your only option.
Beefy Yeah.
Eck I would.

Beefy Yeah.

Eck My cousin, he's really honest. (*Beat.*) He's got the fittest wife I've ever seen.

Ronnie I thought you said he was dead?

Eck That was his brother.

Beefy Yeah.

Eck His wife, she says that honesty's the basis of everything.

Beefy (*hands Eck the joint*) And she's really, really fit.

Pause.

Ronnie I've invited Katie to your party. I'm good with girls at parties.

Pause.

Does she drink?

Beefy No.

Eck (*chokes on the joint*) Damn. (*Hands the joint to Ronnie.*) Will somebody please tell me why I smoke this crap?

Beefy Because you're an idiot.

Eck Oh yeah, that's it.

Ronnie (*shaking his head*) You two. (*He hands the joint back to Eck.*)

Great skunk, but I'm going to have to get a move on if I'm going to . . . I'm going to have to get a move on.

SCENE SEVENTEEN

Ronnie and Katie are sitting together in Eck's back garden at night. The sounds of a huge party in the background.

Katie It's a good job he only invited a select few to this party.

Ronnie I know.

Katie I mean, can you imagine if a lot of people had got wind of it?

Ronnie It would be a disaster.

Katie That's why I had to get out here.

Ronnie Me too.

Beefy, Eck, Kylie and Kelly enter.

Ronnie Hey, come on, can we get a little bit of privacy here.

Beefy (*holding out his phone to Ronnie and Katie*) You have to see this, man.

Kelly It's incredible.

The phone once again projects onto a screen behind the stage.

Eck Carnage.

Kylie All social and cultural order has broken down.

Beefy I told you my moonshine was the best. (*to Ronnie*) The secret ingredient is the Domestos.

We see the inside of the house. Smoke-filled and full of bodies drinking, dancing and in various states of distress. Doors open into a variety of rooms to show:

Li'l Tim giving Krystal a pedicure.

Krystal Who's the bitch now?

Kellie-Marie and Brett snogging. Brett is trapped in her gold chains.

Mary-Anne and a nerd playing chess.

Mary-Anne (*moving a piece with her sovereign-encrusted fingers*) Checkmate, ya arse.

The rest of the Goths and the Neds and the Heathers dancing to the Crazy Frog and hugging each other.

Finally we see Halfmast and Chanelle, locked together on a bed.

Halfmast (*to Chanelle*) For your information.

Pause.

I have already ejaculated.

Back in the garden. Eck, Beefy, Kelly and Kylie are ecstatic.

Kylie We have to get more of this.
Eck Vengeance is mine.
Beefy Think of the bribes we can extort.
Kelly Bribes mean new shoes.

Eck, Kylie, Beefy and Kelly cheer, then exit.

Ronnie I must say I'm stunned that they're couples.
Katie The boys didn't mention it?
Ronnie Not once.
Katie How do you think I knew everything you told me was a lie?

Pause.

Ronnie I suppose that's what friends are for.

Pause.

Katie (*looking up*) Do you know the names of the stars?
Ronnie (*looking up*) What stars?
Katie The stars.
Ronnie What stars?

Pause.

Katie (*points*) There's one up there.

Pause.

Ronnie Where?
Katie (*points*) Over there.

Pause.

Ronnie Is that a star?
Katie I think so.

Pause.

And there's another one.

Pause.

Can't you see it?
Ronnie I think with all the sodium it's only the satellites you can see nowadays.

Pause.

Katie So do you know the names of the satellites?
Ronnie Oh yeah. (*Points.*) Sky. (*Points.*) Telewest. (*Points again.*) CIA. (*Beat.*) Probably watching us right now.
Katie I think you're lying.
Ronnie First one today.
Katie (*puts her hand to his brow*) You feeling okay?
Ronnie Yeah.
Katie Telling the truth isn't making you ill?
Ronnie Well, I don't feel well, but it might just be a touch of the flu.

Pause.

Katie Let's go through it one more time.
Ronnie Okay.
Katie Donnie?
Ronnie Is a stupid name.
Katie Football?
Ronnie Is rubbish.
Katie Witness protection?
Ronnie Nonsense.
Katie Mental problems?
Ronnie Well, I wasn't really thinking straight.
Katie See. That was easy.

Ronnie Maybe not easy.

Katie Well . . . how about . . . a start. It's a start.

Ronnie Yeah. I can go with that.

Katie A start to you being a nice guy.

Ronnie I was always a nice guy.

Katie You've probably never done a bad thing in your life.

Ronnie Not that nice.

Katie Name me something bad you've done in your life.

He thinks.

Katie Did you ever steal anything?

Ronnie Course I have.

Katie Like what.

Ronnie Loads of stuff.

Katie And stealing from your mum doesn't count.

Pause.

Ronnie I don't really like stealing.

Katie Okay.

Pause.

You ever hit someone?

Ronnie Course.

Katie When?

Ronnie All the time.

Katie Where?

Ronnie I've been in fights.

Katie Who with?

Ronnie Let me think.

Katie You've never done one bad thing?

Ronnie Well you tell me something bad you've done.

Katie Okay.

Ronnie And it better be bad. It better be really bad. Evil.

Katie How evil?

Ronnie Really evil.

Katie Okay.

Pause.

Ronnie Come on.

Katie I'm thinking.

Ronnie I knew it.

Katie Evil is such a subjective word. I mean, what's evil to one person is totally normal to another.

Ronnie You've done nothing either.

Katie (*laughs*) So. (*Pause.*) I'm just a cosmetic-loving, argumentative girl who likes discos, handbags and shoes.

Ronnie So, as long as I'm prepared to buy you stuff, argue and pretend to find make-up interesting, I'm fine?

Katie laughs.

I can do that.

Pause.

Katie Okay. Tell me something true.

Ronnie Something true?

Katie The truth and nothing but.

Ronnie Okay.

Pause.

I'm allergic to nuts.

Katie Really?

Ronnie Oh yeah. Bullets bounce off me. Lions and bears are nothing. I can fight fifty kids from borstal, but it'll be a nut that gets me in the end.

Pause.

Katie Now tell me something no one else knows.

Ronnie Something no one else knows?

Katie Something only you know, that you want to tell me.

Pause.

Ronnie Well, I keep thinking there's always this . . . this . . .
I don't know what you call it.

Katie I can maybe help.

Ronnie There's always this thing, when you're first with
a girl.

Katie Alone?

Ronnie Yeah.

Katie In a back garden?

Ronnie Could be.

Katie At night?

Ronnie Probably.

Pause.

Katie Go on.

Ronnie Well, you're there, with a girl, in a back garden,
at night and there's kind of a feeling, a . . .

Katie A feeling?

Ronnie Yeah. A feeling.

Katie What kind of a feeling?

Ronnie It's sort of a . . . a . . . an . . .

Katie Inadequacy?

Ronnie No.

Katie Discomfort?

Ronnie No.

Katie Tension?

Ronnie Tension. Yeah. That's the fella. There's a tension
on a first date.

Katie We're on a date?

Ronnie I think so.

Katie Okay.

Ronnie I asked you, you came along. It's a date.

Katie Are you sure?

Ronnie Aren't you?

Katie I probably would have come anyway.

Ronnie Not according to Eck you wouldn't.

Pause.

Katie Okay then, it's possibly a date.
Ronnie Thank you.

Pause.

Katie You were saying about tension?
Ronnie Oh yeah. I was saying there's a tension on a first date when both people are thinking about what's going to happen with the whole goodnight-kiss thing.
Katie Oh right. That tension.
Ronnie Yeah.
Katie Now I've got you. (*Beat.*) I know what you mean. (*Beat.*) About the tension?

Pause.

It's good that it's not there tonight.
Ronnie What?
Katie Because I've been on some dates and it's just . . . it's unbearable. (*Beat.*) The tension.

Pause.

Ronnie You . . . you haven't . . .
Katie No.
Ronnie Felt . . .
Katie No.
Ronnie Not even . . .
Katie Not a thing.

Pause.

Ronnie Yes, you have.
Katie I haven't.
Ronnie You were thinking when I was gonna try and kiss you.
Katie No I wasn't.
Ronnie Yes, you were.

Katie No.

Ronnie Liar.

Katie I am not a liar.

Ronnie You are.

Katie I can assure you I'm not thinking about kissing you.

Pause.

Ronnie Well, I was thinking about kissing you.

Pause.

And that's something no one else knows.

Pause.

Katie I know.

They kiss.

Ronnie See, there goes all that tension.

Katie Disappeared.

Ronnie Gone.

Katie Evaporated.

Ronnie (*looks up*) Up to the satellites.

Pause.

Katie Are they still watching us?

Ronnie Who cares?

They stand in each other's arms.

Do you want to go back in?

Pause.

Katie No. (*Beat.*) I want to stay here for a while.

The End.

With a Lie and a Smile

Gregory Burke interviewed by Jim Mulligan

A good-looking sixteen-year-old moves to a new school determined to make his mark. We know nothing about him except what we see and what he says and, since he is a congenital liar, it is hard to be certain of anything. The sub-title of *Liar* is *This High School Movie Is a Play*, so it is pretty clear that the play is to some extent an homage to this movie genre.

> I like American high-school movies. They give you a critique of American society. The cliques and strands and tribes that occupy these schools and compete against each other in some way reflect the jocks and nerds and outsiders and beautiful people you find in the real world. I wanted *Liar* to be like that, but to be fresh, and I also wanted it to be about a compulsive liar. I decided I would have as a main character a young boy who is new to a school. When you're sixteen, the main thing you do is lie to girls because there is nothing interesting about you. You're just the same as everybody, so you have to find something that makes you special. Also, when you start a new school it gives you the freedom to lie.

There is an exuberant scene on Ronnie's first day at the school. Eck and Beefy give him a conducted tour, informative but with a good helping of irony. The school has the bog-standard beautiful people, which is a massive achievement in a town with a gene pool this size; geeks; the track-suited and Burberry-hatted Neds; beringed

Femneds, who would not know what to do if Argos went bust; Goths and Moshers, with female self-harmers who focus on diatetic dysfunctions; and skunk-smoking, white Dizzie Rascals. These tribes are the players among whom the principal characters duck and dive and with whom they negotiate. Katie, Eck and Beefy are articulate and in complete control.

> People say there aren't the youth cults that there used to be and at my age I am a little out of touch, but my research shows that they are alive and well with different groups and names: Goths, New Metal, Neds and Chavs. I wanted to show these young people as clever, intelligent and sensitive. I didn't want to write about an issue. Kids of that age are knowing and sharp and they live with issues. Drinking and drugs are there. I'm not glorifying them or legitimising them.

There are a number of repeated linguistic riffs that Gregory Burke uses during the play. One riff is when Katie, Kylie and Kelly discuss each of Ronnie's lies in turn:

> Of course the worst thing about it is by extension –
> By extension?
> Or is it implication?
> – he thinks you look like a footballer's wife.
> No?
> She's right, you know.
> No!
> She's right.
> Shit. I didn't think of that.

Clearly they know the difference between 'extension' and 'implication', if not the first time then certainly on every other occasion. There are similar riffs about whether or not the party will take place, and there is Eck's repeated question, 'Will somebody tell me why I eat / smoke / drink this shit?'

> I use the repetition technique a lot in my writing. Teenagers tend to repeat things. In that period between adolescence and fully-fledged adulthood you tend to do the same things over and over. At that age you don't quite understand things as much as you let on. And they do it because it's funny. They enjoy it. I also wanted to show that everything Ronnie does is public knowledge. Ronnie is the most like me. I'm a terrible liar. And when I say terrible, I mean I do it a lot and am very good at it. That's why I'm a writer. You can get a long way with a lie and smile.

For all Ronnie's cleverness, cunning and deviousness, he does not know until the end of the play that the two groups have been in collusion, winding him up and manoeuvring him. We know that every time Ronnie messes up, Katie will be telling her friends, enjoying her power, keeping him going. She appears to be inviting him to be more outrageous every time, and yet there is an attraction. She offers him the bait, reeling him in. It is touching the way Ronnie is prepared to make clear his feelings for Katie despite the rebuffs she dishes out so easily. And in the end it pays off.

The high-school film is not the only genre from the American cinematic canon which is referenced in the play. There is the gangster movie during the scene in which Ronnie proposes his theory that *The Great Gatsby* is just *Scarface* without the drugs. There are a couple of references to the brilliant satire of the American sports movie *Dodgeball*. And there is the line from the prison movie *Cool Hand Luke* which Katie delivers to Ronnie when he tells her that the reason he lies is because there's nothing special about him. He is just the new boy. Nothing else. 'Sometimes, nothing is a really cool hand to play.'

So we move to the climactic final scene, the party that was definitely not going to take place, but which does. There are some unlikely pairings at the party: Li'l Tim is giving Krystal a pedicure; Kellie-Marie the Ned is snogging with Brett, the scurge of the Neds; Mary-Anne checkmates a nerd; Halfmast and the stunner Chanelle are locked together on a bed – shame about the premature ejaculation.

At the party Katie and Ronnie have a conversation that is almost without lies. Katie decides she is just a cosmetics-loving, argumentative girl who likes discos, handbags and shoes. Ronnie admits the truth and nothing but the truth – he is allergic to nuts. They both agree that on a first date they are knotted up with tension. They negotiate an agreement that this is indeed a first date and that a kiss is in order. They kiss, the tension evaporates up to the satellites and they stand in each other's arms.

Production Notes

Common and colloquial humour infuses the text and should be played out by the actors for all its worth. Dialects can also be explored. Find the specific rhythm that is evident in the characters' conversations. Getting the timing right is especially important to the pace of the gags in the 'repetition scenes'.

The 'repetition scenes' take the drama up a notch and the structure of the scenes and repetition are instrumental, again, to the rhythm. Their purpose is to allow the audience to reminisce over US teenage high-school movies and be provided with a social commentary/critique. Hence the sub-title: *This High School Movie Is a Play*. They also reflect the banality of teenage experience and of doing things over and over again. The scenes provide an insight into the wider social world beyond Katie and Ronnie, though the play focuses mainly on their relationship.

Don't play the 'repetition scenes' too explicitly, as much of the joy lies in the audience's ability to link the scenes for themselves.

The 'beats' and 'pauses' are crucial for points of change and transition of characters. Try to avoid 'wink, wink, nudge, nudge' acting, and play the characters genuinely.

CHARACTER

Discover the wit in the script and Katie's 'light-bulb' moments of response to Ronnie's advances. A freeze and a look on a 'beat' could make the humour override the text. Certain lines could be pushed to achieve this heightened wit and emotion.

Cast carefully, since comic timing is possibly more important than great acting ability. Pace and timing must be cohesive in order to work. Katie and Ronnie really need to carry the piece, so it is important to cast actors who have charisma and intellect. The actor playing Ronnie should be sharp and able to play the verbal gymnastics that show off his intellect to Katie. Explore the logistics of Katie and Ronnie's relationship and how power shifts between the two. It has been Katie's intellect that has always overpowered boys in the past. Discover how Katie and Ronnie are constantly testing each other whilst realising they have a lot in common.

Play with the idea of the three-dimensional characters; tap their energy, and use a formulaic style which will heighten the humour, but avoid presenting the text at face value, as there are deeper issues at the heart of the play. Don't let the narrative sink into a one-story line; each detail and reference should be explored.

Play with the rules of attraction and sexual chemistry in the opening sequence and encourage the characters to delight in each other's lines. There is a powerful physical connection between Ronnie and Katie; their touch should be electric.

ASPECTS OF STAGING

Gregory is amenable to changes being made to his script to suit the location of your company, but it is imperative that those changes don't effect the rhythm of the piece. Likewise, make sure any re-contextualising is appropriate and absolutely necessary. Some jokes might not be appropriate in certain areas. The Fred and Rose West reference might not work if your company is based in Gloucester – it could be changed to Ian Huntley and Maxine Carr.

Push the boundaries of youth culture. Get the cast to observe current greetings, fashion, language, etc.

Use chapter headings to re-title units of the play. For instance, 'Scene One – Ronnie meets Katie'. Headings provide each unit with an identity and are useful to refer to when rehearsing the play.

As the language does not reveal the setting, it is important that you make clear the location of the scenes through set design or the use of projection. You could achieve this with either TV screens or a large projector at the back of the stage that displays iconic images to represent the various environments.

Think about such details as whether the garden in which the play ends is well kept, or if Ronnie and Katie are in the middle of an out-of-hand party. Either choice is interesting and will effect the connection and body language between Ronnie and Katie. Cold weather would mean there would be an urgency to the language, and this would also provide scope for them to be closer together. Take time to explore the best way to portray the final connection at the end of the play that seals the narrative.

BACKGROUND

Watch a few teen movies for a greater understanding of the references in the text. For example:

Donnie Darko – to unravel the mysticism, and explore the importance of its influence.

Ten Things I Hate About You – to play with the idea of a modern context for *The Taming of the Shrew*.

Home Alone – to delve into the idea of Macaulay Culkin and his relationship with the King of Pop.

Dodgeball – for pace.

Heathers – as a benchmark teenage high-school movie.

Workshop facilitated by Matt Wilde
with notes taken by Beth Turrell

THE MIRACLE

Lin Coghlan

Lin Coghlan has written widely for theatre, film, television and radio. Her play *Apache Tears* (Clean Break) shared the Peggy Ramsey Award, and her film *First Communion Day* won the Dennis Potter Play of the Year Award. Other work for the theatre includes *Bretevski Street* (Theatre Centre), *Waking* (Soho Theatre), *Mercy* (National Theatre Studio/Soho Theatre), which was a finalist for the Susan Smith Blackburn Award, *The Night Garden* (National Theatre Studio/Northcott Theatre Exeter), *Rising Blue* (translation for the NT Studio), and *Kingfisher Blue* for the Bush Theatre. She has adapted *Les Misérables* and *Mansfield Park* for Radio 4, and written a number of original radio plays, including *The Lamb's Snow* for *The Wire* on Radio 3. She created *Patrick's Planet*, an original series for the BBC, and is currently developing a feature film with the Northern Ireland Film Commission, as well as writing regularly for television.

Characters

Ron
twelve

Zelda
Ron's best friend, thirteen

Mrs Sheehan
Ron's mum

Ginger
Zelda's dad

Mrs Ginger
Zelda's mum

Trousers
Ginger's best mate

Angela Brickman
seventeen

Mrs Brickman
Angela's mother

Barry O'Donnell
fifteen

Barry's Mum

Miss Lowery
Head of School

Lorenzo Hammond
a soldier returning from the Iraq War

Billy Hammond
Lorenzo's younger brother, twelve, mildly autistic

Header Hammond
Lorenzo's father

Mrs Hammond
Lorenzo's mother

Peter 'Chewy' Zapadski
ten

Elena Zapadski
Chewy's mother

Mr Rodgers
a teacher, long dead

Rosie
Ronda
Renata-May
The Lanky Girls

Lucy Cummings
sixteen

Gran

Maximus Decimus
a lost dog

Some brief appearances by others

*All the characters should be 'represented'
by the young cast, who make no attempt really to
'play' them. We see the people of their town through
the prism of their experience. Therefore old can play
young, girls can play boys, the cast conjure up their
world for us, and tell the story how they like.*

A town, somewhere in the British Isles. Night.

    The population of the town stand looking across the rooftops, as if remembering.

    The rain cascades onto pavements, shop fronts and guttering.

    Ron and Zelda stand amongst the throng. Ron has a pineapple in her hand.

Zelda No one believed us, said we was making it all up, But we never. In't that right, Ron?

Ron Yeah.

Zelda We never. It all happened just like we said, that weird week.

Ron Freak, they said it was.

Zelda That storm.

Ron Rain come down, what was it like, Zel?

Zelda Ain't never seen nothing like it. Wasn't long after that we had the miracle.

Ron Come up through me floor, right next to the bunk beds.

Billy You hear that, Mum? I heard something – next door.

Ron Heard it next door, they did.

Zelda Billy Hammond heard it when he was in the bath, said he heard voices, come up through the plug hole.

Ron But he was having us on.

Zelda I mean, why would Billy Hammond get a miracle up his plug hole?

Ron And you don't get two miracles in one night, do you?

Zelda Don't make sense. Me mum, she never believed Billy Hammond, said he was just having us on.

Ron But my mum said maybe miracles can all come together, like buses.

Zelda But miracles and buses – they ain't the same thing, are they, Ron?

Ron No, they ain't the same thing. Course not. And not long after that, I got me special powers. And I started helping people – least I could do.

Ron and Zelda meet Angela Brickman, seventeen.

Ron How can I help you?

Angela Dunno. I just feel terrible like, right . . . depressed.

Ron Don't tell me no more.

Zelda Best if she uses her powers – to scan you.

Angela waits nervously while she's 'scanned'.

Ron Tongue?

Angela sticks her tongue out.

Zelda Picked up something straight away she did.

Angela (*anxious*) What is it? What d'you see?

Ron You feel your heart sometimes?

Angela Yeah. I do.

Ron Appetite?

Zelda Thin as a rake, she was.

Angela Can't seem to taste nothing.

Ron Thought as much. You want to eat a pineapple, one a day, if you can manage it.

Angela Pineapple?

Ron Come back in a week.

Zelda That was the first time she helped someone, and it just went on from there. Course, not everyone saw it Ron's way, not at first like.

Mrs Brickman Pineapple? But you hate pineapple.

Angela Leave me alone, Mum.

Mrs Brickman I don't know what's the matter with you. Is it that boy?

Angela I'm just taking my pineapple up to my room.

Mrs Brickman Taking yourself so seriously. Don't be silly. There'll be other boys. The world is full of boys.

Zelda We didn't need to advertise or nothing.

Ron Wasn't necessary, was it Zel?

Zelda Word of mouth. Next thing we know, there's a queue, dinner times – kids wanting to see her, for a consultation.

Chewy It's me reading, me words get all muddled up.

Zelda Dyslexic he was.

Chewy Can't read nothing, can't read – sodding – nothing.

Ron I got this cousin can't read.

Chewy But they take the Mick, don't they? I just want to be normal.

Ron (*scanning him*) You get a pain in your head?

Chewy Yeah.

Ron Thought as much.

Zelda Saw a red light – coming out of his head.

Ron It ain't just – *anatomical.*

Zelda Words like that come to her, she didn't know where they come from.

Beat.

Ron You feel . . . sad?

Chewy I do feel sad.

Ron How long you been sad, then?

Chewy Since me dad went off with that Laura.

Ron You got a hot-water bottle at home?

Chewy Yeah.

Ron You put a hot-water bottle on your heart twice a day – see if it shifts it.

Chewy You reckon?

Zelda Soon after that, he started reading.

Chewy (*reading*) 'Whether I shall turn out to be the hero of my own life, or whether that station will be held by anybody else, these pages must show . . .'

Zelda His dad, the one that run off with that Laura, he says Chewy must have been faking it all that time he couldn't read, but Ron's mum, she said . . .

Mrs Sheehan Miracle. Miracle it was. Something good come into our world, into our street. Finally, something really good.

Music.

Zelda Now, about that time, Billy Hammond's brother Lorenzo was a soldier, bombing Baghdad.

Lorenzo This is your brother Lorenzo here, Billy mate, how's things back home in Smallville?

Billy That's what we called our town when Lorenzo wrote me letters, but it wasn't small, it had 93,703 inhabitants. Things are A–okay, Lorenzo.

Lorenzo Good. Had a battle today and we won.

Billy Will you get a medal?

Lorenzo No. No medals as yet. How about you?

Billy No medals 'cause it isn't school games yet.

Lorenzo Right.

Billy School games are in July.

Lorenzo Alright, mate. Signing off now, from the desert.

Billy Alright, Zelda?

Zelda So so.

Billy Letter, from Lorenzo. Had sand in it, from the desert.

Billy pours out the sand into his hand.

Zelda Oh yeah?

Billy There are four main categories of desert in the world, sub-tropical, cool coastal, cold winter, and polar.

Beat.

You seen those big girls up the Parade?

Zelda The Parade was where the shops was, near the school. You mean Rosie O'Donnell and that lot?

Billy Her brother nicked a car last night and drove it through the window of the dry-cleaners down Aldergate Street.

Zelda Her brother Barry was a right head-case.

Billy Say he might go to prison.

Zelda Anyway, next thing we know Chewy says that Rosie O'Donnell's brother wants like a confidential consultation. Ron had to think about it.

Ron The way I see it, Zel, I ain't been given me healing abilities to pick and choose.

Zelda But it weren't easy because we didn't like Rosie O'Donnell or her mates and they never talked to none of us since we come here from Primary.

Ron (*decisive*) I'll see him.

Zelda Next thing we know, he's sitting there, in front of us, down McDonald's.

Barry Alright?

Zelda Rosie and the others was outside, laughing.

Barry People was saying – you had a miracle – up your house.

Ron Yeah. That's right.

Barry And that you got these . . . special powers.

Ron Don't know what I got, but it seems to work.

Barry I remember you when you was . . . this weird kid from up the flats. Always had that plastic goldfish.

Ron What was it you wanted help with?

Barry This is stupid.

Beat.

I got done for nicking that car.

Zelda We heard.

Barry Does God – like – talk to you?

Ron No, nothing like that.

Barry But, you can do stuff?

Zelda He looked out the window at Rosie and those lanky girls she always hung out with.

Ron I'm more a channel me, for the energy.

Barry Me mum, she's sick. Bad she is. Said last night, after the Old Bill let me out, said I was killing her.

Barry looks at Ron.

But, thing is, I've always been this way.

Ron I'll scan you.

Zelda She did. He was in a right state. Thing about Barry was, he was a right hard case, used to cut the names of his favourite goalies into his arms with a penknife. And half the other lads, they wanted to be just like him.

Ron You having bad dreams?

Barry How'd you know that?

Ron You got to find a dog. Make sure you don't nick it, mind, and you got to look after it.

Barry You off your trolley? A dog?

Ron I can only tell you what comes to me.

Barry Find a dog?

Ron Come back in a month, tell me how you're getting on.

Zelda Now, when Ron was a baby, she was right strange, but her mum said . . .

Mrs Sheehan She's my girl and she's the nicest baby I've ever seen . . .

Zelda Her dad worked down Allingtons, in the office. The night Ron was born, all his mates was making this big fuss . . .

Ginger Drinks are on you, Trevor mate . . .

Trousers Drinks are on the big man here.

Ginger Wetting the baby's head . . .

236

Trousers Say she's got a big head, that right, Trev?

Zelda And she did have a right big head, but her mum said . . .

Mrs Sheehan That's for keeping her brains in.

Zelda So this day, about a month it was, after the miracle happened, we was in school like, and Ron gets called to the office.

Miss Lowery I've been hearing some things, Veronica.

Ron What's that then, Miss?

Miss Lowery I've been hearing that you have been promising . . . I'm not entirely sure what . . . promising to help people.

Beat.

Apparently something happened at home.

Ron Something come up through the floor.

Miss Lowery That's right. During the flood down the Dolbys.

Ron A supernatural occurrence.

Miss Lowery Veronica, a real supernatural occurrence must be verified, by . . . by experts.

Ron Why's that, then?

Miss Lowery Because sometimes people get carried away, thinking that there is something happening which is not happening at all.

Ron Don't worry, Miss, I'm only helping people who ask me. And I don't charge no money even though I could.

Miss Lowery But it isn't right, is it, Veronica, to give people false hope?

Ron I don't do that, Miss. I don't promise them nothing. Can I go now?

Zelda 'Bout that time loads of the grown-ups got in a right state about it all, but the trouble with grown-ups is they ain't really got the time to think things through properly, 'cause they're always worried about whether they can get a flat-screen TV and a holiday in Crete in the same year, and whether they should put old people in homes, and whether being a single parent means you'll never get a bloke again and stopping the lad in the family nicking stuff so no one else gets a look in, so they ain't really got the headspace to have much of an opinion about anything, but the long and the short of it was, they didn't like it. That was when we started to go undercover, 'cause, like Ron said . . .

Ron Better lie low for a bit . . . but, the way I see it, we do have a responsibility, to give something back, when you been made a custodian of such a gift.

Zelda Now I know what you're thinking – that I might have found myself being jealous of Ron, the miracle not having come up through my floorboards, and then taking up the role of her – like – assistant, but, tell you the truth, I wasn't bothered. After she honed her skills, she started doing animals, which she said was naturally more receptive then people, being more closely attuned to the universal. Barry showed up with his dog . . .

Barry Found it round the back of the offy.

Zelda Horrible it was. Looked like a scrubbing brush with nasty little teeth up one end and a stump for a tail.

Ron What you called him?

Barry Maximus Decimus, after that bloke – in *Gladiator*. He doesn't half stink the house out.

Ron You got to clean him up.

Barry Why am I doing this?

Ron You got to clean him up and talk to him, he's scared.

Zelda She gave Maximus a scan.

Ron Used to live up north somewhere. Been on the road a long time, says he's hungry.

Barry I give him dog food, he ain't interested.

Ron Give it him on a spoon, come back to me in a week.

Zelda So Barry starts walking round with the dog stuffed up his jacket all the time and now and then he'd put it on the chair beside him down the caff and feed it baby food from a jar, with a spoon.

Barry (*feeding the dog*) Alright, Max, there you go, mate.

The wall down the shops.
Rosie O'Donnell, Ronda and Renata-May, the Lanky Girls, are hanging out when Barry comes by.

Ronda That's your brother, Rosie, with the dog.

Rosie (*trying to keep her cool*) Yeah, he's totally lost it.

Renata Anyone got a fag?

Ronda Least he could've done was get a real bloke's dog. Bull terrier or something.

Renata I'm dying for a fag, I am.

Ronda (*calling over*) You ain't saying much, Barry.

Rosie You finished showing me up yet?

Barry Just shut it, will ya?

Ronda It speaks.

Renata Got any chewy?

Rosie Don't you never eat?

Renata I do eat. I eat chewing gum.

Rosie That ain't eating. It's *chewing*.

Ronda You used to be such a laugh, Barry.

Renata Remember when you smashed down the school wall and Miss Lowery shouted so loud there was like dribble coming out of her mouth? Gross!

Rosie There ain't no rule says you got to stand here, is there? I mean, there's a whole town all around us in case you hadn't noticed.

Barry You left Mum on her own.

Renata I really fancy a burger.

Rosie Yeah, like you have, for the last ten years. Don't you go telling me I got to stay home and look after Mum 'cause you ain't never done nothing for Mum, alright?

Ronda Cheek. You hear him?

Renata Or a battered sausage.

Billy arrives.

Rosie Here we go.

Billy (*to Barry*) Alright?

No one says anything.

You still got that dog?

Beat.

It's up your jacket.

Beat.

If I had a dog I'd call it Rex.

Barry Right.

Billy Which means King.

Beat.

Billy I could walk him for you.

Barry He don't walk.

Barry makes a roll-up.

Billy He don't walk?

Barry Don't like it.

Billy Why doesn't he like walking?

Barry I don't know. He's a lazy bugger. He's only got little legs.

Billy You still stealing cars?

Barry looks at Billy. Billy feels uncomfortable.

I got to go soon 'cause my brother's coming home.

Barry Oh yeah?

Billy He's bringing me a present.

Barry Great. Cool, man.

Billy He's a soldier. Are you going to jail?

Barry I don't know. Maybe.

Billy I got to go.

Barry Yeah. Right.

Billy goes. Barry is left, the words resonating. He leaves. The girls watch him go.

Music. Lorenzo walks on, in uniform, carrying his kit bag.

Everyone
Alright, Lorenzo mate?
Kicked Saddam's arse, did you?
Fancy a real cup of tea?
We're proud of you, son.
We've got your room ready.
No, don't say nothing, you just put that down.
You've got a suntan.
We seen it on the telly.
We seen you in the desert
And we remembered you with your bucket and spade.
We seen you marching into Baghdad
And we thought of you marching round the back garden.
We seen you and we prayed to God to keep you safe,
except your dad . . .
Who don't believe in God.
How'd you know what I believe in?
Alright, I can't speak for your dad, maybe.
Let me speak to the boy, I can speak to the boy.
I prayed to God and I know they've got their own
God . . .
Everyone's got their own God.
But we prayed, that you'd come home, and here you
are, safe.

Lorenzo Hello, Mum. Hello, Dad. Hello, Billy.

Zelda First night Lorenzo Hammond come home from the war they had a drink for him down Squeaky Mary's in the family room . . .

Squeaky Mary's.

Zelda My mum, she was in a right mood . . .

Mrs Ginger Now you listen to me, Veronica, 'cause I ain't going to say this to you more than once. I want you to sit there nicely with Zel and *be normal*. I don't want to hear *nothing* about miracles or special powers or *consultations*. You can both have some crisps and be normal girls for one night, is that too much to ask?

Zelda Problem was, once you're given special powers you can't just turn them on and off like a tap, can you, Ron?

Ron No way.

Zelda And when that Lorenzo come in. Ron was immediately affected by the terrible state of his auric field.

Ron Never seen nothing like it.

Header Here's your pint, son.

Mrs Hammond I never thought your dad and me, we'd see you home.

Header Wait till he tells you about that Saddam's Palace.

Mrs Hammond That Saddam Hussein, he killed babies, isn't that right, love? What kind of man would do that? Poison babies?

Lorenzo Alright, Angela . . . how you been?

She looks at him.

Ginger I want to thank you, son, for what you did . . .

Lorenzo Alright?

Ginger You acted for all of us out there, in all our names.

Lorenzo It was just a job.

Ginger Just a job? See that? Modesty? What did I tell you?

Lorenzo (*to Angela*) You want to get out of here?

She looks at him.

Dad, I was thinking, that I might not stay.

Ginger But you can't go home, son, the party's for you.

Mrs Hammond We got all the bunting out . . .

Mrs Ginger Last came out for the Silver Jubilee . . .

Ginger What do the Royals know . . .

Mrs Ginger As I was saying . . .

Ginger That Edward couldn't even get in the Marines . . .

Lorenzo (*to Angela*) Don't go . . .

She looks at him.

Mrs Hammond Didn't they feed you out there?

Lorenzo How'd you mean?

Mrs Ginger He's skin and bone . . .

Ginger Representing your country . . .

Lorenzo There were people there from all over . . .

Ginger But the British Army, it's the best in the world . . .

Header He needs another drink, the boy's glass is empty.

Ginger Should have joined the Territorials . . .

Trousers You what?

Ginger I ain't too old, I should have joined up, could have served out there – in Iraq.

Trousers You're too old.

Ginger No I ain't.

Mrs Ginger How d'you make it that you're fit to serve in the Territorials when you can't even put up a shelf?

Ginger Don't be so stupid.

Mrs Ginger What's stupid about that?

Ginger It ain't the same thing, woman, is it? Serving your country and putting up sodding shelves.

Mrs Ginger There ain't no glory in putting up shelves . . .

Ginger Glory? Glory? What do you know about glory?

Zelda And soon it was getting right out of hand, with my mum and dad having a right go at each other . . .

Mrs Ginger Nothing! I have to make do with the little things – the little victories, like making the beds . . .

Ginger What you haven't got . . .

Mrs Ginger What haven't I got?

Ginger What you haven't got is the size of a head that can entertain a concept like *service* . . .

Mrs Ginger God give me patience . . .

Ginger What would you know of patriotism . . . of *camaraderie* . . .

Mrs Ginger What would you know of it, the nearest you've ever come to testing your character is watching *Full Metal Jacket* on the telly . . .

Ginger I wouldn't shrink from my duty if I got the chance . . . I wasn't made for a life like this.

Mrs Ginger You wasn't made for any kind of life, you never get up off the sofa except to go down the pub . . .

Ginger I'm sick of listening to you. Where's the boy? Lorenzo? I want to hear it all, I want to talk to you – about the war.

Lorenzo (*to Zelda and Ron*) Here we go . . .

Barry comes in with Maximus.

Barry Alright, Lorenzo?

Ginger You seen real action over there?

Barry Give us a pint . . .

Mrs Ginger It's only soft drinks for kids.

Barry Who're you calling a kid?

Mrs Ginger Trev, you tell him.

Trousers You heard her, Barry.

Mrs Ginger And he's got that smelly dog stuffed up his jacket.

Ginger You brought back any souvenirs?

Lorenzo Souvenirs?

Ginger You can tell me – like one of them Republican Guard cap badges . . .

Mrs Ginger (*about Barry*) His poor mother, she's that poorly with cancer and what does he go and do? Steal cars? That's how he helps her out.

Ginger That's what they did in the last war, nicked their helmets, brought 'em back, made flowerpots of them.

Mrs Ginger His mother might not live to see the New Year and what does he do? Steals cars.

Angela Alright, Barry?

Barry Thought you didn't talk to rubbish like me.

Angela Must be feeling charitable.

Barry You still with that wanker Paul Fraser?

Angela No. I dumped him.

Barry Thought it was the other way round.

Angela You here with your girlfriend then, or do you find it difficult to get off with girls while you got a dog stuffed up your jumper?

Angela walks off.

Header Bit of hush. Alright, alright.

Lorenzo Dad . . .

Header Now I know he doesn't want no fuss made but he deserves a proper welcome home.

Cheers.

Header 'Cause a little bird's told me he was a credit to all of us over there . . .

Ginger Well done, Lorenzo lad.

Mrs Ginger Oh, can't you ever stop?

Ginger What?

Header And I know it can't have been no holiday for you, son, but we was with you every step of the way, so here's to you, Lorenzo . . .

Others Speech! Speech!

245

Angela Make you wish you were a hero coming home, Barry?

Barry I wouldn't fight in their shitty war.

Ginger Watch your mouth, you!

Barry Who are you, then, the talk police?

Ginger You come outside and say that.

Mrs Ginger Oh Ginger, just let it go.

Header Round of applause for Lorenzo, our hero.

Applause. Lorenzo stands in the spotlight.
A huge silence. Discomfort grows.

Lorenzo Don't know what to say . . .

Header Tell us what it was like, son . . .

Billy It was hot, wasn't it, Lorenzo?

Lorenzo Yeah. Hotter than the hottest day you ever get down Brighton . . .

Ginger Wasn't no joyride, was it?

Lorenzo So, thanks for coming, and have a good drink.

Suddenly Lorenzo is finished. People start to clap, uncertainly.
Lorenzo finds his way to Angela.

Give it ten minutes, alright? Then we'll go.

Lorenzo goes to talk to some of the others. Barry approaches Angela.

Barry You've pulled, then.

Angela What's it to you?

Barry You always fancied him.

Angela Maybe you've got it wrong. Maybe he always fancied me.

Zelda Must have been a week or so after that we was called into Miss Lowery's office one day, me and Ron, and our mums and dads was there two.

The Head's Office. Zelda, Ron, Mrs Sheehan, Ginger and Mrs Ginger.

Miss Lowery It's been going on *clandestinely*.

Ginger Talk straight, woman.

Mrs Ginger Oh, why can't you just listen for once?

Ginger What's up with you now?

Miss Lowery Veronica is clearly the main influence.

Zelda She talked like I didn't even have a mind of me own – in't that right, Ron?

Miss Lowery She's been meeting people – in the toilets.

Mrs Sheehan Ron?

Ginger What kind of people?

Miss Lowery She's been giving them advice, for their problems, suggesting treatments.

Mrs Sheehan Ever since the flood . . .

Miss Lowery I am aware what happened at your house, Mrs Sheehan.

Mrs Sheehan It was – wonderful.

Ginger Here we go. You told the Pope yet, have you? Next thing we know she'll have a plaque over the door and it'll cost you a fiver to go in and take a look around the place.

Miss Lowery I understand some debris was washed up when the canal burst its banks.

Mrs Sheehan Veronica woke up with a statue of St Anthony in her bedroom. In the bottom bunk. I've always felt very close to St Anthony.

Miss Lowery I believe the entire contents of St Saviour's was affected by the high rainfall that night.

Mrs Sheehan But to find St Anthony, in your bedroom . . . I mean – how did he get in?

Ginger (*sneering*) Maybe he came down the chimney, like Santa Claus?

Zelda My dad always said stupid things like that, I mean, Ron didn't have a chimney in her bedroom, did she?

Miss Lowery There were all sorts of things washed around the streets that night. My own neighbour found her microwave stranded on the pedestrian crossing at the end of her road.

Mrs Sheehan But that wasn't the case with us. We were virtually untouched by the storm. It's got to be an omen, at least.

Ginger An omen? What planet are you living on, woman?

Mrs Ginger He has no faith in anything.

Ginger What are you asking me to have faith in, a bloody statue coming down the chimney?

Zelda It didn't come down the chimney!

Mrs Sheehan I mean, he wasn't even storm damaged. He looked – pristine.

Ginger Who did?

Zelda St Anthony!

Miss Lowery Veronica, have you anything you'd like to say?

Everyone looks at Ron.

Zelda Thing is – she didn't. I mean, what was the point? See, our street, our town, it's full of things that used to be different, things that have got stuck, things that are like shells of themselves. From the top of our street you can see the roof of the old mill that's been empty for years and years . . .

Ginger That was work. Jesus, that was work in those days. A man would break his back for his family in those days.

Mrs Ginger Fancy yourself, do you, coming home on a Friday night? The man of the house? The lord and master?

Ginger All I'm saying is . . . oh, forget it. You wouldn't understand.

Zelda And up the road there's the school with the bell where they had to close it down after the First World

War when all the boys went to fight and only two
come back . . .

Mrs Sheehan That's the nun's school, Ron, look, you can
still see the apple trees the sisters planted before the
war, and they had their own donkeys and every donkey
was called after a saint, and my granny remembers
being given a ride on Bernadette and the donkey bit her
and she went running in to the Mother Superior crying
that she'd been bitten on the bum by St Bernadette!

Ron and Mrs Sheehan laugh and laugh.

Zelda There's the place that used to be a snooker hall,
and then they made it a gym and then a kick-boxing
place and then a snooker hall again . . . There's the
flats where the Irish lived, and then the Asians, and
then the Turkish, and then the Kurds . . . There's the
house that used to be where old people went to die,
and then a residential care place for boys, and then
one of them clinics where you get needles stuck in you
all over, and then a sex shop . . .

Mrs Ginger Don't go near that place, Zelda, you hear
me? What did I say?

Zelda And there's the people. My dad, who wanted to be
a policeman but wasn't tall enough so he went to work
in Bentley's, behind the counter. And Ron's mum, who
was going to emigrate to Australia and work on a
sheep farm but her sister got sick and she had to stay
at home, and then it was too late for her to go because
she had a husband and baby . . .

Mrs Sheehan Everyone has their moment, Ron, when
their destiny comes right along and taps them on the
shoulder, everyone has their moment.

Zelda There were people all through those streets with
problems, and it seemed to me only Ron here wanted
to help. So anyhow, they made us promise that it was
finished, and we wouldn't do it no more.

Chewy Ron, you got to talk to me.
Zelda She ain't allowed.
Chewy But it's an emergency.

Ron and Zelda stop and look around, scared they're being watched.

If you stop using your special powers, what's going to happen to me reading?
Zelda He had a point. Maybe if Ron packed it in, everything would start going backwards.
Chewy See – I can't go back to being thick.
Zelda You wasn't thick, Chewy.
Chewy Whatever, but I can't go back.
Zelda And we was just starting to think about what our responsibilities was when Angela Brickman comes legging it in saying the Old Bill have only gone and picked up Barry O'Donnell for a car that he nicked down the Hollings, and his mum went mental, and Barry's come back and took his uncle Bill's machete and he's up the playing fields swinging it over his head and there's loads of police . . . Course we only had one option, didn't we? We had to go, see what we could do to help out.

The playing fields.

Police Come on now, Barry, don't be a right wanker.
Barry I've told you, I'll top meself.
Police With a machete? What you going to do, chop your own head off?
Ginger What's all the noise?
Trousers That kid what nicks all the cars . . . says he's going to top himself.

Ginger (*shouting*) Get on with it, then! Do us all a favour!

Police I'm sorry, kids, we've got a bit of a situation here, you can't come through.

Zelda Course it was all their fault, the Old Bill, 'cause Barry never took that car at all, because he was turning over a new leaf, 'cause of his mum being poorly . . .

Trousers Stop being such a stupid bugger, Barry!

Barry I never touched no car and you ain't going to put me inside.

Ginger Should throw away the key, they should. All kids like you are doing is using up valuable oxygen.

Barry I want to talk to *her*.

Zelda Everyone turns, and he's pointing at Ron. I mean, what could she do? The way she saw it, it was her civic duty to help out,

Barry I never done it, Ron. Look, I still got me dog, like you said. Why would I go nicking a car when I got me dog and me mum to look after?

Zelda Ron, give him a quick scan . . .

Ron I believe him. You've got the wrong man.

Zelda The press was there and next thing we know Ron's on the front of the *Shopping Gazette* . . . 'Local Girl at Heart of Police Drama'. But – like I said back then, Ron never sought no publicity . . .

Ron I never . . .

Zelda But, when you've got special powers it ain't easy, to keep things low-profile.

Miss Lowery's office.

Miss Lowery (*examining the local paper*) I'm very disturbed by this, Veronica.

Ron I was only helping to avoid a miscarriage of justice, Miss.

Miss Lowery looks at her.

Miss Lowery I would ask you merely to think about this logically, Veronica.

Ron Yes, Miss.

Miss Lowery If God had decided to reveal himself through a miracle at this time in the world's history, why do you think he would choose to reveal himself to you?

Ron Don't know, Miss.

Miss Lowery Reacquainting myself with your long history at this school, I think it's only fair to say that you have not been without your challenges while you've been with us.

Ron In what way, Miss?

Miss Lowery I am right in saying, am I not, that when you first came to us from primary you had problems making friends?

Ron stares at her.

And it was felt necessary to see if you needed to be statemented for special needs.

Ron But I'm alright now, Miss.

Miss Lowery What I'm trying to say, Veronica, is that, for a girl like you, an isolated girl, a girl who has problems fitting in, to be seen as some sort of – celebrity – it would have its advantages.

Ron But I'm not a celebrity, Miss. I mean, I didn't ask to be given my special powers.

Miss Lowery What do your special powers feel like, Veronica?

Ron It's hard to explain.

Miss Lowery A sense of excitement?

Ron I dunno.

Miss Lowery It is exciting, isn't it, to be important in people's lives, to have people needing you, thinking you're special?

Ron I dunno.

Miss Lowery We'd all enjoy that, wouldn't we, being so popular, being so – valued?

Ron I ain't doing no harm.

Miss Lowery But you are. You're giving people false hope. That's a terrible thing, Veronica. And you're pretending you know things you can't know.

Ron But I do know them.

Miss Lowery No you don't, Veronica. You cannot know whether a disease will heal or if a boy is innocent or how to help a child to read. Some of these things we can never know, others can only be deduced with the assistance of trained minds. Do you have a trained mind, Veronica?

Ron No, Miss.

Miss Lowery So if you have no appropriate training, we must assume that the source of your knowledge is direct intervention from God. Do you consider yourself a religious person Veronica?

Ron I don't know, Miss.

Miss Lowery So can you explain to me why, of all the wise, pure, gifted and spiritual people in the world, God would choose to reveal himself to you?

Ron says nothing.

Miss Lowery Peter, you can come in now.

Chewy comes in, looking scared out of his wits.

Now Peter, I want you to tell Veronica what you told me earlier.

Chewy looks at Ron desperately.

I spoke with Peter and his mother at their home yesterday, and he has something he'd like to say to you.

Chewy I made it all up – that you helped me. I was always able to read. I was just pretending.

Miss Lowery So you see, Veronica, you are just a normal girl, an ordinary girl, and being ordinary, it really isn't such a burden to bear, is it? We all have to struggle on knowing that we are most of us really very unremarkable. That's what growing up is all about.

Zelda I said she must have put Chewy in the slammer, beat him up with electricity cables to make him say what he said, but it turns out . . .

Chewy They never. My mum just started crying and said she couldn't take no trouble at the school, and that she just wanted everything to get back to normal and that if I didn't stop telling lies it would kill her 'cause her blood pressure was through the roof as it was and that second job she was doing down the Hollings would be the death of her and did I really think everything circulated round me? So I had to, Ron. I had to say what they told me.

Zelda They put Barry in this foster place till his case was due to come up . . . He met Ron the day before, up by the old garage on the roundabout.

Barry You better take me dog, Ron.

Ron He needs you.

Barry Nobody needs me.

Ron You was good with that dog.

Barry He's a right awkward bugger. If he wants to, you know, go outside, he looks at you.

Barry hands Ron the dog.

See you round.

He goes. Ron is left holding the little scruffbag of a dog.

Zelda People started talking after that, 'cause the whole miracle thing, it became this joke and no one wanted to look like they'd been taken in. Angela Brickman, she was the first to kick off . . .

Angela Yeah, that's right. I had a right laugh – went to her for 'advice'. And you know what she tells me to do? Eat pineapples!

Zelda Ron just looked at her, said nothing.

Ronda You lost your 'special powers', Ron?

Ginger I always said there was something wrong with that girl.

Mrs Ginger And you're the expert, are you? You can tell the world what normality is?

Ginger All I'm saying is, that girl's never been right.

Zelda Things were bad just then, with Billy in the halfway house, and Ron in trouble, and being, I would say, sort of vilified for simply trying to lend a helping hand, then over at Lorenzo's house things took a turn for the worse.

Mrs Hammond You've got to talk to him.

Header I don't know what to say.

Mrs Hammond I can't do this any more on my own.

Header looks at her, gets his nerve up, turns to face Lorenzo.

Header Your mother . . . she thinks . . .

A beat.

We think, that you should come out of your room. Eh?

Lorenzo looks at them.

Play a game of football. Get some air, son.

Lorenzo looks at them.
Header looks at his wife.

Mrs Hammond The corner shop, they said, there was some . . . mistake.

255

Lorenzo There wasn't no mistake. I took the biscuits.

Mrs Hammond Why would you take biscuits? We have biscuits. Were you hungry? You could tell me if you were hungry. You never eat anything as it is.

Header Did you steal biscuits from Mr Shah's shop?

Lorenzo You know something, he used to have this sign in the window, when we was at school, 'Only two kids at a time.' Pompous git. Sits behind that counter, listening to that stupid radio . . . singing along to that stupid music . . .

Header I'm not sure if I understand this . . .

Lorenzo He deserved it. Look . . .

Lorenzo takes out the remains of the packet of biscuits and shoves one in his mouth, munching it, shocking his parents.

Call the police.

Header Are you ill?

Lorenzo laughs.

Mrs Hammond Mr Shah's always been so nice to us.

Lorenzo What does a packet of biscuits matter?

Header I don't believe I'm hearing this. You've stolen these biscuits – from the corner shop?

Lorenzo That doesn't matter. What do biscuits matter? Look at the world.

Header What do you mean, 'Look at the world'?

Lorenzo Look at the world we're living in. What do biscuits matter?

Zelda A few nights after that, there was this massive row, Ron and me could hear it, 'cause our flats are third floor and the noise carries, if the wind's the right way . . .

Header hammers on his son's door.

Header Lorenzo, open this door. D'you hear me?

They wait.

Mrs Hammond Lorenzo, it's Mum.

Header What's he doing in there?

Mrs Hammond Lorenzo! If you need the toilet, come out.

Header What? Why are you saying that to him?

Mrs Hammond Don't go on at me . . .

Header I'm not going on at you, I'm asking you a question.

Mrs Hammond He's started going to the toilet in his room.

Header In his room? What do you mean, 'in his room'?

Mrs Hammond In the wardrobe. He's not well.

Header (*yelling and hammering on the door*) Not well? LORENZO, open this door!

Lorenzo Come on, then! Come on!

Mrs Hammond Lorenzo, I'll send Dad away . . .

Header Send me away? Why would you send me away?

Mrs Hammond You frighten him . . .

Header He's not a little boy any longer . . .

Mrs Hammond You've always frightened him.

Header Don't be so stupid.

Mrs Hammond He only joined the army to get away from you.

Header And if it hadn't been for me, he'd have settled for this, this, backwater . . .

Mrs Hammond It's all you. You're the one that wanted to get away, but you drove our son out of the house instead . . .

Header I should have gone, I would have gone if anyone had ever encouraged me . . .

Mrs Hammond Always blaming others . . .

Header I had to stay! What could I do, leave my mother in that house all alone? What kind of a man would that have made me?

Mrs Hammond Our child could have been killed in the war . . . would that have made you happy? Maybe it would, all those stories to tell down the pub, all that sympathy . . .

Header stares at her, speechless. Suddenly Lorenzo comes out.

Lorenzo I'm going out.
Mrs Hammond Why don't you change your clothes?
Lorenzo I don't care about clothes. Do you? I don't.

He goes, leaving them shaken to the core.

The sound of traffic. Lorenzo and Angela Brickman in a stolen car.

Lorenzo (*laughing*) Out of our way, you buggers!
Angela You're mad, you are.
Lorenzo You only just noticed?

They laugh.

Angela I didn't know you had a car.
Lorenzo There's lots you don't know about me.
Angela Man of mystery, are you?
Lorenzo Come on, let's drive up the Maltings, it's quiet there.
Angela (*looking at him*) Alright.
Zelda The night Lorenzo took Angela Brickman up the Maltings, Ron was coming home when she run into those Lanky Girls.
Ronda Watch out, everyone, here comes the witch.

Ron looks at them.

Do us a spell then, Ron, 'cause I've got this awful boil on my bum.

Renata Anyone got any sweets?

Rosie (*to Ron*) You've gone and made my brother go mental, you have.

Ronda He was mental before if you ask me.

Renata You got any money? We could go get a kebab.

Rosie That's what they used to say about you, wasn't it, Ron? That you was mental.

Ronda She had to have one of them special assistants to sit with her in class in case she did something.

Renata Miss Roberts. I liked her. Always had Maltesers in her pocket.

Rosie Everyone hated you at Primary, didn't they, Ron?

Ronda I'd have topped meself if I'd have been you.

Rosie And now everyone knows what you been doing, how pathetic you are, your life is going to be so bad, girl. So so bad. I feel sorry for you. I really do.

At the Maltings. Lorenzo sits with Angela.

Angela You really want to sit up here?

Lorenzo What's wrong with here?

Angela Those lads from Raincroft come up here. They beat up a boy from the estate a few weeks ago. He lost an eye.

Lorenzo They won't touch us.

Angela Why's that then? You going to take them on, all your own?

Lorenzo looks at her.

Lorenzo Might do.

Angela Oh yeah.

Lorenzo Might have a gun. Might have brought a gun back with me, from Iraq.

At Lorenzo's house.

Header Military police, they're at the door.
Mrs Hammond Military police? Why?
Header They say up Lorenzo's barracks, there's a gun missing.

At the Maltings.

Lorenzo You got to go now, Angela.
Angela Why've you got a gun?
Lorenzo You've got to have a gun. How would you protect yourself if you didn't have a gun?
Angela Let's go back, eh?
Lorenzo Got to always carry your gun.
Angela What's the matter with you? Are you having me on?
Lorenzo What?
Angela You're acting . . . funny.

Angela looks at him.

It's cold, lets go.
Lorenzo You go back.
Angela On me own?
Lorenzo Yeah. You go back on your own.
Zelda That Angela was well fed up, had to walk four miles in her heels.
Ronda Ohhhh Angela, that's a blister. You want me to burst it, I've got a needle here somewhere . . .
Angela No thanks.
Renata Didn't he take you for nothing to eat?
Angela I don't want to talk about it.
Renata I would have got him to take me up the Taj Mahal. Had a Chicken Madras.

Ronda Why'd he make you walk home?

Renata With pickles.

Angela 'Cause he's lost it. Alright?

Zelda Ron could sense there was something up . . .

Ron That army boy, he needs help . . .

Zelda But when the police found him, there wasn't no gun.

Header Of course there was no gun. My son, he's a hero. He's served his country. He was out there when you were all sitting at home on your backsides watching it on TV. Now you come here, accusing him . . . you make me sick.

Zelda Then, one day, he was gone. They looked for him, but they couldn't find him nowhere. Looked all over. Lorenzo's dad, he was going mad. Sticking up posters everywhere, with Lorenzo's picture on, sticking them on lamp posts he was . . .

Angela Like he was a lost cat or something.

Ronda 'Have you seen my son?'

Zelda Picture of him sitting having his Christmas dinner, smiling.

Ronda Paper hat on . . .

Header I'm going out looking again.

Mrs Hammond Don't go.

Header I'm going out. I have to go out.

Zelda And blow me if one night Mr Hammond didn't turn up at Ron's house.

Header (*awkward*) Alright?

Mrs Sheehan I heard . . . about Lorenzo. I can't imagine.

Header Is Ron in? I wondered, could I talk to her?

Zelda Like I said, Ron, she'd stopped seeing people, but this time, she made an exception.

Header I can't find him. I've looked, I keep looking, but I can't find him.

Header looks at Ron.

Will you help me, Ron? You can do it. I know. You can use your powers to find my son.

Zelda Ron had to think about it. She sent Mr Hammond home, said she'd stopped doing that kind of thing, but she knew, she could see, exactly what was just about to happen, and she had to decide if she was going to do something about it. Must have been a week after that, Ron went out late one night, she took a torch and her big overcoat, the one everyone laughed at. It was going to be the last time she ever used her gift. The town was quiet, on edge you might say, like deep down everyone knew that something was going to happen.

Chewy It's my fault. Everyone's having a go at Ron now, because of me.

Elena Zapadski Don't be silly, Peter.

Chewy But it is. 'Cause I lied, didn't I? I lied, about her helping me.

Ginger When we was kids, we used to go up the back of the town with Mr Rodgers, looking for bats.

Elena Zapadski Peter, you take everything too seriously.

Chewy But I lied. I betrayed her. I've ruined everything.

Ginger He'd meet us by the old school and give us each a metal torch, with a silver ring on it so you could hang it up after, and we'd lie with our backs against the rocks and wait for the bats to come . . .

Mr Rodgers See that, boys, there they are . . .

Ginger Yes, Sir . . .

Mr Rodgers The world is full of mystery, things we can never hope to understand . . .

Ginger I like mysteries, Sir . . .

Mr Rodgers Never lose that appetite for knowledge, boy. You stop asking questions of the world and you'll be a poor excuse for a man.

Ginger I loved him, that teacher.

Mrs Ginger What's the matter with you now, are you drunk?

Ginger Never mind.

Zelda Barry knew what was happening – he was in this foster place down Allingtons, emergency overnight stay it was, and he was in the toilet, looking out the window, knowing there was something going on . . .

Ginger, Mrs Ginger, Barry and Chewy all look up into the night sky.

   Ron meets Billy Hammond. They're both bundled up against the cold.

Ron What you doing here, Billy Hammond?

Billy (*suspicious*) Nothing.

Zelda It was Billy's thirteenth birthday. Ron knew Lorenzo wouldn't miss it.

Lorenzo appears out of the dark, bedraggled, as if he's been sleeping rough.

Lorenzo What'd you bring her for?

Billy I didn't. She was just here.

They all stand in the cold night.

You got to come home, Mum's going mad.

Lorenzo I told you, Billy mate, I can't go home no more.

Billy It's not fair. I'm stuck there, all on my own.

The people of the town look out across the black night-time horizon.

Mrs Sheehan I still think of the landscape of Australia. I see it shimmering, translucent in the heat – and those ancient people, aboriginals, so close to the earth, and us, so close to . . . nothing.

Billy, Lorenzo and Ron stare out across the town.

When I was thinking of going to Australia, I must have been pregnant with Ron – only – I didn't know that, did I? And I was – looking – gazing into these brochures – of Australia – those flat-topped mountains – a redness over everything, and the dreams I had – such dreams – I had to wonder – if Ron was dreaming too.

Ron You go home now, Billy, and don't tell no one that Lorenzo was here.

Lorenzo Do as she says, eh? Go home, mate, it's late. Happy birthday.

Reluctantly, Billy turns and goes.
Lorenzo stands, cold.

Ron You like it then, the river?

Lorenzo I used to come up here when I was a kid.

Zelda There was a river run down through the moor . . .

Mrs Sheehan Run all the way from the hills right down to the back of Bentley's, where it turned grey as it met the town . . .

The sound of hundreds of bats taking flight, flapping their leathery wings against the cold night air.

Mr Rodgers (*pointing to the sky*) See that, boys, see the bats over the water . . .

Barry My dad took me up that river once, winter it was.

Mrs Sheehan Rivers have magic in them, Ron . . .

Barry Where's the water come from, Dad?

Dad What you mean, 'Where's it come from?' What sort of a question is that?

Barry Don't matter.

Mr Rodgers People used to be baptised in rivers long ago, boys, because of their cleansing properties.

Ginger All the boys got in and swam, under the moon . . .

Mr Rodgers Careful, boys, careful . . . and no ducking each other.

Ginger Why don't you come in, Sir?

Mr Rodgers Because it's my job to look after you.

Ginger I remember him saying that.

Mrs Ginger My mother used to say there was something odd about that teacher.

Ginger Why can't you leave me alone? Can you not even . . . ? I mean, what's it to you? My memories?

Mrs Ginger What's the matter with you now?

At the river, the girl and the young man stand in silence.

Lorenzo You've got a dog stuffed in your jumper.

Ron It's Barry O'Donnell's dog. They've put him in care.

Lorenzo I know.

Ron He didn't take that car.

Lorenzo I know – I did.

Ron (*turning on him*) And you let them think it was Barry?

Lorenzo They never come asking, did they?

Ron But they're going to do him for it.

Lorenzo You think it would make any difference if I put me hand up and took the rap? Barry O'Donnell's been nicking cars since he was twelve years old. He nicked his dad's car and set fire to it. He nicked a bus off the council, and you're telling me he's like this innocent kid carrying the can for something I did?

Ron Still isn't right.

Lorenzo There ain't no right and wrong no more.

Ron What d'you mean?

Lorenzo There ain't no right and wrong.

The community of mothers, fathers, teachers and children stand gazing out across the town, each in their own world.

Mrs Sheehan The spacemen, when they come back to earth – land in the foamy ocean – they report spiritual experiences in space – not scientific – spiritual.

Ron I think there's right and wrong.

Ginger I think – if we have spirits – whatever – Mr Rodgers would be walking over those moors right now, on a night like this – with his bats.

Mrs Ginger You're the one who's bats.

Ron I've finished with this town.

Beat.

Lorenzo Yeah.

Ron Be a while, a few years maybe, but one day I'm leaving.

Beat.

Lorenzo Take Billy with you when you go, will you? I don't like to think of him, with Mum and Dad, alone.

Ron Take him yourself.

Lorenzo Maybe I won't be here to do that.

Ron Yes, you will.

He looks at her.

Lorenzo See into the future and all now, do you?

They stand together.

Ron You know what tonight is?

Lorenzo How'd you mean?

Ron It's midwinter.

Lorenzo Oh yeah?

Ron Midwinter night if you catch a fish in your hands in the river, you can make a wish and it has to come true.

Mrs Sheehan Don't you know that, Ron? Everyone knows about midwinter night.

Lorenzo You've lost it, you have.

266

Ron That's why I come up here.
Lorenzo You're a right head-case, you are.

Ron ignores him.

Where's your fishing rod, then?
Ron You don't catch them like that.
Lorenzo Right.

Lorenzo and Ron stand.

Ron It's got to choose to come to you. You've got to call it and it's got to come to you.
Lorenzo You're off your head, you are.
Ron No, I'm not.
Lorenzo You've always been round the bend.

Lorenzo looks at Ron, realising he's said something he shouldn't have.

It's just something people say. It don't mean nothing.

They stand together for a moment, neither knowing what to say.

Ron This is the last night, that I'm using me powers. That's my wish, to be normal again.

She looks at him.

You can have my last consultation.

He looks at her – long and hard.

Zelda There was different ideas about what happened that night.
Mrs Sheehan Midwinter . . . the shortest night.
Mr Rodgers You see that, boys, the constellations. The light from the stars takes thousands of years to reach us – we are looking at the sky of ancient Rome, we are sharing the night with Caesar.
Ginger You think they might have gone up the Moors?

Mrs Ginger Why would they have gone up the Moors?

Lorenzo and Ron take off their socks in preparation for getting in the river.

Lorenzo You know something, Ron, I can't wear me socks no more. Because of the sand. I can't stand nothing between the skin of me feet and me shoes.

Header Used to put his socks on inside out when he was little. Didn't like the seams to rub.

Mrs Hammond I did that. When did you ever dress him?

Header I know. But I remember.

Lorenzo (*smelling the air*) What is that? Is it petrol? Oil?

Lorenzo and Ron stand taking in the air.

Header When they got to the desert, the oil wells were burning. Darkness never fell, because of the glow.

Ron It's just the smell of our town.

The soldier and the girl stand barefoot in the night.

We got to wait. That's what we've got to do. Give it long enough and one day, we'll be older. This will all be gone.

Lorenzo Christmas I'll be nineteen.

Header Born Christmas Day, he was. Come early, caught us all off guard.

Lorenzo and Ron walk into the river.

Ginger Found some boy up Derby with that gun. Couldn't say why he took it.

Mrs Ginger Had that disease they get when they crack up.

Ginger Some poor boy.

Mrs Ginger They had it in the First World War, only they give it a different name.

Ginger He hid it in the baby's cot.

Mrs Ginger They shot boys with it in the First World War.

Ginger Didn't do no harm, just hid it.

Mrs Ginger Shot Davey Barratt's Uncle Les.

Ginger Said he felt safe with having it near.

Mrs Ginger He was only sixteen.

Lorenzo Water's cold.

Ron Yeah.

Ginger Reeds there was in that water, soft between the stones . . .

Miss Lowery I'm very concerned to hear that Veronica is missing . . .

Zelda You said some bad things to her, Miss.

Miss Lowery What I might or might not have said to Veronica is of no concern to you, Zelda.

Zelda It's a bad thing to tell a person that what they had to give wasn't wanted.

Miss Lowery I'm sure I never said anything of the sort . . .

Zelda Thing is, Miss, when they found electricity – they didn't know how it worked but no one said it was a bad thing when they saw all that light. And you know why that was, don't you, Miss? It was because of having vision, which is seeing beyond the everyday. Truth is, nothing great would ever have been discovered if everyone went round using what they already knew as the yardstick. That would have buggered up Einstein and everyone in no time, and that's what you done with Ron. You went and killed her potential.

Chewy You went and said that? To Miss Lowery?

Zelda Felt I had to, least I could do.

Lorenzo (*looking down on the city, shivering*) They're all down there – Ron, Mum and Billy . . . Mr Shah in his corner shop, the lads will be going bowling just about now, Thursday, be heading up The Tilers for a pint . . . down the bowling alley, jackets off, shirtsleeves, looking at girls sideways, roll-ups, then down to McAllen's punching each other's arms, heading down McAllen's where the smell of deodorant and dry ice cuts through the strobes. Alright, mate? Let's get fucking rat-arsed –

past Lucy Cummings from sixth form whose brother
got killed in the back seat of a Ford Fiesta doing ninety
when they was all off their heads . . .

Lucy Alright, Lorenzo?

Lorenzo Put him up a headstone that looked like a racing
car, the grandmother paid with money she got from
the Christmas Club . . .

Gran How can I have my Christmas when I know one of
me grandchildren don't have no headstone? What's the
point of Christmas with him laying up the cemetery in
an unmarked grave?

Lorenzo Down the Hamlins . . .

Ron Rashida Perez in those shoes.

Lorenzo 'I got them for me modelling.'

Ron 'You need good shoes.'

Lorenzo See you in Paris, losers!

Ron Lives up Frenton now, got a baby, called him . . .
Claude . . .

*Suddenly they both laugh and laugh and laugh in the
cold and the dark.*

Lorenzo You're alright, Ron.

Beat.

Zelda Someone said they saw them.

Mrs Ginger Course *you* think you can do something
useful, you're the one that has to get involved . . .

Zelda Someone said when they got up the Moors, Ron
and Lorenzo, the boy that come back from the war,
they was standing, in the river . . .

Ginger Moon come up as bright as anything . . .

Trousers (*calling*) Ron! Lorenzo!

Header Lorenzo! Son!

Ginger They're in the river!

Mrs Sheehan (*spellbound*) Oh Ron! Midwinter night!

The whole 'town' looks up.

Barry I want to change things, make 'em better, but I just keep being pulled back in. I dunno, I'm fifteen now, maybe it's too late for a second chance.

Elena Zapadski Go to sleep, love.

Chewy I can't. I keep thinking, about what I said, about Ron, she was the only one who helped me . . .

Elena Zapadski Didn't your dad or me, didn't we help you?

Chewy I just wanted to read good so they'd stop calling me names . . .

Elena Zapadski You'll be alright, love . . .

Chewy But what if we all get killed by something, what if all the water gets poisoned and we're forced to eat GM food and we get diseases and the terrorists come and get us?

Elena Zapadski They're not coming tonight, I promise. No one's coming tonight. Now go to sleep.

Ginger (*calling*) Ron! Lorenzo!

Zelda Now some people think that everything in life is like – in your own hands, and others, they see it as fate, all mapped out, and you ain't got no choice about it, you ain't got no responsibility, about what happens to you . . .

Lorenzo and Ron stand in the water, waiting.

Ginger Wouldn't it be something, to get a second chance?

Mrs Ginger What's the use in asking something like that?

Ginger To start all over, with a will to do it better, to use what's been learned from life and still have time to put things right . . .

Lorenzo closes his eyes in the river.
Ron closes her eyes.

All across the town, everyone closes their eyes –
Ginger, Mrs Ginger, Trousers, Angela, Chewy, Elena
Zapadski, Billy, Header Hammond, Mrs Hammond,
Miss Lowery, Barry, the Lanky Girls – it is as if the
whole town were longing.
Music.
From the depths of the black river two silver fish
leap, shimmering against the black star-studded sky.
High into the air they rise. Lorenzo and Ron stare in
disbelief. It is as if the whole community senses what
has happened. Ron and Lorenzo reach out, and catch
the fish, and almost as quickly they're gone.

Zelda When Ron and Lorenzo came home that night,
they were changed . . .

Ron and Lorenzo join the rest of the community,
standing under the night sky, as at the start of the play.

They didn't talk about it, but Ron, she never used her
powers again. She was thirteen that year, she joined the
drama group at school, boys started to notice her,
sometimes people would laugh and say, 'Don't you
remember, Ron, you used to be such a weirdo?' and
she'd just smile. And Lorenzo, he got married, to that
Rashida Perez . . .

Lorenzo stands holding a baby in his arms.

Lorenzo Got a wife now, Ron, and a baby.

Ron and Lorenzo look at each other.

Ron That's good.

Lorenzo We're moving away. Making a new start. Billy's
going to come, weekends.

They look at each other.

Like a wish come true it is.

Ron smiles at him.

Rosie What's he doing, going off with that Rashida Perez?

Renata Anyone fancy some chicken nuggets?

Ronda Someone told me that he'd taken her to Paris for the weekend . . .

Angela Shut up, Ronda.

Ronda But it don't make no sense.

Rosie And he's taken on that baby. That funny little baby, Claude. What'd he want with a baby that ain't even his own?

Ronda I heard he bought her shoes in Paris. Carried that baby all over, he did, in a rucksack, on his back.

Zelda Ron's mum, she sent St Anthony back to the church. Wrapped him up in a blanket and popped him in the wheelbarrow . . .

Mrs Sheehan Don't seem right pushing a saint through the streets in a wheelbarrow . . .

Mrs Ginger Probably likes it, Gail, probably having the time of his life . . .

Zelda Lorenzo told the Old Bill Barry never nicked that car and Barry went home to look after his mum, got the dog back and all, something had happened to him, no one knew what, but he was good after that . . .

Barry I've made you scrambled eggs, Mum.

Mum When you were a baby, you used to make me cry, just looking at you, I loved you that much.

Barry You eat something, eh? Make you better.

Zelda Chewy wrote a story that got published in a magazine. He gave it to Ron, said it would never have happened without her.

Zelda stands looking out across the town.

Zelda What you reckon happened here, Ron? What d'you think this was all about?

Ron Don't suppose we'll ever know, Zel. Maybe it ain't for us to know. Maybe with something like this, you just got to take it . . . like a gift.

Ron, Zelda and the community look out across their town.
    Lorenzo holds the baby.

The End.

Sowing the Seed of Hope and Redemption

Lin Coghlan interviewed by Jim Mulligan

In a town somewhere in the British Isles the population stands looking across the rooftops, as if remembering. *The Miracle* is starting, and thirteen-year-old Zelda guides us through the town, allowing us to witness strange events that are transforming lives. The changes in people are profound, but the triggers mundane: eat a pineapple a day to get rid of depression; use a hot-water bottle to cure a reading problem; befriend a scruffy dog to turn away from a life of crime.

I think miracles are happening all the time. On one level you have thought processes that appear to affect the physical world, but on another level there is something more practical that is about taking responsibility. I am intrigued by the concept of a person of good character who makes a difference, by the idea that things can be changed in an extraordinary way when people take action, by one person standing up for what they think is right. Sometimes we are not even in contact with our own sense of responsibility. In a way *The Miracle* is about one girl deciding to take action that has repercussions.

Zelda introduces us to a number of people who have not realised their potential. The men seem to fare worse than the women. Header Hammond, who couldn't join the army because of family responsibilities, tries to live out his dream by encouraging his son to join up, and only succeeds in losing both his sons. Ginger, after a promising start with an inspirational teacher, appears to have given up on everything and is bitter that there is no longer any work for him. Mrs Sheehan, however, is philosophical about the fact that she had to look after her sick sister instead of going to work on a sheep farm in Australia. 'Everyone has their moment,' she tells Ron, 'when their destiny comes right along and taps them on the shoulder.'

> Mrs Hammond is much less dominant that Header, but he is more unhappy. She accuses him of living his life through Lorenzo, and neither of his sons turns out to be what he expected, but in the end he goes searching for Lorenzo and goes to Ron for help. I have a lot of sympathy for him. The past is haunting all of them, but Ginger in particular is terribly stuck. Mrs Ginger has a lot to put up with, yet she doesn't understand anything. I feel for Ginger.

Zelda shows us the shell of a town where everything used to be something else, including the people. They were all something else, but they have forgotten their true natures, so they too have become shells of themselves, like the old empty buildings on the outskirts of the town. But the present intrudes. The armchair warriors, the jingoists and the stupid, greet Lorenzo. In the pub they celebrate his return from the desert war with crass remarks and bonhomie. The war has come to the town, but in a very indirect way.

> I wanted to show the effect of war on a young person coming back. I didn't want to tell the story of whether war is justified or not, or discuss the politics of what is happening in Iraq. In fact Lorenzo could have been coming back from the First World War. In *The Miracle* we do not need to go to the war itself. There is enough information about the effect of the war on Lorenzo, about the jingoism of the characters in the pub, in

Barry's comment that he wouldn't fight in their shitty war.

The climax of the play is, if not miraculous, at least magical. The strands that have been twisting in the windswept landscape form a pattern: Barry at bay, wrongly accused of nicking yet another car; a missing gun that was not stolen by Lorenzo; Ginger's memories of swimming in the river and looking at the constellations; Ron using her powers for the last time; and everyone in the town closing their eyes, combining in one powerful psychic surge that causes two silver fish to leap shimmering against the black star-studded sky, high into the air.

I hope part of the debate will be about fate and destiny. Can we change what happens to us? Do we have to carry the burden of the past? If Lorenzo hadn't crossed paths with Ron, if Ron hadn't put on the long coat that everyone laughed at and taken the torch to find him, would they have come home to ridicule and arrest instead of coming home changed?

In their last exchange, Zelda asks, 'What d'you reckon happened here, Ron? What d'you think this was all about?' And Ron replies, 'Don't suppose we'll ever know, Zel. Maybe it ain't for us to know.' We do know some things: that Lorenzo survives his ordeal, marries Rashida Perez and takes on her baby; that St Anthony went back to the church wrapped in a blanket; that Chewy got a story published in a magazine; that Barry is a reformed character who looks after his mum; that Billy is going to spend weekends with his brother. But we don't really know what happens to anyone in the long run.

This is not a play about happy endings. There is too much loss. There is an enormous amount of longing.

Although we feel that Lorenzo has survived, we don't know what will happen to any of the characters. I wonder about Zelda – where she will be when she's seventeen. Will Ron be able to escape? I feel that everything you write should have your spirit in it. You have a responsibility about where you leave your audience. If you leave them with a happy ending you run the risk of them getting something that's sentimental and unearned. It doesn't tell anyone very much about anything. If you leave the audience with questions you are sowing the seed of something intriguing: there is the possibility of hope and redemption.

Production Notes

Lin Coghlan completed *The Miracle* following her decision
to write something for herself that she enjoyed. She has
worked extensively in prisons, with companies including
Cleanbreak, and has met many young people in trouble.
Barry, Ron and Zelda's stories all come from this
experience. Theirs are stories of a community that never
quite got its chance. The play is about lost potential, and
longing: it is both epic and interactive.

The majority of modern English plays are set indoors,
in rooms. Lin writes things outside, in the open, which
allows her to sweep over a town and its gardens, parks
or allotments. She does not want to root the play in a
naturalistic setting. The scenes take place on an open
landscape or stage.

Nothing in the play is unnatural, but it is put together in
fast-moving montages/collages. If you use lots of images
it can make up fascinating, rippling pictures of the play.
However, if you try to do too much visual representation
you will find that the action is too fast-moving and
supple to accommodate fantastical scenery. The play is
going to be more flexible than any scenic representation
you can contrive, and while the lines are taken from
life, the way they are put together is something we are
unused to.

It's very clear that Ron and Zelda are in charge of telling
the audience things about themselves and about other
people. Their task is to pursue the storytelling. The ongoing
function for everyone else is to keep it alive. Ron and

Zelda talk to the audience mid-scene, and their thoughts are free and conscious. Actors instinctively talk to each other and make naturalistic choices. Here the actors will need to speak to the audience directly.

Explore the spatial relationship between the cast and the audience. Think of the play as a landscape. The characters are on this landscape, not unlike the characters in Dylan Thomas's *Under Milk Wood*. The storytelling shouldn't be naturalistic.

EXERCISES

Play the entire play for voices. Make this an exercise in purely vocal storytelling.

Have the actors talk directly to one audience-member when the lines suggest it. Use all the space, have them make sure they do not attempt to stand next to the person they are talking to. Discover how, when the characters are talking to the audience, they can become more distinct than when they are talking to each other.

When Billy has a flashback without it being announced – 'You hear that, Mum? I heard something – next door' – the line is a scene within itself; it is important to make such moments vivid.

Note the differences between private and public action, when the lines have been *said*, remember what hasn't been *seen* on stage.

CHARACTERS

RON • Aged twelve. • Wants to help people. • Is mature but not arrogant. • Makes goodness interesting. • There is a worldliness about her. • When Ron and Lorenzo are together, it's not sweet. • Ron might well be the same when she is older.

Ron has a father called Trevor or Trev. Ginger and his best mate Trousers refer to him, but he never speaks. The moment he might talk is the night Ron was born, as the drinks are on Trevor. Decide if Ron's dad still lives with them, as we know he was definitely around at the birth.

BILLY • Aged twelve. • Is autistic: he can store up facts and be very competitive. He needs to get everything right. • His brother receiving a medal gives Billy a sense of achievement he can relate to. He has a literal way of thinking. • He is the most erudite character in the play, but is considered not normal. He represents the absurdity in this world and can be slightly pompous.

BARRY • Aged fifteen. • Half the other boys want to be like him. He has both his following and his image to live up to. He is not really bad. He doesn't know how to act until Ron shows him. • He's not really a male role-model. He is already unusual because he's come to Ron. • Barry is categorised as a type, he wants to change but finds it hard. • Barry's sister doesn't approve of his new behaviour at all. His hardness moves to strength. By the end of the play he has changed: decide how.

The Lorenzo and Billy scene is written like a letter, but the tone is as a phone call. Decide whether it's an email or a dream.

ASPECTS OF STAGING

There aren't many stage directions in the play, so when there is one, take it very seriously: sand has to come out of Billy's letter and is important, as it conjures up the desert and then disappears in a way nothing else can. Something received in a letter means a lot and can have a powerful effect. Lorenzo knew his brother very well, and knew the effect the sand would have on him. This action shows the closeness of the relationship between the two brothers and a lot is learnt about their relationship through this event. It's like part of a patchwork throughout the play.

The sand is as important as the pineapple. These are the only two things that are specified as being required, and give the play a sensuality. Make sure the pineapple and sand aren't just passing props casually dropped in.

The Miracle is set in a landscape parallel to ours. The support of music conjures a landscape as nothing else can. It should be introduced when something needs to be there which isn't in the text at the moment. Rhythmically, the text sometimes asks for these things, like a breath or a beat, before it continues. Similarly, the music both mirrors and partners the landscape.

Read pages 236–239

The grown-ups are worried about not having control and about the different things that are coming into their lives. There is a misunderstanding and concern from the adults that the kids are behaving inappropriately. Decide from whose point of view we are seeing the play. Is it from Ron and Zelda's perspective, which might be why Miss Lowery is depicted in a certain way? Ron and Zelda are at the centre of something that's very intriguing.

We only see fragments of Miss Lowery and Mrs Sheehan, and a lot is left unsaid – this is a puzzle in the play.

The adults know that there has been a flood at the Dolbys'. The houses and buildings have been severely damaged, and some domestic items moved around. The contents of the church have been swept away, the shop has lost its stock, there was a microwave on the zebra crossing, and St Anthony wound up in Ron's house. Ron's mum is very moved by this. The mystery and ambiguity is vital, as the play is deliberately elusive.

The play happens two weeks after the flood. The clean up has started, but St Anthony has not been returned. He is the saint you pray to when you have lost something, and is normally depicted holding an open book with a baby Jesus on it. He is a gifted speaker, and attracted crowds everywhere – even the fish wanted to listen.

There is a shift in the story when Ron starts doing animals. Decide if she scans the animals, or whether they come to her independently. Lin once went on a course to explore inter-animal relationships, at the end of which she accurately read a horse's mind. She feels there is a connection between humans and animals.

Read pages 239–241

This part of the play feels naturalistic and you don't get a sense of role-play. It's not narrated by Zelda, and Ron is not involved. Renata is always fantasising about eating, but the Lanky Girls say she never eats. She does eat, but acts like she doesn't. Maybe they have had enough of her constantly going on about food. Find the dynamic between these three girls, aged fourteen to seventeen.

Barry is caught between the two groups. He has his old life with his sister, then Billy enters and he feels awkward.

He is unsure of where to place himself within the two sides. Barry and his sister are arguing about their mum – decide what they think of her, and what they can say in public in front of other people about her. This type of conversation is awkward for Barry, but feels like one it is important for him to have.

There are animals in all of Lin's plays and the dog is important, but an actor doesn't have to play the dog. If you do get an actor to play the dog, don't play it for laughs. There is a protective quality about Barry and the dog: it shows Barry in a different light.

The Lanky Girls are the counterpoint to Ron and Barry: they ground the story. When Billy enters you see the awkwardness that arises for Barry. He is left feeling exposed, embarrassed and uncomfortable. Explore how long the pauses can be. Discover the difference between a beat and a pause. Billy is isolated in those pauses because he is different – this is a different silence, stressing the fact that Billy does not fit into the community, so when his brother Lorenzo arrives it's important for him in terms of his sense of belonging.

If you have a problem with Barry making a roll-up, get him to do something else with his hands, otherwise it will affect the rhythm of the scene. If he is doing something, there is a tension going on. In these actions a lot of things are going on in his character.

This group of people know each other very well. We can see that they are completely at ease with one another and can finish each other's sentences. When Barry says, 'You left Mum on her own,' he is getting back at his sister.

Discover how the length of the pauses can bring a new dimension to the scene. Billy asks questions that no one else dares to ask. Find the scene's intention and choose whichever route you want to play, but remember that the small moments reveal the bigger picture.

Read pages 241–246

Perform a version of the scene with one person playing Lorenzo, and the other characters walking around the space. When they pass Lorenzo get them to pick up on the next line in the scene – stop and genuinely ask Lorenzo the question. Make sure it is asked directly to him.

Ask what it might feel like for Lorenzo to be bombarded, caught, trapped, exposed and vulnerable. What Lin intended is for the questions to be authentically asked: they all have to be specific. Lorenzo does not have answers – he hears the questions but can't put faces to them. The key to this scene is to hear the questions and for them to be real. Ask what these questions leave Lorenzo thinking about.

Squeaky Mary's scene

Discover the difference between the outside and the inside. Decide how to make the scene feel like a pub. Note the difference in Lorenzo when he is talking to his mum and being with his friends.

In this scene there is a very public argument. Decide how this makes the characters feel. Explore the sense of community, of all these people being in the same room. Look at the arrival of Barry in the pub and how it affects the dynamics. He doesn't come in very often, so it's strange when he does. See what happens if you get the other characters to shift positions when he enters.

Angela is playing Barry and Lorenzo off against each other. It is a total shock for Barry that Angela is speaking to him; he can't compute this, it's very strange.

Every time there is an argument or tension, the focus is taken off Lorenzo. Lorenzo's dad (Header) constantly tries to bring attention back to him. Decide why his father sent him off to war and what he gets out of this relationship.

Angela is on the fringes of the Lanky Girls, but she isn't one of them. She is slightly older (seventeen) and at once more outrageous and more interesting. She has an antagonistic relationship with Barry – decide if there's something going on between them, and now that Lorenzo has come back whether she is playing them off against one another. She stops talking to Barry to get Lorenzo's attention. She has a lot of confidence and knows how to play the boys off against each other. Barry takes the blame for stealing the car. There is a huge dynamic between the good boy Barry wants to be and the actual Barry. Discover how the local community puts Barry in this 'bad boy' role.

Read pages 247–250

Ron and Zelda come out of the scene and have a moment together. Decide how much conversation actually went on in the room when Ron and Zelda stepped out.

Ron isn't just meeting people, she's meeting people in the toilets. Decide what's been going on there, what type of people meet in the toilets. As far as the grown-ups are concerned it could be a cover for taking drugs.

Miss Lowery chooses her words carefully and very pointedly: she is trying to undermine Mrs Sheehan. The two of them are having an argument; the tone is not yet decided. It is a clear disagreement about what actually happened and is not really about Ron at all. Mrs Sheehan believes that St Anthony came to her because she has been calling for him. Each line Miss Lowery speaks steps up the argument, and she is very specific in her use of language, worrying at it like a dog with a bone.

Decide on Mrs Ginger's religious beliefs – she says that Ginger has no faith in anything.

Zelda comes back into the scene here. Ron and her mum have a moment together – she could be showing Ron this scene in the distance. Zelda likes winding her mum up which shows when she tells her about the sex shop. When the two of them are narrators or storytellers they talk about the other characters.

Everything the children say is the truth. The adults protect the children from the adult moments. What the adults want to be true is as important as what is actually true.

Decide how Ron gained her powers. Did she recognise them or did someone tell her? Maybe she became suddenly aware that she can sense things at the same time as Zelda, and starts to look at people in a different way.

Zelda is the voice of reason and presents a very grown-up attitude to things. Maybe that is the miracle, and that is what is relevant. Make sure you're not just making the play all narrative.

Read pages 250–251

This is Barry's chance to be a movie star – it is his moment. Remember that Zelda is telling the story and that Zelda is thirteen, so there is an excitement in it – don't get caught in the poignancy.

Read pages 252–255

Miss Lowery can be light and played with a caring attitude, but remember she can be devious when it suits her. There is a change in tone from when she is exploring things to her becoming an adult and drawing a conclusion. She is not vicious in her intentions, but she does try and demolish Ron's point of view. Find out when she's trying to understand Ron's position and when she has to draw some sort of line under it. Some of what she says is quite demoralising.

Barry still cares about the welfare of the dog. This is heartbreaking, as he has given up on himself, but do find a way of doing it without it being mawkish. Show this through the reactions of the other characters. Barry is like a parent with the dog when he gives it to someone else.

In this section of the play the idea is being conveyed differently from how it was being told before – there is a sense of pace, and of reasons behind why the story is being told.

Read pages 255–258

When Header gets involved, his missed opportunities become clear. In trying to find the light and shade, one suddenly understands why Lorenzo went to war. His dad is trying to live his life through him. There is a different way of arguing between these parents and between Mr and Mrs Ginger, as there is a lot of sadness in these two. Mrs Hammond rarely raises her voice at her husband, and Header is speechless; they are not having the kind of conversation they normally have. The key to the scene is finding the love that the parents have for their son, even if it is misguided. Lorenzo is looking but not speaking – he is losing it. Underneath these moments lies the real truth. Know when the characters are lying to themselves as well as to each other.

Each of the characters' names has a history. Trousers is called Trousers because he has a story in his life – what that is, is for the actor to discover. It gives each character a strong sense of identity.

Header is not the only one who has frustrated ambitions: all the characters' ambitions are frustrated because none of them have realised their dreams. There are different shades of this dynamic of missed opportunities throughout the town. There are also references to caring for parents throughout the play – generation after generation are still in the same community.

Ron has the opportunity to break the chain and that is what is at the heart of the play.

Read pages 258–261

The key with the Lanky Girls is to make them funny: find that flavour, the laughter is relevant.

Angela is quite high-status as a character. Lorenzo has driven all that way, then kicked her out of the car. Maybe she does have different concerns. She needs to carry some of that atmosphere from the car into the Lanky Girls.

Read pages 261–265

We see Ginger as a boy. Mr Rodgers is the kind of teacher who took kids out to have experiences – he is a fine chap. He is the counterbalance to Miss Lowery.

The bat noise is a specific type of noise – it has to sound like bats.

Barry's dad is not around any more – he is long gone.

This is a part of the play that needs very complex staging: all the layers are moving. Time is overlapping, and the emotional resonances of the piece are building with a poignancy that represents all the different layers of Ginger's memory.

Everyone is present in this scene. The play is reaching its conclusion.

Read pages 265–274

This long chunk is all interconnected. Take the reaction of the townspeople out of context of the play, and look at Ron and Lorenzo's scene in isolation. There is a clear journey, and it is practical in terms of rehearsal. Do the same with Mr and Mrs Ginger.

Midwinter night is the shortest night. Don't worry about the shifts in time and who is saying what to whom. Make it work as an ensemble.

If the scene is physically static it could be interesting. Keep it simple.

The fish moment: start with an extreme, look at what is the most bizarre way of staging this, and often you will find a way in. Introduce a magical way of making the fish appear. Don't be too literal, and keep it light. It is about a personal experience for Ron and Lorenzo. Whatever happens needs to affect the whole community.

Workshop facilitated by Paul Miller and Tim Stark
with notes taken by Sophie Hobson and Des James

PACK UP YOUR TROUBLES
THE MUSICAL

Snoo Wilson

created from an original concept by Aubrey Powell,
with lyrics by George Asaf, Felix Powell,
Aubrey Powell and Snoo Wilson,
and music by Felix Powell, Aubrey Powell
and Nicolas Bloomfield

Snoo Wilson's first professionally produced play, *Pignight* (1971), was so shocking it prompted questions in the House of Commons about the suitability of artistic subsidy to Portable Theatre, the short-lived but influential touring theatre founded by Tony Bicât and David Hare. However, *HRH*, a play about the Duke and Duchess of Windsor, was equally scandalous – though the times had changed – but played in the West End in 1998 with not a boogler in sight. Many of his plays are published by Methuen, and he has also written book and lyrics for a number of musicals as well as libretti for opera and original films (*Shadey*, 1984). His fourth novel, *The Works of Melmont*, is published by Barkus. He also wrote *Bedbug* for the Connections programme in 2004.

Nicolas Bloomfield is a composer, writer and director. He was the co-founder of GLORIA. His works include: *Sarrasine* (London and New York); *A Judgment in Stone* (*Time Out* 1992 Award); *Night after Night* (Traverse/Royal

Court); *The Picture of Dorian Gray* (Lyric Hammersmith); *Lady into Fox* (Sheffield/Lyric Studio); *Seven Sacraments* (Artangel/East of England Orchestra); *The Game of Love and Chance* (National Theatre); *Twelfth Night* (Goodman Theatre Chicago). He was a member of BLOOLIPS. As Musical Director: *The Marriage of Figaro*, *Die Fledermaus*, *Cinderella*, *Eugene Onegin*, *The Ghosts of Scrooge* (which he wrote and directed) and *The Bar*. TV includes the *Omnibus* title theme and *Now That It's Morning*.

Characters

Felix Powell

Felix 2

Felix 3

George Powell

Mabel
wife of Felix

Leila
wife of George

Aubrey Powell
Felix's grandson

Recruiting Sergeant

Joan Bellamy

Sarah Bonham

Mayfair Minnie

German Tenor

Charlie Chaplin

Judge

Neville

Compere, Lurland

Court Attendants

Bookies

Siren Girls

Fast Eddie

Choruses

British Army

German Army

Civilians

Racegoers

Pubgoers

Pearly Kings and Queens

Brighton Barmaids

Hoods

Charlie Chaplins

Cowgirl Dancers/Singers

Joan Bellamy Backup Dancers

Mayfair Minnies

*Large choruses appear in different and recurring
costumes throughout and will be identified
as the need arises.*

*The stage is divided by lighting into two or more
performance areas as needed. There is a place for a
permanent object, roughly the shape of an upright piano
but larger, with useful performance ledges on it, which
can be trucked on: other musicians can play in a pit band
or onstage. Felix Powell can mime playing on the symbolic
piano, or he can use a real piano, or his fingers can call
forth the piano and other instruments out of the air.*

Mabel and Leila in Pierrot ruffs are performing or rehearsing in a spotlight. On another part of the stage, George and Felix, dressed in suits, are composing at a piano.

Mabel *and* **Leila** (*soulful close harmony*)
Private Perks is a funny little codger
With a smile, a funny smile.
Five feet none he's an artful little dodger,
With a smile, a funny smile.

They stop abruptly, puppetlike, as the music halts. The action moves to George and Felix.

George Go on then, Felix. Let's hear it.

First line of 'Pack Up' intro, played on a piano with one finger.

You changed it. Is that marching time?
Felix The chorus has to be. Nothing else.
George Alright, how does it go?

The two groups are now being watched by a man in a modern bomber jacket, Aubrey Powell.

Mabel *and* **Leila**
Flush or broke, he'll have his little joke,
He can't be suppressed.
All the other fellows have to grin
When he gets this off his chest . . .

Music ends. Aubrey turns to the audience to introduce the two groups.

Aubrey Meet the Powell family! My grandfather Felix
Powell is even now composing the tune, Felix's older
brother, my great-uncle George, has written or re-
written the lyrics, and it is being sung here by their
wives, the lovely Mabel and Leila, the former Brooks
Sisters, later of the Harlequinaders, long-ago stars of
the music-hall circuit. Felix was the one who became
famous, but he later died by his own hand, illuminating
a gulf between the chipper advice dished out in the
song – 'What's the use of worrying, it never was
worthwhile' – and what he felt. Just before my mother
died, she had mentioned she had a few things of
Grandpa's. So after I had been finally orphaned, as the
last surviving Powell, I went up into the attic, to my
grandfather's chest.

*Music (if you have a band/orchestra, this is their first
entrance). Aubrey approaches the near-piano. He
draws up the lid. Lights, music, a reveal. Enter Felix 2,
a character wearing the front of a pantomime horse,
miming a gallop.*

Just a minute, who the hell are you?

Felix removes the head.

Felix 2 I am the ghost of Felix Powell. I have run ahead
of my back end to tell you to get a move on.
Aubrey You can't be the ghost of Felix Powell. Felix is
over there, playing the piano!
Felix 2 Two Felixes can tell the story twice as fast.
Aubrey, crack on with the introduction, make it short,
and then get lost. (*to Felix 1 and George*) Almost
there! Keep it up, chaps.

*Musical swell. Felix 2 exits and Felix and George go
back to work. Aubrey turns to audience.*

Aubrey In the chest were tour diaries of his hectic
schedules as a music-hall performer, sheet music of
'Pack Up Your Troubles', much other music, published
and unpublished, a tambourine with his World War
One tour dates inked on it, and a war-booty German
pistol without its ammunition. I discovered Felix had
been a child prodigy, a cathedral organist at twelve
who ran away from the house of God to the boards.
A man who wrote the best-selling marching song of all
time. A man who became a star, went to the front in
the First World War armed only with a piano, who
then shot himself through the heart twenty years later,
dressed in his Home Guard uniform. Ladies and
gentlemen, I give you my grandfather, Felix Powell.

He exits.

George I've re-written the words now, look.

*The song comes out experimentally, with increasing
confidence.*

Felix 1 *and* **George**
Private Perks is a funny little codger
With a smile, a funny smile.
Five feet none, he's an artful little dodger,
With a smile, a funny smile.

*The music continues under the following which needs
to be said in sixteen bars.*

George What's the connection between the Bradford
Picturedome, the London and Manchester Hippo-
dromes, Doncaster Palace, Sheffield, Finsbury Park
and a dozen other Empires? They won't let us leave the
stage till we give it to 'em. Felix, little brother, since it
won Best Marching Song, do you know how much
money that song has made us?

Felix Mabel handles the accounts.

Mabel *and* **Leila**
Flush or broke he'll have his little joke,
He can't be suppressed.
All the other fellows have to grin,
When he gets this off his chest –

We introduce, from nowhere, a massive chorus. Men dressed as soldiers, as women; women dressed as nurses, as factory workers, as vamps – a First World War tableau.

Chorus
Pack up your troubles in your old kit bag
And smile, smile, smile.
George We've hit the jackpot!
Chorus
While you've a lucifer to light your fag,
Smile boys, that's the style –
Chorus
What's the use of worrying,
It never was worthwhile. So:
Pack up your troubles in your old kit bag
And smile, smile –

Song halts abruptly.

George The money's enough to free us from the treadmill of performance. And to think it was rescued from the bottom drawer! But I have to confess, little brother, I am already conflicted about taking money for words endorsing tobacco products.
Felix But it won't stop you taking the money, will it?
George The Germans have already put new lyrics to the tune.
Felix I'm not surprised they don't want a straight translation. Private Perks getting all his pals to enlist so they can kill some more Germans!
George I based Perks on you.

Felix That was perceptive, George, because I'm going to join up.

George You! Going for a soldier! What an idiot! The war is a collective insanity. Why? Do you want to get killed?

Felix Mabel says we have made enough not to tour any more.

George Yeah but did she tell you to enlist?

Felix She doesn't suspect. She'll find out when my papers come through.

Mabel appears, extravagantly dressed as cowboy – chaps and stetson on a pantomime horse – to a mighty drumroll.

George (*to audience*) Ladies and gentlemen! For the finale tonight, in their triumphant farewell tour of the world's most modern music halls, the globally acclaimed and deeply patriotic Harlequinaders!

Music.

A big hand, please, for Mrs Mabel Powell, as Lethal Larry, our own, new and surprising Guardian of Britain's shores, Dauntless Dick Deadeye!

Mabel (*patter*)
From Timbuktu to Rotterdam, Gay Paree to Nepal,
Sharpshooters, tremble and retire, for I outdraw y' all.
Sometimes the job could break your heart, I freely
confess.
Once, a kid and his mother both refused to get dressed;
Strictly between us, she was called – Venus.
But the gods of love, who we adore,
Are not above the frontier law. Venus
Went on encouraging her son to infect everyone.
Cupid would not stop firing arrows. They both
mocked my arrest;
They was buried in Tombstone Creek, last week.
I plugged the pair of them; straight through the chest.

Cowgirls

> Lethal Larry, the frontier's hope,
> Coming to get you by gun or by rope.
> Lethal Larry, the frontier's pride,
> Beware of the peacemaker at his side.

Mabel

> So this here is a music hall. 'Fine Entertainment Stars ,
> Women passing off as men?' – Most peculi-ar.
> If my wife strapped on my chaps, I swear, I'd whup
>   the tar.

Chorus

> Lethal Larry always takes it too far!

*Cowgirls perform a dance break, joined by Gwilliam,
Larry's pantomime horse.*

Mabel

> I'm gonna ping the chandeliers, to make y'all leave
>   quicker.
> Cross-dressin' is worse wickedness than breakfast with
>   no likker.
> Frustrating for the preacher man who's tryin' to get
>   folk tied.
> If both of you is wearing pants, you can't tell who's
>   the bride!

Cowgirls

> Lethal Larry, a stranger indoors,
> His high code of chivalry we all applaud.
> Divorcing his horse because of her snores,
> And when Britain needs him, he is all yours.

Mabel

> I heard a Chinese whisper passing through the prairie
>   grass
> Of Hunnish misbehaviour, now I can't let that one pass.
> I'll take the hand of Uncle Sam, and then enlist, what's
>   more

We'll drill the Boche with more durn holes than my
old outhouse door.

*The singing segues into a whistled 'Pack Up Your
Troubles'. Mabel fires three times at German spiked
helmets on a wall: each time she fires, the helmet is
'hit', pulled off and disappears. Cowgirls continue to
dance in background. Chorus march off to this, with
Mabel at the head, saluting proudly. Lighting change
and, without leaving, Mabel is 'offstage', taking off her
cowboy gear, meeting Leila, another cowgirl who
leaves the muted performing line of cowgirls.*

Leila What do you think about Felix joining the army?

Mabel I won't be sad to stop this lark after what it's
turned into. Cut-price patriotism. Fanning the fires of
blood-lust night after night. Recruiting officers
rounding up their quotas with under-age boys at the
end of the show. We're making a significant contribution
to getting our audience killed. And dragging America
in, wonderful – that'll make it a *complete* world war.
It's funny, the first time we played Bradford they threw
orange peel from the gallery at the stage, and they're
still doing it now. That's what Felix will be fighting for.
The British right to throw orange peel.

Leila The risks are worst for officers, aren't they?

Mabel Felix would never make an officer.

Leila How I hate this war.

Mabel What's George going to do?

Leila He's going to be a conscientious objector.

Mabel Don't they make conchies work on the farms?

Leila George said he was going to get a caravan and we
were going on the road to sell herbal remedies. For
poor people who can't afford doctors.

Mabel If you only treat poor people, how are they ever
going to pay you? Why does everything have to be so
precarious! You always enjoyed the worst things, like,

aged eight, singing for your supper squirming on some wharfinger's knee in the Isle of Dogs.

Leila As Dad played the squeezebox, remember? You did the accounts even then.

Mabel I sometimes think we should have followed little Charlie Chaplin's footsteps. He's so wealthy now.

Leila He was always a smart fellow.

Mabel As well as being hung like a horse. Missed your chance there, girl. No, I mean the chance to get into film. We could have taken the Mississippi riverboat engagement the Harlequinaders were offered, after we were in Cape Town. And then Baton Rouge to St Louis, and then by train to California.

Leila Why didn't we go?

Mabel Felix got cold feet and then to cap it, lost his voice. We've never had security before. I'm already getting misty-eyed about my retirement!

Leila I never thought Felix would pull it off. Why would he want to join up after hitting the jackpot?

Fade on Mabel and Leila. Lights up on Felix and George: long coats, fedoras, at the piano.

George Brass monkeys! This has to be the coldest office in all of Tin Pan Alley. When are we going to have some heat in our place of work, Felix? Sod 'When we can afford it'.

Felix I've sent out for a heater.

George Did Mabel knit you that pair of mittens?

Felix She did.

George Tell you what. Give me the left-hand one. You can play the melody with your right. Forget all that flophouse left-hand.

Felix Have you ever heard me playing flophouse with my left hand?

George Never. And more's the pity. You got *snobby ears*.

Felix (*indignant*) I got what?

George Snobby ears. You hate jazz because it's got
feeling in it, but not a *feeling* you were taught was
proper.

Felix Can we just leave it that I don't like jazz?

George (*forgiving*) Alright! Competition for marching
song, so: marching time, four-four, left-right, left-right.
Not too challenging for you?

Felix I've already done my bit. What about your end of
the business?

George It came to me when I was at my ablutions.
Private Perks is now a murderous little shortarse.
He has the same violent feelings for the enemy as you
have for filthy New Orleans jazz. By verse two, see,
we're in lockstep with the prevailing mood of the
country. Chuck it at the wall, now, and see what sticks.

Music. Felix plays.

George (*sings*)
Private Perks went a-marching into Flanders,
With a smile, his funny smile.

Felix Private Perks hasn't killed anyone yet.

George I bet you a tenner he will before the bleeding
heater arrives.

George (*sings*)
He was loved by the privates and commanders
For his smile, his funny smile –

Felix *and* **George** (*sing*)
When a throng of Boches came along,
With a mighty swing,
Perks yelled out, 'This little bunch is mine!'
Keep your heads down, boys and sing, hi!

*Stage fills with massed chorus, marching and singing
softly behind the action.*

Chorus
Pack up your troubles in your old kit bag . . . *etc.*

303

Felix A hundred quid would be handy.

George If we win this competition, sod Mabel's purse-strings, I'm going to buy a car.

Felix It's good enough to try out in the act, certainly.

George It's good enough to reach the world, this one! From Alabama to the Hindu Kush. Everyone's going to be forking over their hard-earned dosh and marching along to it. All the colours of humanity. Pink soldiers. Red soldiers. Yellow soldiers. Brown ones.

Felix There was that enlisted black British footballer who rose to captain –

George – and died. But we can still give his merry men something to sing, as they follow their officers over the top.

Chorus (*to whistling*) So –!

George I got offered two white feathers today, for not being in uniform. The second was from a different woman to the girl who normally tries to give 'em out in Trafalgar Square. But she had exactly the same blank expression as she handed them out, reminding cowards still in civvy street of their duty.

Felix I've seen her, yes.

George I looked this new madam straight in the eye and said, 'Thank you madam, but unless you are joining the armed forces yourself today, I suggest *you* hold on to it, and pin the white feather on *your* bosom.'

The marching chorus leaves the stage, music fades.

Felix If we're done, I'm going to make a fair copy.

George (*arch*) *I* can't do any better, I know that. Tune's sharper now, but probably still a dud. Hey, ho.

Felix Are you a hundred per cent sure about Private Perks? The name . . .

George Alright, I'll change it. Won't cost you a thing. What about Private Taffy?

Felix (*scathing*) Private Taffy? Doesn't scan.

Enter Recruiting Sergeant with Felix's uniform, which Felix starts to put on. Felix moves away from piano.

George (*sings unaccompanied as he exits*)
Private Powell is a funny little fellow
With a smile, a funny smile.

Sergeant Name, rank and number?

Felix My name is Felix Powell. My rank is a private. My number –

Sergeant You're in His Majesty's Army now, Powell. Address me as Sergeant.

Felix Yes, Sergeant.

Sergeant And what is your flippin' number, then? Come on, Powell, don't keep me hanging about. The Boche could launch a surprise attack in the time you're taking!

Felix 315948 . . . Sergeant.

Sergeant Congratulations, Powell. Correct. And your posting . . . ?

Felix I don't know what my posting is, I'm afraid, Sergeant.

Sergeant If you shut up for a moment, I can tell you! Immediate attachment to 142 Cavalry Division. I take it you're experienced.

Felix What as?

Sergeant It says here you are a heavy lorry driver.

Felix I've not driven a lorry. Ever. I'm sorry, Sergeant.

Sergeant Heavy lorries is what you're leaving Blighty tonight to drive. Waterloo Station eighteen hundred hours, report to the duty officer on the platform for your travel warrant.

A Station Guard blows his whistle.

Sergeant When you get to the other side, Powell, don't try and score a Blighty with a self-inflicted wound. We can always tell if a soldier has been drilled by the

Boche or has deliberately shot himself. Powder burns.
It counts as desertion. Cowards what shoot themselves
get shot!

*Exit Sergeant. Felix goes back to the piano. Enter Leila
and George.*

Leila Where you off to now, George?

George I got my call-up papers. I'm going down the
town hall to tell 'em to get stuffed.

Leila Why didn't you stop Felix joining up? Don't you
ever discuss things?

George Never! We wouldn't get any work done. We leave
chatter to the girls.

Music.
   *Spotlight on Joan Bellamy dressed as Private Perks,
plus burlesque back-up dancers wearing gas masks.*

George And now, ladies and gentlemen, a warm, a very
warm, and put your hands together please for the
delicious, delumptious and utterly scrumptious armed
forces' sweetheart, Joan Bellamy, on her first outing to
Gallipoli!

Joan smiles and waves. Whoops and hollers of crowd.

Joan (*sings*)
Private Perks he came back from Boche shooting,
With a smile, his funny smile –

*At the same time as the song unfolds, Joan removes
her uniform in a striptease. On another part of the
stage a wigged lawyer accompanies George to stand
before a Judge in flowing robes, in simultaneous
action. Court attendants.*
   *Alter volume as necessary to make both song and
scene comprehensible. The Lawyer should start his
speeches and scene about now, to play out in parallel.*

Joan
Round his home he then set about recruiting
With a smile, his funny smile.
He told all his pals, the short, the tall,
What a time he'd had.
As each enlisted like a man
Private Perks said, 'Now my lad' – Mmm . . .!

Lawyer M'lud, my client George Powell wishes to register his conscientious objection to serving in His Majesty's armed forces.

George This is such a waste of everyone's time. You got people told to come back in six months 'cos they can't process the flood of lambs to the slaughter.

Judge Could your client tell the court what he does for a living?

George I am on the boards, m'lud.

Joan
Pack up your troubles in your old kit bag
And smile, smile, smile.
Smile boys, that's the style –
What's the use of worrying?
It never was worthwhile
So, pack up your troubles in your old kit bag
And smile, smile, smile –

Judge The boards of which companies?

George The 'boards' of a theatre. (*Aside.*) You silly old goat!

Joan is 'killed' when a German soldier comes up and ritually bayonets her. She 'expires' patriotically and her backing group carry her off, all still singing. End song.

New parallel scene: lights on Felix at the organ, churchy vamping. A young Felix, Felix 3, at twelve years of age, mimes organ playing.

Judge It does not sound as if your objections to serving your country are reflected in your patriotic words, now sung by our brave Tommies worldwide, Mr Powell.

Organ ends.

George (*indignant*) I never expected it to be taken literally! It's a song what because of the mad times, m'lud, got totally out of hand.

Judge Alright, go and be a pacifist then, you dirty unpatriotic little Welsh conchie!

George Think I'm not brave enough? Try me! Call me up and place me under enemy gunfire mortar and gas attack – I'll stay till Fritz bastes my birthday suit in phosphorus, if you release my brother from his soldier's oath!

Judge Not a chance of a snowball in hell to that.

George (*to Judge*) Not so fast, m'lud! A musical prodigy, my brother, beloved by all of us, impressed Druids to the extent he was put in charge of sacred music at St Asaph's Cathedral aged only twelve. Left to his own devices, m'lud, I swear he would still only write holy tunes. Which is a waste of time because nowadays, sadly, God is dead. A nearby shellburst – an everyday event, I know in wartime – could spill l'il Felix's fragile cocktail of talent.

Judge Case dismissed.

Judge and any Attendants exit.

George A genius; but if his loved ones aren't around to cushion the cruel shock of reality, he may crash and burn. Let some higher power lead him back out of the chemical quagmire. Felix, you weren't made for the exploding wilderness of mud. Let me burn my white feathers and perish in your stead! (*Pause.*) What's this rising before my eyes? A broken church!

Scene changes to a church with bomb damage. Felix 3, aged twelve, and Felix 1 at different organs, playing 'Ave Maria' fragment. A suggestion of broken stained-glass colours in lighting.

Enter Sarah Bonham, a stylishly dressed woman in khaki, who listens to the tune. 'Ave Maria' continues on and off through conversation.

Bonham Apparently the east window had some of the best medieval stained glass in Europe.

Felix The organist's father told me he had repaired the keyboard, in memory of his soldier son. His tombstone's outside but they never found his body.

Bonham Excuse me, I was sitting in the back pews, listening. I hope you don't mind. I never associated you with sacred music, Mr Powell.

Felix I won the Eisteddfod classical composition prize when I was twelve. My father was so proud of me he cried that day. He died soon after, so he never knew the rest.

Bonham Sarah Bonham, former assistant manager, Finsbury Park. You won't remember me from civvy street, but you once sent me out for flowers to placate your wife.

Felix (*laughs*) And it didn't work, did it? What are you doing here, Sarah?

Bonham Journalism – *The Wipers Gazette*. The only thing women are allowed to do, apart from nursing. The British forces newspaper is keen as mustard to do a proper double-page spread on you. Can I ask, how did you come up with the prizewinning formula of 'Pack Up Your Troubles'?

Felix The music publishers Francis Day and Hunter called it a prize. They offered a hundred pounds for a marching song, but it was *actually* an advance on royalties. Still, not bad. My brother wrote the words.

Bonham I expect you both do pretty well out of it. Where is your brother enlisted?

Felix Nowhere. He heard the troops embarking at Southampton for the Somme singing our song, from which time he became a pacifist.

Bonham That's going to make future collaboration tricky, isn't it?

Felix Pacifism once almost stopped this war. In Christmas 1914, whole divisions on both sides put down their weapons and met in no man's land and sang 'Silent Night' in their own languages. This Christmas, you try singing 'Silent Night' holding a candle above the parapet, the sound from the other side will be machine-gun fire. Three years in, we aren't brave enough to practise pacifism anymore.

Bonham But you don't condemn your brother's view as cowardly?

Felix No. It's easy for me, the only thing I fight with is a piano.

Music.
   Scene melts into exterior: no man's land.

Bonham Do you think your music can help bring this war to a speedy end?

Felix I've seen it raise the spirits of the troops. When blinded by mustard gas their only consolation, their connection with the world they've lost, is a song. And yet the song changes nothing. In the year I've been here, the front line has stayed in the same place. As for songs keeping the British side going, they does as much for the Germans. You can hear them at night, even though we don't get royalty statements from Berlin.

Massed gas-blinded chorus, with bandaged eyes, weave on, hands on the next man's shoulder. Men as women, women as soldiers, ad lib. They sing softly to

'*Vesper Time*', *as shells thud rhythmically, searchlights play, machine guns orchestrate.*

Chorus
  Never forget, my darling pretty one,
  That through the dark I'll see you.
  You'll never change for me,
  Ageless, remain with me,
  For love is blind, love is blind, lo-ove is . . .
Bonham I'm afraid we won't be able to print any of your observations.

Second chorus continues under the following.

Felix And here's something else unprintable. My band, The White Knights, presides over orgies. The army stopped local prostitutes coming to the dances, to halt the spread of clap. So the younger soldiers stepped in the gap, and arrive at the dance halls dressed as women. Miss Bonham, I spent twenty years in music hall, but nothing prepared me for playing keyboards for cross-dressing Tommies, on their last night on earth, who then go and roger shamelessly in the shadows.

The blinded soldiers pair off and slow-dance.

Chorus
  I'll prove them wrong,
  The ones who said I'd ne'er get back to Blighty.
  Your soft arms encircling me,
  Tenderly, mercif'lly,
  For love is blind, love is blind, lo-ove is . . .

Music and dance effects end. Lights change.
    Music.
    Felix, isolated in no man's land.

Felix Why should I put the slap on every night, devise entertainment to disguise the fact that round here men

die in a fight without a prize? Just a few steps into no
man's land, and they say it's over in thirty seconds.

Sergeant (*from side*) Private Powell! If they find you out
in no man's land when you're meant to be playing,
that's a court martial. You could be shot for desertion!
What are you doing, going that way!

Soldiers (*variously, from side*) You bloody suicidal fool!
Oy, Fritz, don't shoot our pianist! Felix – come back!

The male chorus of soldiers reform around Felix.

Felix

I can see this used to be a wood.
War's a game not quickly understood.
Now before my naked eyes, armed conflict names
    its price,
The swollen corpse of politics exploding with the lies.

Soldiers

In no man's land; it used to be a wood.
War's a game not quickly understood.
Now before your naked eyes, armed conflict names
    its price,
The swollen corpse of politics exploding with the lies.

Felix

Why should I be forced nightly to perform a lie,
Why not turn a traitor to the cause of this war
Where death is the reward?

War's the game, we play it night and day,
War's the game, but music paves the way.
We're safely on the sidelines, paid to play in marching
    time
And thank a brother pacifist who wrote these bloody
    rhymes.

Chorus

In no man's land don't fall on your own sword.
God is dead, and great is your reward.

No countenance divine observes the slaughter and the
  rime
Welcome to the hell on earth built from man's design.

Felix

Machine-gun Fritz, drop the curtain on my final bow,
I'm so agreeable to my dispatch, I'll light this match,
I'm ready now.

Come on, Fritz, can't you see it in my face?
Diagnose a catastrophic case.
I get no sleep, I can't compose, my soul has gone away,
Continuing survival is a torment, day to day.

Soldiers

Gunner Fritz says step right back in line.
Won't shoot you now, no matter what your crime.
We're sick of the excuses, sit down, no one jumps
  the queue,
You'll have to postpone suicide till war's next in the
  news.

Felix

Come on, Fritz can't you see it in my face?
Diagnose a catastrophic case.
I get no sleep, I can't compose, my soul has gone away,
Continuing survival is a torment, day to day.

Soldiers

Gunner Fritz says step right back in line.
Won't shoot you now, no matter what your crime.
We're sick of the excuses, sit down, no one jumps
  the queue,
You'll have to postpone suicide till war's next in the
  news.

Felix

Come on, Fritz can't you see it in my face?
Diagnose a catastrophic case.
I get no sleep, I can't compose, my soul has gone away,
Continuing survival is a torment, day to day.

Soldiers
　　Gunner Fritz says step right back in line.
　　Won't shoot you now, no matter what your crime.
　　We're sick of the excuses, sit down, no one jumps
　　　　the queue,
　　You'll have to postpone suicide till war's next in the
　　　　news.

Exit chorus. Felix, alone. Sound of clip-clopping hooves.
Enter panto horse pulling cart on which is written
GEORGE & LEILA POWELL'S HERBAL REMEDIES. ALL
YOUR MEDICAL PROBLEMS SOLVED BY GWILLIAM
THE SAPIENT HORSE.
　　Music. German treble choir under, softly, 'Stille
Nacht'.

German Choir
　　Stille Nacht, heilige Nacht,
　　Alles schläft, einsam wacht,
　　Nur das traute . . .
Felix George . . . Leila? This is a war zone. You're meant
　　to be in England!
George (*to horse*) Easy, Gwilliam, easy.

The cart stops and George gets out and puts a haybag
on the horse's head.

Felix Get away from here! It's highly dangerous.
George I should cocoa!
Leila It is, to some foolish folk!
George Leila and me an' faithful Gwilliam, we are
　　invincible: such stuff as dreams are made of. Right
　　now we breezed in, through the German lines, and not
　　a sentry turned his head. If it was dangerous here now
　　for us, Gwilliam the Sapient Horse would bolt.

Horse paws ground.

Gwilliam thinks it's dangerous for you, though, here!
　　Very dangerous!

314

Horse paws ground emphatically.

So, brother, how have you been feeling recently?

Felix I don't have a future.

George You do if you were to stop poncing about here in no man's land, *trying* to get topped by Fritz.

Felix You're alright, touring round country lanes in Stroud and Gloucestershire selling quack remedies. Death is the only way out of the abyss I'm in.

Leila We do understand your feelings. About how terrible it is for you and . . . the rest of the Private Perks.

George Being able to waft through the wires as we can, we've seen the destiny of so many Private Perks written here in blood.

Leila German Perks, French Perks, Indian Perks, Austrian Perks –

George Turkish Perks, Russian Perks, Perks of all nations!

Leila With their insides draped along barbed wire. Depressing. And it's exactly the same the other side, a mirror of suffering.

Felix That is why I'm here. My life is going to be over too, in a minute. I'm quite determined.

George Is there anything herbal from the gypsy caravan we could give him, Leila?

Leila For suicide? Nothing that would lift the spirits in time.

George consults horse.

George Gwilliam says there's only one thing to be done – send for Mabel.

Felix I don't want to argue with Mabel. They'll say I was shot here – there have been plenty of others, brave men who have done this!

Leila (*calls*) Mabel! Mabel!!

George Felix is about to kill himself over the state of the war. Over here, Mabel!

315

Enter Mabel, in Wild West gear.
   Music.

Leila *and* **George** (*sing*)
   She's always there when trouble starts, 'cos trouble
      she adores
   She'll take the hand of Uncle Sam, and enlist, and
      what's more
   She'll drill the Boche with more durn holes than my
      old outhouse door!
Mabel Yer doing what, Felix? Do trees volunteer to
   become planks? Not so fast to the sawmill, pardner.
   Leave him to me, boys.

   George and Leila exit with the caravan and horse.
   Mabel brings her counselling skills to the fore,
   revealing an unexpected side of her Lethal Larry
   persona.

All things pass, Felix. This is the most horrible, freezing
   muddy depressing landscape, all pitted with shell-
   holes, full of rotting, stinking corpses, enough to
   depress anyone for eternity. But in fifty years mother
   nature will come back and obliterate the sins of man
   here with songbirds and greenery. Should we not look
   beyond all this?
Felix I can't compose any more.
Mabel Then, I allow, killing yourself is a very reasonable
   reaction. On the surface. But couldn't you wait and
   see if the tunes came back? Fer three minutes, the
   benchmark time of all the greatest music-hall numbers?

   Machine gun clacking.

Felix It's too painful.
Mabel What if people were listening now? Are you
   telling them you can't pull any resolving melodies out
   of your hat, or wherever you guys keep tunes before

316

they're writ? You got a lovely little wifey at home, haven't cha? Now Mabel keeps the accounts, and she tells me there's so much money from the song coming in, she can't barely catch it in her lap.

Felix (*bitter*) That'll make her happy. Mabel's always been materialistic.

Mabel Yeah, materialistic enough to want her man in the flesh and not have him throw himself away like the phantoms of the half-million putrefying corpses we're standing on right now. None of them have wives now, there are just weeping sweethearts and widows . . . Is there going to be an empty chair at the piano when The White Knights play tonight at the Armentieres Saloon?

Felix What do you think I should do, then?

Mabel Quit making a silhouette for snipers, f'r a start.

Mabel pushes Felix over.

And follow me. Sometimes the only cure is cheap and despicable American music.

Music.

The dance hall. The White Knights playing 'Alexander's Ragtime Band'. Mabel leads Felix to a different area, where he stands.

This ain't so bad! I can see handsome wimmin here! Lethal Larry's bin unattached for a while, so this ain't no sin. I'd like to entertain a genuine lady with a dance, how about it?

Lethal Larry dances extravagantly with drag soldier. Music. Optionally, music can segue into a slow dance, 'Queen of Summer'.

Sergeant Alright, everyone. As has become customary, it's always the ball on the night before Waterloo, here

till the stroke of midnight when you all turn back into
soldiers again. You lads are going to be putting on
your kit and marching into battle tomorrow very
shortly, and you might be aware that normal practices
and customs have been suspended in the entertainment
area, due to some wartime shortages. Not a man here
will disgrace the colours of his regiment when the call
comes, don't matter what he's wearing tonight. Have
your fun now. Fritz will be waiting to test your mettle
at dawn with a warm greeting, but now, please, a
warmer welcome to Felix Powell and The White
Knights, introducing our special guests tonight from
Mayfair, The Angels of Death!

*Music. Dance ends. Applause from dancers, male and
female. Mabel sets off after another soldier in drag,
Mayfair Minnie.*

Mabel That one's mighty purty!
Felix As well as being under-age. No recruiting officers
can resist fourteen-year-olds.
Mabel Mmm! Recruiting officers might have a point!
What's your name, lady?
Minnie Guess! It begins with M.
Mabel Muriel. Mildred. Maureen. Mavis!

*Minnie shakes her head each time, and the song
begins.*

Minnie 1
Your champagne bottle empty, and my caviar was dry,
You were trying to flag the waiter down, till you
caught my eye,
Then the charm offensive started and we took that
fatal prom-
-enade near Flanders Field, you said, handy for the
Somme.

318

A chorus line of Minnies forms.

All Minnies
Mayfair Minnie, yer Angel of Death,
One little wink, and you draw your last breath.

Minnie 1
Mayfair Minnie, remember my name,
Don't drop it casual, but drop it the same.

Minnie 2
The price of stepping out with me, some might say, is
steep
Don't matter what your title is, what company you
keep,
I charge the same for officers as other ranks; I'm cheap,
I'm Mayfair Minnie, your own Angel of Death –

Minnie 1
Watching every morning when brave lieutenants blew
Their whistles and the privates knew they'd not outlive
the dew.
The lucky ones were gassed at Wipers, shoulda seen
the mud!!

*The Minnies all sigh, then swoon as if gassed. Minnie 3
rallies.*

Minnie 3
It made one quite nostalgic for the days of Noah's
flood.

Minnie 1
Mayfair Minnie, votre ange de la mort –

All Minnies
French-kissing young boys who set off for war.

Minnie 1
Mayfair Minnie, remember my name,
Don't drop it casual, but drop it the same.
The shells that mean so well always miss me by miles,
I am the skull that looked at all the men in single file.

That was me, at Passchendaele, a-widening of my smile.
I'm Mayfair Minnie, and I'll have you all.

At Mons there were some angels, or so wise generals
said.
The truth is, I was up there, a-gorging on the dead.
I took 'em as their lips reached out, like I was mother's
milk.
They died for King and Country and their souls tasted
of silk –

All Minnies

Mayfair Minnie, der Engel des Todes,
No wonder the Huns all say she is a goddess.
Mayfair Minnie, remember her name,
Don't drop it casual, but drop it the same.

Minnie 2

There's some who say that Minnie's just a girl for the
good time,
But some who say her bold embrace is preferable to
wine.

Minnie 1

I'm sworn against advertisement, or spinning of a line.

All Minnies

We're Mayfair Minnie, your own angel of death,
We're Mayfair Minnie, your own angel of death.

Blackout.

George and Felix at piano.
Music.

George It doesn't happen often, but I'm miserable. Why
are we stuck working like this? Here we are, sat in
Tin Pan Alley, just like eight years ago, same grotty
lettering over the windows as it was when we were
knocking out marching songs. We won the war,
correction, you won the war, but the economy's in

ruins and Felix Powell and George Asaf still can't afford proper heating.

Ghostly chorus sing 'Pack Up Your Troubles' in German.

Men (*sing*)
Weit ist der Weg zurück ins Heimatland,
So weit, so weit.
Dort bei den Sternen, überm Waldesrand,
Liegt die alte Zeit.
Jeder brave Musketier
Sehnt heimlich sich nach dir.
Doch hoch weht die Fahne nun trotz aller Not,
Wir folgen ihr.

Felix (*over chorus*) I'm sorry, George, I was miles away.

George The 1919 Treaty of Versailles was gonna squeeze Germany till the pips squeak, so where are our royalties? The Krauts pinched the tune and used it. That's an act of theft.

Felix They made new words.

George Insolence! Did they even ask if they could change them? We should squeeze their music publishers for tune and words till their pips squeak.

Felix I think we'll be alright without invading Germany to claim royalties.

George I feel like going to Berlin, going to a gramophone record shop and asking for it –

Felix It's called 'The Forester's Song' in German –

George I'll get a whole stack of 'Forest' songs and – wham! – break them over me head. It's our song!

Felix The future of music isn't in gramophone records, any more than it was in wax recording disks or sheet music. It's in radio.

George Is radio the same as wireless?

Felix The same. And you can send music all over the world.

George Then everyone is going to be like the Germans,
not needing to pay. We were in a golden age and never
knew it. I bet you have a wireless in the pub you and
Mabel bought. What you go and buy a pub for? Aren't
there enough pissed people out there already?

Felix It was what Mabel wanted. Security. It's got a
piano.

George You said it was untunable after a customer threw
up into it.

Felix It's still no worse than some joannas I've been
lumbered with in my career.

George If I'd gone through a war as a hero, like you, I'd
have wanted more than having me felt hammers come
unglued with puke!

Felix I'm no hero, George.

George You are to the common man. They shoulda given
you a medal.

They are suddenly surrounded by beery drinkers.
The Black Swan, Hungerford. Felix plays the piano.
A woman approaches Mabel. Music.

Felix (*plays and sings*)
  At a country farm in Somerset
  See the little ducks at play,
  Gobbling up the worms of Somerset,
  Romping in the mud all day.
  Some are lame, some tame,
  Some game for anything
  Some love a stand-up fight,
  Some won't rise in the morning
  And some stay out all night.

Felix vamps under the following.

Woman Where's me change?

Mabel There's your change.

Woman (*to Mabel*) Blimey, you don't get much!

Mabel Three G and Ts and a half-pint of mild comes to seven and thruppence, it doesn't matter how you count it. You gave me a ten-bob note with the corner torn, remember?

Woman Next time I'm going to be drinking at home.

Mabel We'll all miss the company, to be sure.

Woman leaves.

Man Excuse me, love.

Mabel I would, gladly, I've been on my feet for twelve hours.

Man Excuse me, love. Point of information. I came in here last week I think and . . . Where are we?

Mabel Exactly the same place, if last week was the same.

Man Yeah, but wassername of the pub?

Mabel The Black Swan, Hungerford.

Man Hungerford! That's it. I was here last week, then.

Mabel Were you the rowdy military reunion?

Man The Hampshire Pals. Sorry about that. Not many of us pals left, see, love? The rest of them all marched off to perdition . . . Can't hold down a job mind . . . Nothing much seems steady, unless I'm with me pals, the ones who made it through . . . Would he sign something for us, love?

Mabel Would who?

Man Doesn't he play the joanna here, love? The man who . . . ? You know, love? Would he sign me beer mat?

Man drunkenly approaches Felix and stops him playing.

Man Play 'Pack up yer Troubles'.

Felix This is one I wrote earlier.

Sings and plays.

Have you seen the ducks go by?
For their morning walk?

All
> Quack quack!

Felix
> Waddling along, oh my,
> You should hear them talk.

All
> Quack quack!

Felix
> There's the ma duck, the pa duck, the grand old drake,
> Leading the way, what a noise they make!
> You can hear them, when you're near them,
> Or a mile or two sky high . . .
> Have you seen the ducks once more
> Come a-rolling home,
> Feeling very sad and sore
> As the lanes they roam.
> Of the pond they are fond, but they stay too long
> Whiling the time with wine and song.
> Have you seen them, have you seen them,
> Have you seen those ducks go by?

> *Applause. Dispersal.*
> > *Lighting changes. Next morning in the pub.*

Mabel I've had hardly any sleep again, Felix, I'm sorry,
I can't be doing with this any more!

Felix George was really rude about those words I did,
they're no worse than some of his.

Mabel I mean, you in front playing for customers and
me with no help. I want to sell this place. It is hell on
earth. I want to go somewhere where I don't have to
smile all the time at drunken idiots!

*Enter Neville, a slick Canadian in a sharp suit with a
briefcase. Mabel watches him accost Felix.*

Neville My name's Neville and I'm starting a township
on the Canadian model , and I'm looking for celebrities

324

to put it on the map. You must be the famous Felix Powell.

Mabel Presently a bar pianist.

Neville Mrs Powell, I'll be frank with you. Life is full of ups and down. Right now you are being offered a showhouse with full plumbing on *extremely* favourable terms, in what is shortly going to be the ritziest, priciest, most exclusive resort in the UK. My vision is a township on the Canadian model, on land I've bought by the sea, just outside Brighton.

Mabel If it's not a pub, we'll take anything, if it's below market value.

Felix Can I bring my brother? He writes my words.

Neville This is so fortuitous! I am also looking for someone who does words, to create a magazine covering the development. There's only one showhouse built so far, but think you could get your brother to come too?

Felix I could ask him.

Mabel Ask? Felix, Leila would kill to get out of that caravan. (*to Neville*) Alright, so where are we going?

Neville South! There's a competition for the most popular name, but I've fixed it. You can tell your friends you're moving to Peacehaven. The first buildings to be completed will be a cinema doubling as a grand hotel overlooking the cliffs next to the Lurland, the most modern dance hall in England. But don't take my word for it. See for yourselves.

Scene change to Lurland Dance Hall. Spotlight on compere.

Compere My Lords, ladies and gentlemen, members of the armed forces of all ranks, coxswains, and grinning seadogs! This evening's dance programme on the BBC is being brought to you from Peacehaven, snug in the arms of the Downs above Brighton, where here in the famous spanking new Lurland Dance Hall, the only

one in England to be actually sprung on golfballs,
Mike Fadden and his Dixie Jazzers are going to swing
their musical niblicks and make sure everyone gets a
hole in one! But first, the audience here are going to
see something special, the finalists of the Peacehaven
Charlie Chaplin lookalike competition will perform
with the words and music of those two retiring but
intensely talented locals, Felix and George Powell!

*Music. Applause. Joan on stage in Charlie Chaplin
outfit. She does 'Life is Just a Puppet Show'.*

Joan (*sings*)
    First born in this life, what a mystery,
    Like opening up a book, some history,
    But as you turn the page, girls start to come of age
    Until an aged Pantaloon rises from the stage – and cries
    You are not too young to know
    Life is just a puppet show,
    Take your time in the limelight glow –
All
    Heigh-ho.
Joan
    As for words you have no choice though you may not
      lose your voice
    You are not fortune's pet, you're the new marionette,
    Life's a puppet show, life's a puppet show.

*Band plays. Joan peels away from the line-up, who
hum sotto voce. She approaches Felix.*

Joan Mr Powell! don't tell me you're not up there with
    the finalists! It's your song, after all.
Felix I was going to give the prize, but they got a surprise
    guest.
Joan Who? Not the little tramp himself!
Felix I discovered he was making a brief visit, and
    phoned him at the Dorchester.

Joan Don't tell me you know him.

Felix We used to tour together.

Joan And he agreed to come to this dump?

Felix Yes. My wife and I have just moved here.

Joan How incredibly brave. I'm waiting for Peacehaven to become more than desperate publicity and a whiff of bad sewage!

Felix With these kind of dance nights, and the motor car, the new town is coming together fast.

Joan Do you know, one of the first solos I did was 'Pack Up Your Troubles' at the Hammersmith Palais?

Felix It's a good little number, isn't it?

Joan Nowadays it seems the only way I can get shows on is with my own money.

Felix That means at least you've got some money to lose!

Joan Not for long. My husband is running out of patience. I hear you have been putting on shows locally. Excellent shows.

Felix Yes. In the new kin-ema.

Joan Is that how you pronounce it! I'm looking for a lyric muse for my next professional production, Mr Powell.

Felix What's it about?

Joan Book and lyrics together would be about seven and a half per cent of the gross, after recoupment. Are you very busy at the moment?

Music cuts out. Enter George, dressed as Charlie Chaplin.

George That's me out. Disqualified, for over-actin'.

Felix Yesterday I was playing piano for a hundred thousand unemployed while conducting them singing 'Pack Up Your Troubles'.

George That's right, he's got two pairs of arms.

Felix Joan, this is my brother George, who works with me and also edits the *Peacehaven Gazette*.

Joan A man of many talents! I was hoping to seduce your brother into writing something else for me, George. Do you think it's possible?

George He won't need asking twice. Look at him.

Felix Who is producing?

Joan I am. I'll give you a call midweek, darling.

She kisses Felix lightly on the head and sweeps out.

Felix How do you like being the *Peavehaven Gazette* editor?

George It beats working. But it's amazing the number of people who call up thinking that Mr Neville owes them money.

Felix Does he?

George They can't all be wrong.

George To make room in the *Peacehaven Gazette* for the Little Tramp's surprise visit, Neville told me to turn down a really interesting article on the origins of music which are apparently birds singing. Did you know Mozart gave his starling a hero's burial?

Felix Yes, I wrote the article.

George I should have kept it in, because Neville's been arrested in connection with some financial holes in the Peacehaven New Mortgage company, and he can't tell what's on the front page. I should do a 'broken promises number' – total absence of rail transport, roads, gas, electricity, sewage and water. It would close the town and the paper, so I won't do more than hint at the inexplicable absence of running water, so close to the sea, too.

Felix We've always had water.

George You had the showhouse. Every time my septic tank overflows I think of our founder, on remand in Brixton nick, and I think, 'I hope you smell what I'm smelling, Mr Neville.'

Music.

> *Meanwhile a succession of Charlie Chaplins wait for the prizegiving.*

Charlies
> Heigh-ho, heigh-ho,
> Heigh-ho, heigh-ho,
> Heigh-ho.

George Remember Charlie at the Sunderland Empire, mooning the stage from the wings?

Felix It was funnier than anything he did on stage.

George Good news about Joan, though – for you, I mean.

Felix I'll see how it goes. George, does Leila know why Mabel's turned against me?

George Since when?

Felix Since we came here.

George Mabel's mum got pretty crabby round Mabel's age. You could have bottled her piss and sold it as battery acid. But it's not inevitable. If you'd followed Charlie's example and married a woman forty years younger, you wouldn't have any of this trouble and strife you're getting.

> *Charlie Chaplins mount a stepped podium, like athletes who have won a race.*

Compere And here to present the prize on behalf of the British Broadcasting Corporation at the Lurland Dance Hall with its patent Neville-sprung floor for the winner of the Charlie Chaplin lookalike competition, is our surprise guest Charlie Chaplin!

> *Applause. Charlie Chaplin, smartly dressed in a grey suit, shakes hands with the competitors, giving a bunch of flowers to the winner – not Joan Bellamy.*

George You know Charlie entered a Charlie Chaplin

lookalike competion himself, a couple of years ago in Biarritz. He came fourth.

Felix Are you not going to say hello?

George I stood on his foot once in the Hull Empire. He won't have forgotten. He never forgave anyone. Memory like an elephant. Similarly endowed elsewhere as well, I hear.

Felix What does Joan's husband do?

George He's got a factory making camouflage paint. He steps in when her accounts are in disarray. Don't lend her any money, Felix.

Music. All the Chaplins do a song and dance number, 'Come to Lurland', with the pantomime horse.

All (*sing*)
Come let me lead you to Lurland and leave your tears behind.
Come and be happy in Lurland, and see what we shall find.
Sunshine and gladness fill every hour, no sorrow can enter there,
Its just the right place for your sad little face.

Music abruptly ends.
Exeunt all, leaving Felix 2, who reveals himself as the front half of pantomime horse.

Felix 2 Welcome to six miles west of Peacehaven, on the Royal Brighton Racetrack. Standing here, you can just see Peacehaven. But no one in Brighton's jealous for a second. They have Lurland. We have the Prince Regent's Brighton Pavilion. We have a horsetrack. They don't even have *dogs*.

Air raid siren. Effects.

And now, with Germany once again the enemy, vapour trails of Messerschmidt, Hurricane and Spitfire tangle

overhead. Why are the Jerries dogfighting over our
lovely racetrack? Why do they want to bomb the
Royal Pavilion and the piers and the attractive housing
back into the Stone Age? Why do they want to suppress
Brighton's world reputation for getting barmaids
pregnant? As the Prince Regent, remarked, that will
never do.

*Music. Smoke, effects, and the effigy head of the
Prince Regent, a large Victorian dandy, is carried by a
chorus of heavily pregnant Brighton Barmaids, dressed
for the year of their sashes, reading 'Barmaid of the
Year 1899'; 'Barmaid of the Year 1914'; 'Barmaid of
the Year 1918', etc.*

Barmaids (*one or more reciting over music*)
The Prince Regent built a truly royal pavilion, down
   in the town,
Money no object, spilt it like wine,
Golden onion domes, a tasteless stately home,
Mistresses thrashing, and colours all clashing,
   vermilion 'n' incarnadine.

*The Barmaids cast down the large mask and come
forward majestically.*

Above the town for royal relaxation,
Where velvet greensward never turns to brown,
The Prince decreed an entertainment built here,
A race track to be raised on Brighton Downs.

Sung or recited.

The Sport of Kings takes place on hallowed ground here,
For punters, the grandstand's their chapel, on earth –
When God caught Adam in the Garden, so they say,
God sent him down, forgetting that Adam could nick
A sod of Eden's perfect racing turf . . .

*The stage fills up with punters dressed as Pearly Kings
and Queens, etc., and Bookies with tick-tack men
signalling to them. The bookies stand on rows of
boxes with their names on – Honest Joe, Firm Tom,
Brighton Business Books, Hove Turf Accounts, etc.*

Bookies Weighed in! Weighed in!
Bookie Lucifer ten to one!

*All the Bookies move to change their odds whenever
a new odds is called.*

Bookies (*sing*)
Brighton is the seedy side of England's pride,
Steamily dreaming, viciously wise.
Take the special Pullman from Victoria,
A must for a flutter, an hour to the seaside –
Bookie Private Perks fifty to one!
Bookie Harlequinader evens!
Barmaid
Brighton Race Course, magnet for the underworld!
Racegoer
All of the gang is here –
Second Racegoer
– unless they're inside.
All
Once a year the Brighton Corporation wakes and
Announces a purge which will reverse the inexplicable
moral slide!
Bookie Shoot the Pianist odds-on favourite!
Bookie Peavehaven a snip at fifteen to one!
All
See the bookies fleece the punters expertly –
Bookies
Don't pick a quarrel, we all have knives –
Pearly Kings and Queens
Snatch the chance to catch up with nefarious chums,

And rather like Ascot, the bigger the villains,
The bigger the hats on their wives!

Bookie East Pier, five to one!

Bookie No Problems, three to two!

Bookie Anyone for Charleston?

All

See the suited thugs, not once arrested for
Murders horrific, corruption and theft.
Country houses stripped of their antiquities, it is
    iniquitous,
Nothing of Olde Englande left –

Bookie My Stallion, seven to two!

Bookie Star of Peace, evens!

Bookie Come on, ladies, you'll never find the favourite
winning today, so have a flutter. The State I'm In,
twelve to one –

Break out the shampoo because they're friends of
    mine.
It's like a pantomime,when we get together.
Star of Peace came fourth, I heard, at Cheltenham –

Pearly King

The jockey's not beltin' 'im –

Pearly Queen

And the horse likes this weather!

All (*rallentando*)

Star of Peace came fourth, but that was Cheltenham,
It was deliberate, no shadow of doubt.
Today the cunning money's on the Star to win.
Never mind The State I'm In, Star of Peace by a snout.

Read the horseflesh like it was a form book.
Look at the ears first, then at the eyes.
Calculate the odds against My Stallion,
Proving them wrong at a hundred to one although
    he bucks and shies.

A mimed horserace takes place. Music tempo climaxes.

All
Can't get any closer than the horse's mouth.
Star of Peace's been held back for this race.
Can't get closer than the horse's north and south.
Put your money down, or die in disgrace –

*Suddenly to elegiac: was there a winner? We may
never know. It would be good to have Star of Peace
triumph. Anyway, the race is over. Sunset. Evening
comes. Crowds disperse as lights change to night.
Punters sing softly.*

Pearly Kings and Queens
Something sad about the ending every time,
All the excitement just dribbled away.
West of us must be a race just starting up,
The sun god galloping overhead, marking out
Each precious blazing second . . . of the . . .
    endless . . . day . . .

*Felix finds himself caught up in a whirl of working
girls and boys who are striding in their evening outfits
in a pack round the stage.*

Felix I'm looking for Fast Eddy. It's essential I find him
today.
Girl Reelly? The smart money's usually on avoiding Eddie.
Felix I was going to be here earlier but I got held up . . .
Stupid, I know. I was given his name by a friend, Joan
Bellamy.
Girl Joan Bellamy! I don't know her. She a friend of
yours?
Felix Business friend. Is Eddie here?
Girl I can't say I've seen him.
Felix Does he not work as a bookie?
Boy In the good old days, before he went away, he did.

But then the corporation barred him.
He looks after ladies, now.

Felix What kind of ladies?

Girl What do you fink?

Felix If you girls know him, maybe you could give me his
phone number.

Girl Why don'cha just keep on with us, till we hit the
Parade? If he wants to, he'll come to you.

*To star cloth and Brighton Pier, further magical
transformation.*
    *Music. The song can be divided up with selected
lines amongst a number of principals with all girls in
chorus, or sung en bloc.*

Girl
    Night comes to Brighton, a spectacle delectable,
    Down on the seashore it's dark and less respectable,
    But who needs a love-light, when Cupid's blind?

    Hardworking girls offering comfort here,
    Can't pawn the baby if the rent's in arrears,
    Best to negotiate a sensible price.

    Night comes to Brighton, a spectacle delectable,
    Down on the seashore it's dark and less respectable,
    Look where he comes now, Lord of the Flies.

    Girls need protection and Eddie gets to supervise,
    He takes a cut of every ladies' enterprise,
    Cock of the walk here, under the pier –

Girl (*to Girls*) He's coming!

Girl (*to Felix*) He's coming!

Girl He must *like* you! You're alright then! What's your
name?

*Enter Fast Eddie in a camel-hair coat with a gang of
bodyguards.*
    Music.

Fast Eddie

Well, I can smell bad credit a mile off,
I'm going to be perfectly frank.
Everyone 'as got their reasons
And you know I charge more than a bank.

You might have heard Fast Eddie done time.
Trying to impress a girlfriend of mine,
The sort of thing that young men do, when they don't
   have the money to –

Hoods

'E should never, ever, ever, ever, ever have done time!
Never, ever, ever, ever, ever have done time.

Fast Eddie

It's a celebrity society we live in.
The stars are close as we will ever get to heaven.
If Joan had been known to be on my arm,
They would have overlooked the harm.

I should never have done time.
When a stabbing's patriotic, you can't call it a crime
Of course the jury would've agreed, if she'd spoken up
   for me, me, me –

Hoods

He should never, ever, ever, ever have done time.
Never, ever, ever, ever have done time.

Fast Eddie (*spoken*) If you're born within the sound of
Bow Bells – close in my case – bear in mind that I'm a
native – it's an insult to the race. I was called a *puddin'*.

(*Explains.*) Sago, dago, and I coulda swung
For responding to this insult in our ancient Cockney
   tongue.

I should never, ever, ever, ever, ever have done time.

Fast Eddie *and* **Hoods**

He should never, ever, ever, ever, ever have done time.
He should never, ever, ever, ever, ever have done time.

*Hoods advance and ritually present Felix with
Gladstone bag.*

Hoods
Pleased to oblige you, and Eddie's got the readies here.
Keep tight to what's agreed, don't you get in arrears
Or it could get physical, to make our meaning clear.

Here is the news, that we could always break a limb,
Stitch you up back and front, and even do you in,
Depending what's overdue, or what Eddie requires –
Fast Eddie
I should never, ever, ever, ever have done time.
Hoods
Never ever, ever, ever have done time.
Fast Eddie
It's best this is understood between us now,
I'll give it to you straight.
Ten grand comes back as twenty, come first of May,
No way is there a wait.

Unless you have a life insurance plan,
Don't take the mick, leave out the spick 'n' span.
Show respect and don't tempt fate, and if you're ever
   late
We'll nail your hands to Brighton Pier, now do you
   understand?

*Lighting change. Canned applause. Joan comes on
with showy dress and battered bouquet.*

Joan It went well for a provincial tryout. Twenty people
in my dressing room. Brighton audiences have always
loved me. But look at this! Someone has deliberately
stood on my bouquet.

Three girls perform an air-raid siren noise. It fades.

Joan Is that the all-clear?

SNOO WILSON

Felix That's the all-clear.

Joan I still don't understand why Hitler would want to bomb anywhere, let alone Brighton. What good will it do him to blow up the Grand Hotel? You can't tell me this war is anything more than pure unadulterated malicious spite . . . Has somone told your wife about us?

Felix I don't think so. No. If they have, it wasn't me.

Joan If they have, what will become of us, Felix?

Felix I don't know . . . I'll leave the deposit off tomorrow at the Savoy.

Joan No, darling. I've arranged for our show to go into the Duchess Theatre. Didn't I tell you? The deposit is another fifteen hundred, but we can run indefinitely there, although we open a month later than planned.

Felix A month later? I've only got a short-term loan.

Joan You're going to have to extend it!

Music.
    Split stage: Lyon's teahouse set, with Leila and Mabel. Apart, Felix and George at piano, in their 'working' mode.

Felix (*sings*)
    I've got problems –
George (*sings*)
    Best advice is letting your problems all go.
Felix (*sings*)
    I've been threatened by a backer
    If I don't give back his dough.
George What's his problem? You're sold out in previews!
Leila (*sings*)
    What's with Felix? Such great prospects,
    He is topping the bill, like old times.
Mabel (*sings*)
    It's that woman, she's bewitched him,
    And she's stealing what's rightfully mine.

338

George (*sings*)
> Felix – now's no time to get in a stew,
> Your wife bargains better than you.
> Send Mabel, she'll know how to extricate you

Felix (*spoken*) NO!! Don't involve Mabel. I'll get it
somehow.

Leila Mabel, it's time to name names.

George Felix, why borrow from people who will break
your legs? You could ask any bank for a loan.

Felix I didn't know she was going to delay the opening.

Mabel Second name, Bellamy. Joan.

George Mabel mustn't know! I see.

Mabel Well, she's not going to break up my home.

Leila It's a mistake; you haven't been thrown over!

Mabel Oh, you've always been such a simpleton, Leila.

> *Chorus make air-raid siren warning – up-down, up-down.*

All (*over vamp*)
> Blame it on the Blitz . . .
> Blame it on the Blitz . . . (*etc.*)

Mabel He gets nothing, he signed all rights away to this
tart.

Leila Surely the composer gets something at least?

Mabel Nothing – I can tell you, my hand on my heart.

Leila My advice is, don't rock the boat now, wait for the
opening. Then if it's a hit, tell Felix to have a quiet
word with the –

Mabel
> Producer?!
> I stamped on her bouquet, the cow.
> It gave me great pleasure – producer!
> All Brighton knows what she is now!

All
> Oh, what dreadful scenes on tour,
> The star was an opportunistic whore.

We got problems, of which jealousy,
The green-eyed monster, is one.
Second problem – involving repayment of sums.
Money clashing with love, good heavens above,
Suddenly there are voices with choices and,
Heaven forfend, there's a gun.

George

You're making this more complicated than it need be,
Just wait, the problem will remove itself if
You can give it time.

Mabel

An actress and a prostitute who sleeps around with
criminals,
Will be exposed for what she is, the lowest class of
slime –

Leila

She's putting on your husband's show, he was naturally
infatuated,
But no more, so simply let it go.

Felix

I'm less afraid of gangsters than if Mabel gets to know.

Leila There's our waitress!

Mabel

Really, she is disgracefully dressed!
Lyon's Tea House renowned once,
Now I'm not impressed.

Leila They've got one poor girl running round covering
all the tables.

Mabel And the usual excuse – wartime. As if all the
waitresses were needed for fighting.

George

You be firm now, you just tell 'em,
They'll just have to wait to get paid.
What you need now is a minder,
So your head can be clear for the play,

    If I understand you
    They don't sound too bright.
Felix True, they don't normally invest in shows –
George
    Then they are just flying a kite,
    Tell 'em you don't give a shite.
Mabel
    That skirt she's got on's too tight.
    Waitress!
    I'm not going to sit here all night!
Announcement (*tannoy, from the three air-raid girls*) All
    shops and places of refreshment are now closed. An air
    raid is imminent. If there is no shelter provided in the
    basement of your building, make your way down to
    the platforms on Leicester Square Underground
    Station. And remember, careless talk costs lives.
Mabel
    Cross your fingers. Joan could always die in this raid.
Leila Don't say that, Mabel. Don't wish a doodlebug on
    anyone.
Mabel
    Let the bombs drop, so her debt to society's paid.
Leila She may have driven a hard bargain with Felix, but
    he's getting lots of exposure –
Mabel
    Exposure!?
    Breaking his marital vows?
    You'll read all about this –
    Exposure!
    Society will punish them now!
All
    We got problems, of which jealousy,
    The green-eyed monster, is one.
    Second problem – involving repayment of sums,
    Money clashing with love, good heavens above,

Suddenly there are voices with choices and
Heaven forfend, there's a –

*Transformation: explosion, then music – the theatre
has been bombed. A proscenium arch with a velvet
curtain is lowered from above onto the the stage.
Rubble tumbles down in large polystyrene boulders.
Joan appears, sobbing theatrically from behind,
sooty.*

Joan Direct hit. The back is even worse. Not a dressing
room has been left standing. Catastrophe, Felix.
Catastrophe has struck.

Felix We lost the theatre, I know. But it's not the end of
the world. There are places in the provinces that we
could tour . . . Norwich hasn't taken a single bomb.

Joan I'm not touring to cathedral towns. I invested too
much in all this. I declare my career over.

Felix If you won't tour, how am I going to repay the
loan?

Joan Money? Money seems such a stupid subject at this
time.

Felix I'm worried that if I don't come up with twenty
thousand now, Fast Eddie's going to go round to
Peacehaven and break Mabel's legs.

Joan Fast Eddie! You never got the money from Fast
Eddie! You fool!

Felix You put me on to him.

Joan Did I? You can't have been listening properly. If I
had mentioned Eddie it would have been as a dreadful
warning. He knifed a man. Eddie claimed the man had
called him a . . . rude name, a snippo, a gyppo, or
something, and this was an intolerable insult, I didn't
even hear it. The next moment, there was a man on the
ground and blood everywhere.

Chorus
Heigh-ho!

Joan exits, lighting change. We are in Lurland dance hall. Enter George.

George Look at that long face! Wasser matter now?

Felix Joan won't tour and I have to pay her bloody gangster back. Plus the mark-up.

George How much?

Felix Double.

George Does Mabel know?

Felix No.

George Where will it come from?

Felix lays his finger on his lips.

Felix The Peacehaven Mutual Society.

George I thought the accounts were all frozen after our dear founder's arrest?

Felix If I pay it back inside six months, no one will know.

George Blimey, Felix, you're having a powerful late change of personality here! What you propose is legally called embezzlement!

Felix Well, you're not offering to help.

George I'd love to help, Felix, but I don't have twenty grand under my mattress. What with the future of civilisation at stake, there are more important things going on. Think of the big picture and make a clean breast of it to Mabel. Honestly, what are you more concerned about? Hitler, or upsetting the wife? Next week the south coast could be the front line.

Felix I know. I've joined the Home Guard.

George I can see the headlines in the *Peacehaven Gazette*! 'Embezzler Redeems Himself by Heroic Stand. Light-fingered Local Composer Routs Panzer Division: Nation Applauds and Forgives.'

Felix I'm not a bloody local composer! George, they won't get me for embezzlement, will they?

George (*aside*) What is embezzlement? A word! Now
Felix, about this light-fingered approach you have been
developing to the Peacehaven Building Society. I
should tell you, the fraud investigators are being
bleeding thorough. They are looking to put our dear
founder away for fifteen years.

Felix Whatever they do to me, it couldn't be worse than
how I feel now. I can't write.

George Will you talk to Mabel?

Felix Not now. I've got to go on duty.

George That's a good idea! It could be reviving to the
spirits to defend Brighton now – just the thing you
need. Promise me you'll talk to Mabel when you come
back.

Felix I'll see how I feel.

George No. No! We've all been seeing how you feel for
too long, Felix!

Felix Well, that's an easy problem to remove.

Exit Felix. Enter Leila.

George Something's stuck inside my brother.

Leila I'm not setting him up with no enema. He was
always so bloody rude about our herbal remedies.
It always had to be a regular doctor with him.

George It's not something that Syrup of Figs can release.
I've not seen him like this since we got hissed in
Hartlepool.

Enter Mabel, furious.

Mabel Before anyone says anything, why are we
rehearsing this terrible old chestnut of Felix's?

George The Lurland Dance Hall is having a gala, to have
its balls resprung.

Mabel I thought we were all meant to be economising in
wartime. That doesn't sound very austere!

George No, actually, I was pulling your leg. We're raising money for a fighter's propeller to be dispatched to Malta.

Mabel Nobody asked me if I wanted to help Malta out!

George We sort of assumed. Like me not being a conchie this time round. Can we get on with rehearsing, Mabel?

Mabel I want a fresh tune. And proper lyrics. Or I'm not singing. (*She storms out.*)

George Leila, can you see if you can go and calm her down.

Leila Mabel, dear, we're all trying to help, don't be like that!

Leila exits. Enter Felix, in Home Guard uniform, with gun.

George You forgot to tell Mabel we were rehearsing!

Felix Everything is going to be alright, because I am going to kill myself.

George You can kill yourself any number of ways. Or you can have a conversation with Mabel.

Felix Poor Mabel.

George If it's 'Poor Mabel', how are the rest of us going to take it? What about your son? What is he going to do if you top yourself?

Felix I don't know. He'll find something.

George This is getting truly ghoulish. I am going to tell your commanding officer you should not be left alone with a rifle.

Felix As staff sergeant, there is no one senior to me on duty tonight.

George Oh, so it's going to be tonight, is it?

Felix Don't try to stop me, George, because if you make it difficult, it just gets messy.

George You have not thought this one through, Felix. Deserting your post by suicide – fail, and you could get court-martialled. Is that what you want from your domestic problems? Have you considered how hard it is to kill yourself with your trusty Lee-Enfield rifle? Because if you place the muzzle up where the bullet's going to make the desired difference, like inside the mouth, you're never going to be able to reach the trigger.

Felix I've written to Mabel.

George Let me guess what it says. 'Dear Mabel, sorry about dropping all this in your lap but really it serves you right, you've been a right cow.'

Felix No. It just says I've not been feeling too well – she knows that – and I haven't been able to compose for some time.

George You cold-blooded selfish bastard.

Felix I'm not even hinting she's anything to do with the decision, so don't you tell her.

George It doesn't matter what I say, she's going to spend the rest of her life castigating herself. Do I get a farewell note?

Felix Why, do you want one?

George To fill out the obituary in the *Peacehaven Gazette* after 'Local Composer Dies. Eleventh February 1942. "Smile Smile Man" Shot. Felix Powell locked himself inside the famous Lurland Dance Hall, and shot himself with a service rifle, having never recaptured popular acclaim after his one hit twenty-five years earlier. His note to his main collaborator, his elder brother said . . .'

Felix 'Goodbye, Home Guard. Sorry it has to end like this. Signed, Staff Sergeant F. Powell.'

Felix on stage, taking his sock off and using his toes to try to fire the rifle which is pointed at his heart.

George Bang!

Felix falls down, having shot himself through the heart.

'He appeared to have been aiming for his own heart, but took several hours to die. It is proposed that the dance-hall floor will have to be taken up, to remove the blood that has seeped down over the famous balls. The inquest concluded a suicide while the balance of the mind was disturbed. Cremation took place at Brighton, and the ashes were later placed in the Peacehaven garden of George Powell, the deceased's brother. Floral tributes were sent by the Seaford Amateur Dramatic Society and the Peacehaven Home Guard.'

Enter Joan Bellamy, leading a coffin draped in a Union Jack, with military pallbearers. George and Leila enter, dressed for the funeral.

Leila Who the hell invited Joan Bellamy? Mabel told me Felix killed himself over her.

George Not really, and the funeral would be a bit light on celebrities otherwise.

Music. Joan Bellamy appears, glamorously funereal, by the coffin. Mabel is helped in, sobbing.

Joan (*sings*)
    One single soldier's burial –
    Freed now from cares.
    He who has given life to all
    Will hear our prayers
    And judge not this dear departed soul
    Who served his country well.
    He gave our soldiers heart to sing,
    Marching through their living hell.
George *and* **Leila**
    Lord, mercifully judge this one,
    Set him apart.
    He caught the tune that Everyman

347

Plays in his heart.
Award him his immortality,
Each of us has sinned,
And all of us now gathered here, pray,
Saint Peter, let him in.

All

One single soldier we entrust,
Much loved, to you.
Take up his soul, now he is dust.
Give him his due.
For he has sought a better place
Till the centuries roll
And all are folded in, to know that
Love is of the soul,
That love is of the soul.

*Rolling smoke over stage. Still in church. Exeunt all
except George, who is met by a German Tenor with
big wings, angelic.*

Tenor Ah, George Powell. All my life I have been
wondering what I would say to you, and now the
moment has come after your dear departed brother's
funeral, I have come to say . . . I am sorry.

George There's only one person I want an apology from.
It's the bloke who wrote those dreadful words to the
German version of 'Pack Up Your Troubles'. Is that
you?

Tenor Yes, they are pretty bad, but I never was paid.
And no one goes to hell for bad lyrics; luckily for you.

George Yeah, well. I was often under a lot of pressure.
Felix would pump out these tunes like rabbit pellets.
And the funny thing was, that with all that frantic
activity, what he really wanted to be in his heart was
with you fellas. The angels.

Tenor Yes, we can see that very clearly from here.

George You you didn't really come to say sorry. Angels don't say sorry. So what do you really want?

Tenor Your brother found a key, something everyone in the world can truly call their own. We want your opinion of the latest sacred arrangement.

George You mean it is sacred, what he wrote?

Tenor Not just him. You saw that man makes war upon himself and is debased in the process. Felix would be doing this job, but the violent shock of his death has temporarily untuned his soul.

Music. Two choirs, starting with 'Pack Up' in English, and seguing into German. The Tenor conducts, then brings in Dutch, Japanese, Russian and Filipino versions of the song. He continues to conduct while talking to George.

Tenor (*cueing*) Dutch! And now Japanese! And Russian, and Filipino! Xhosa! Norwegian! Spanish! Hindu! Classical and demotic Arabic together! Latin! Greek! Yiddish! Hebrew! Siberian Inuit! Polish! French! *Vive la différence!* All together now, the family of man, in one doomed, delicious, delightful, dangerous planet, one of countless millions in the infinite prodigality of time and space –

The choirs all sing 'Pack Up', in different languages, perhaps with flags. The Tenor conducts.

Triumphant End.

War's a Game Not Quickly Understood

Interviews by Jim Mulligan

Snoo Wilson pays a tribute to Aubrey Powell, the
grandson of the composer Felix Powell, by placing him
in the opening scene of *Pack Up Your Troubles*. Here the
character tells how he discovered his grandfather's chest
with unpublished, handwritten manuscripts and the
detritus of the composer's life. The discovery was repeated
when Aubrey brought the chest round to Snoo Wilson
and asked him to write a musical that would be a tribute
to a man who had been excised from the collective
memory of the Powell family. Snoo Wilson:

> The problem was to condense the story into a
> psychologically convincing set of characters, and
> I decided the way to do that was to concentrate on the
> quartet of George, Felix, Leila and Mabel. These two
> couples were professionally linked and successful
> music-hall stars on a par with Charlie Chaplin. In
> 1914 they were touring together, with Mabel running
> a tight ship, and then Felix and George wrote 'Pack Up
> Your Troubles', the best-selling marching song of all
> time. From then on they were comfortably off, but
> they never had another hit. George became a pacifist
> and Felix, at the age of thirty-seven, enlisted.

Felix Powell was a child prodigy, classically trained and,
at the age of twelve, organist and musical director of
St Asaph's Cathedral. Before he was twenty he gave up
all of that and embarked on the gruelling life of touring
the music halls. Nicolas Bloomfield:

The bulk of Felix's music is Edwardian. This period was a huge cultural watershed, but Felix was untouched by it. Music was changing all around him. Schoenberg and Stravinsky were contemporaries. Black musicians were playing jazz at the Hammersmith Palais, there were big bands and swing, but the unpublished pieces I found when we opened up Aubrey's chest were sentimental, violets-in-springtime stuff. The music I've written has resonances of Felix Powell's writing, but it tends to go slightly against the grain of his writing in the sense that it deals with critical situations that would have had no place in his music – things like him going to war and the difficult relationship he has with his wife.

It is impossible to say how much Powell was affected by his early encounter with organised religion, nor do we know what led to his rejection of it. According to Snoo Wilson, Felix was a very complete musical perfectionist who was driven to repeat the success he had experienced with 'Pack Up Your Troubles'. The difficulties he encountered in his personal life were probably compounded by his inability to stay the star he had once been. Snoo Wilson:

I think the relationship between Felix and Joan was a case of mutual exploitation. She wanted the name of Felix Powell and he wanted a fresh chance to write a proper score for a musical. In fact he ended up writing incidental music. By that time, if they weren't lovers, they were as close as makes no difference. The psychological impact of this woman's proximity to him was very considerable. He was probably monogamous by instinct, but the situation between him and Mabel had become quite acid and so he looked somewhere else for comfort, as people do. It's not even a tragedy. It's an everyday event. Unfortunately, suicide is a permanent solution to everyday problems.

Family records show that Felix's death was, in a very real way, avoidable. If he had only had the courage to ask Mabel for the money he owed, the matter could have been settled. Snoo Wilson:

> After he died, Mabel turned up with a bag of fivers and settled the debt. The money was there all the time. The problem was that if Felix had taken the money from their account, Mabel would have noticed and she would have thought he was having an affair. It's all very sad, an elementary misunderstanding.

Nicolas Bloomfield did not write a full score for *Pack Up Your Troubles*. This gives companies great freedom and scope to produce the musical that matches their resources. Nicolas Bloomfield:

> People can take the music and, in a sense, do what they like with it. The songs are there. They could do it successfully with a piano. That would make it an intimate piece. You could easily do it as if it was all in Felix's head, with him sitting at the piano. Or you could do it with massed bands and choirs.

Although *Pack Up Your Troubles* started off as Aubrey's tribute to his grandfather, it is also about George Powell, the pacifist. It must have been difficult for him to hear troops singing his song on the way to their deaths and, despite all his highest intentions, knowing that his family's security rested on the income the song was bringing in. Felix must also have been troubled by his song raising the troops' spirits only for them to be killed or blinded. And he cannot have been unaware of his troupe, The White Knights, presiding over orgies. Snoo Wilson:

For some reason this aspect of the war has been white-washed out. In any intense war situation sex becomes commercialised, but the generals were so concerned about troops contracting sexually transmitted diseases they banned prostitutes from dances and the under-age soldiers gallantly stepped into the breach. Scoring a Blighty by having sex was a very peculiar aspect of this war.

Many people are only familiar with the chorus of 'Pack Up Your Troubles', but this musical makes the most of the verses. They speak of Private Perks and his adventures. He goes to Flanders and he shoots the Boches, but the Germans in their turn write words of their own. Private Perks is Every Soldier, Everyman, and everyone can relate to him. Hence in the finale the German Tenor exhorts us: 'All together now, the family of man, in one doomed, delicious, delightful, dangerous planet.' And the choirs all sing 'Pack Up Your Troubles' in different languages.

War's a game not quickly understood.

Production Notes

Aubrey Powell's parents would never discuss the life or death of his grandfather Felix. However, Aubrey's mother revealed the existence of a trunk in her attic that belonged to his grandfather and was filled with artefacts of his life. Felix Powell had spent some of the war in the trenches, and the trunk contained items such as his gun, tambourine, writing desk, scrapbooks and manuscripts.

Felix Powell was a frustrated classical composer. He had been a child prodigy, having won an Eisteddfod at the age of ten, and was a cathedral organist at twelve. By the time he was twenty, he and his brother George were in music hall; and when they moved to the Midlands they became involved with a family of four sisters, leading to the formation of The Harlequinaders. Within a short time they were at the top of their profession, appearing all over Britain and touring as far as South Africa and America.

Felix had a huge hit in America in 1911 with the song 'Queen of Summer', of which Florrie Forde made a record. He wrote the song with George, with whom he also wrote 'Pack Up Your Troubles'. Originally intended as a music-hall song, they entered it at the start of the First World War in a marching song competition, and this caused friction in the family because George was a pacifist while Felix was going off to the trenches. The brothers didn't meet or write again for many years.

Felix wasn't conscripted, but asked to form a troupe, called The White Knights, to entertain the men at the front; and he became a kind of trench pop star, always whisked away to safety from the front. This compounded his feeling of guilt, and he once walked into no man's land – probably his first suicide attempt.

Felix was greatly affected by the fact that men were singing his song as they marched to their deaths. But by the end of the war he had earned £20,000 in royalties, and there was a tremendous confusion in his mind: he'd made money out of a war he'd never fought in himself. Meanwhile his brother George had rewritten the words as a conscientious objector.

After the discovery in the attic, Aubrey contacted EMI about other music written by his grandfather. He discovered that Felix had written massive hit tunes and melodies of his time. The verses were very Edwardian in style, and not necessarily appropriate for this musical, but although Snoo reworked the lyrics they remain faithful to the essence of the music.

Primrose Time wasn't a hit, but the writing team took pieces of music from it, which Nicolas Bloomfield rearranged while Snoo reworked the lyrics. The music comes from the period between 1910 and 1937, and isn't in chronological order, but the order Snoo felt best fitted the story. David Croft acted in *Primrose Time*, and his mother, Anne Croft, was the producer, and had an affair with Felix. Snoo changed her name to Joan Bellamy. When Felix needed money to stage the show in London's West End, he borrowed the equivalent of about £80,000 today from a gangster, but had no way of paying it back, or so it seemed.

Snoo has changed some details. The gangster is now a Brighton criminal; half-Italian and half-English. The horseracing scene in which he is introduced is a homage to the Ascot sequence in *My Fair Lady*. It's set in Brighton because that was the area the brothers gravitated to after the war, and where *Primrose Time* was a big hit. And Felix was a gambling man who enjoyed hanging about with a racetrack crowd.

If you stand on Brighton racecourse (as the team did when they were researching the piece) you can see Peacehaven – now a grim, run-down place, though after the First World War it was intended as a sort of utopia. Felix and George went there because they thought they were going to be big fish. They were celebrities. George even edited the monthly paper.

One very important event in Peacehaven was the building of the Lureland Theatre. Intended as a dance hall, Felix took it over and produced full-blown Gilbert and Sullivan operettas; and at the height of his fame Felix hosted massive stadium singalongs where up to 90,000 people would turn up to hear popular songs from the war as well as contemporary numbers. But by 1930 he had a longing to get back to the limelight and the West End with the doomed production of *Primrose Time*.

When Felix shot himself in 1942 he left a note saying he couldn't take any more. Being dressed in Home Guard uniform at the time might suggest an obsession with war was to blame. He wrote two suicide notes. One was to his Commanding Officer apologising and the second to his wife, in which there was no apology.

So the moral fulcrum of this story is: how can you best stage a musical in which the leading character kills himself? His action could make sense of everything and give it guts.

POINTS FROM THE WORKSHOP

Two sisters marry two brothers. • Mabel was the
backbone of the tribe and kept Felix together, but when
he had an affair she found it so contemptible that her
reaction didn't help him to have a rational view. • He
was obsessive about his music and had two pianos in
every house, one upstairs and one downstairs. • South
Wales, where he grew up, had many Welsh Methodists
marrying into Romanian Jewish families. • Felix's father
was a master painter. • His father died and his mother
married a man from Liverpool, and so he acquired
stepbrothers and sisters. • George, who was a clown and
a non-stop joker, died not long after Felix.

'Pack Up' is in everyone's psyche and language, and is
still heard and played everywhere.

The story stretches three decades in its primary narrative,
but reaches much further as Aubrey embraces the
present, which nudges us towards the relentlessness of a
world at war. • The music-hall acts use the timeless
characters of Venus and Cupid to conjure the universality
of the struggles of love. • There are contemporary echoes,
such as the damage war leaves behind – and as this
workshop was taking place, Gulf War Syndrome was
again in the headlines.

This is the story of a man who achieves many a triumph
but with each triumph becomes more reluctant to stay
alive. • In the play Felix is ever present. It is not necessary
for the actor playing Felix to *show* everything he goes
through in each scene – the whole play will serve to
summate his character, and each scene could be viewed
as an exploration of an aspect of it – Felix the artist, the
soldier, the depressive, the brother, the deceiver.

MUSIC AND SOUND

Joan's voice should feel like it is the most trained. She is more of a star than the other women.

Don't be scared about having some of it spoken/sung.

The instrumentation can be done with piano only. Nicolas Bloomfield has put in suggestions for solo instruments and it would work with a small dance band – a violin, double bass, drums and keyboard. To a degree what is going on in Felix's head happens as he is sitting at the piano. So the piano might be the most appropriate sound.

Applause features very strongly, in the second half in particular. Consider what this sound does for both the artist and audience. Is it congratulatory for the artist night after night, or does it become a monotonous audible mush? If the sound effect of canned applause is treated in some way to illustrate that the applause Felix keeps hearing isn't doing anything for his self-esteem, it might be an interesting punctuation.

Find a way of using applause so that it isn't typical. You might subvert the habit of clapping.

NOTES ON STAGING

If naturalism is the anchorage and the four main characters do their backstory work well enough that they live as fully fleshed people, this provides the bedrock from which anything is possible.

At the beginning of the piece it is clear what is real life and which are the 'set-piece' music-hall numbers and the mini-shows-within-the-show. Later on, the Fast Eddie sequence is written like a vaudeville number and yet is intended to reflect real life. Felix's personal life mixes with the theatrical until the two become indistinguishable.

Establish strongly the two distinct styles (theatrical and realistic) at the beginning and start to play with them. For instance, there's a whole stretch of the piece that slip-slides from the church where Felix is talking very rationally into no man's land, where he is being bombarded by voices from his past – here the two styles collide. Spend time exploring the real and imaginary and how both are presented.

Raise the stakes with the Fast Eddie scene – make him more rough and ballsy. It wouldn't be right if the stakes are higher in no man's land than in Fast Eddie's, because both are about being killed.

The crucial note to each actor would be to play everything truthfully and let the arc of each dramatic unit, whether naturalistic or otherwise, take care of itself.

The first duet is unaccompanied. As it is the opening number the actors need their notes before the play begins. Make it mysterious in style, it's quite a tricky harmony.

Felix is picking out the tune on the piano – it's the first time we hear it. Keep the pedal down to create a sense of haziness. The duet should be unaccompanied, but rehearse it with accompaniment as long as necessary.

The beginning should be a dreamscape, with a sense of something not quite born yet. Felix is composing. George is leaning on the piano. The girls are elsewhere, perhaps in the dressing room? Both pairs are in different places but should be kept in view at all times. The girls could be wearing pierrot ruffs/part-costume, contrasting with the boys in suits. You could immediately see that the girls are rehearsing with part of their costumes on.

When Aubrey arrives and watches them, it needs to be made clear that he is not in the same time zone. Choose one of the best non-singing actors for Aubrey. He needs to do the same amount of backstory work and have an instant rapport with the audience; he must charm them with positive energy. He can intermingle physically with characters from the past.

The piano could be a box on wheels that could be used as a box of tricks throughout the play. If you choose to do the show with piano only, it could be incorporated somewhere within the set. Be consistent with whatever you decide. It could be a real piano, two real pianos or one could be real and the other fake. If the actor playing Felix is a very good pianist you could have him playing the music throughout.

What you first see can't be too surreal – it has to be anchored in realism or there's going to be nowhere to go.

The second duet is more perky, detached and less soulful. A general rule – when you are going from music to dialogue, just cut in: surprise the audience.

Because none of these characters exist in their actual age, it follows that they are all alive and dead at the same time. Time is pushed. Character should have authority rather than getting caught up in the ageing process.

The first piece of music is tantric foreplay – it's teasing the audience into almost joining in 'Pack Up Your Troubles'.

Ask who Private Perks is and what is his role. Once rehearsals are under way this question should inspire a discussion that may throw up several interesting leads.

There's a location shift into music hall with Mabel's 'Lethal Larry' song. It is a big number. Hold the Cowgirls' entry until she has done the verse. Get across the idea of Mabel playing the Angel of Death – it's an anti-love song, Mabel has found out about the affair. The tune is repeated in the Angel of Death sequence, when Mayfair Minnie is with boys in drag before they go to their death. Here, it is a vulgar version of the Angel of Death. Mabel is pretending to be an American – it's not a realistic accent. Her songs are all quite low: mainly chest-voice if necessary.

Bring the panto horse back in the dance during 'Lethal Larry'. The number needs to look over-rehearsed. They have been performing it day after day in venues all over the country.

The following chorus entry is the marker that we are now in the First World War. All the people are workers who happen also to be singing. They should be seen to be doing their work or on their way to or from it.

Just before that is the first of two stunts (the second is Joan being stabbed by a bayonet) – after each 'smile' is a gunshot as each German helmet is hit.

The following vocal score has the chorus in half-time and should sound like a weary background to what is still up-tempo dialogue. The whistling continues with the dialogue over the top of it.

Felix isn't afraid of the sergeant; it is not his destiny to be destroyed by him. His threats don't affect him, but the sounds of the war become increasingly disturbing to him.

Set up the Joan scene, then contrast it with the serious scene in the courtroom. You don't have to split the stage. She could be in the centre with the court scene happening around her. This is a prophetic sighting of Joan – she hasn't yet entered the story.

Joan dies very dramatically and at length. (Eventually we learn her attraction to Felix was a factor in his suicide.)

The big chorus with soldiers in/out is all commentary. This isn't a showbiz number – rather, it is a turning point when we learn how troubled Felix is. The German choirboys could all be girls or younger boys with unbroken voices, in contrast to the soldiers.

The horror is that they were attacked the night before battle while they were in drag. This is Felix's experience of the war at its worst. Perhaps old-fashioned footlights could lend distortion and eerie shadows to this scene. Use make-up on the drag artists – make it look rushed, put on over bandages, layering horror and showbiz.

As Felix's mind is increasingly disturbed, there's a distraction into the pub scene – the drunken man and mouthy woman are very specific, and this anchors the scene in naturalism. The back story of the Hampshire Pals is a useful marker of the lives of the survivors.

The dance routine could perhaps be ducks tap-dancing (tap was a big craze before the Second World War) or even glove puppets coming out of the piano. The applause starting to ring thick and fast could be a motif. At the end of the number the dialogue comes in quickly.

The 'heigh ho's are harmonised in the puppet show.

In the Brighton section, incidental music should start quietly, mysteriously, and build up. The bookies' dialogue is boomable and raucous. They should shout over the top of one another.

The barmaids' collective identity is like a Greek chorus and the number should build up.

'Night Time' is not a pretty chorus: it should sound hard against the niceness of the music

'Producer' is sung by Mabel as an outpouring of her rage.

Disaster strikes for Felix when the theatre is bombed and his life is exploded. The scene should explode with it. Joan could enter covered in dust – a visual development from the trodden-on bouquet of flowers, now the rose herself has been squished.

Improvising off-text will help with working out what Felix and George are doing.

'Transition' is about being impelled towards a conclusion, and should be as simple and as clean as possible. Felix remains anchored, and through body language we have to know that location and time have changed.

When Joan exits and George enters the scene moves to Peacehaven/Lurland. The slip-sliding of locations at this point starts to control him.

There is a surreal subversion with the entrance of the coffin. This is a good opportunity for big ensemble staging. Dramatically the funeral marks the end of his life. Structurally it brings the solemnity that you want at the end of a piece like this. Make it simple: perhaps light candles, dress the cast all in black and give them black umbrellas. Rain would be good. The funeral was modest, not a grand ceremony or hero's burial. The closure with George is important, not unlike in the film *It's a Wonderful Life*.

For the final song an empty space should be invaded by singers, dancing, marching. It would be great if there were flags of all nations.

This piece thrives on surprise – with one final one at the end in not singing the final 'smile'. Avoid a cosy ending. It could be a moment of seeing the silence, with the lights fading slowly.

Workshop facilitated by Anthony Banks
with notes taken by Mairi Coyle

THE MUSIC

l. lyrics by; *m.* music by; *p.* published by

Pack Up Your Troubles, *l.* George Asaf, *m.* Felix Powell, *p.* EMI Publ's Ltd

Lethal Larry, *l.* Snoo Wilson, *m.* Felix Powell, Aubrey Powell, *p.* PUYT Ltd © 1998

Ave Maria, *l.* Snoo Wilson, *m.* Felix Powell/Aubrey Powell, *p.* PUYT Ltd © 1998/Snoo Wilson

No Man's Land, *l.* Snoo Wilson, *m.* Nick Bloomfield, *p.* Snoo Wilson/ Nick Bloomfield

Alexander's Ragtime Band, *m.* Irving Berlin

Mayfair Minnie, *l.* Snoo Wilson/Aubrey Powell, *m.* Felix Powell/Aubrey Powell, *p.* Snoo Wilson/PUYT Ltd © 1998

Pack Up Your Troubles (German version), *l.* Anon, *m.* Felix Powell, *p.* EMI Publ's Ltd

Have you Seen the Ducks Go By, *l.* Felix Powell, *m.* Felix Powell, *p.* EMI Publ's Ltd

Puppet Show, *l.* Felix Powell/Aubrey Powell/Snoo Wilson, *m.* Felix Powell/ Aubrey Powell, *p.* PUYT Ltd © 1998/Snoo Wilson

Come to Lureland, *l.* Felix Powell/Snoo Wilson/Aubrey Powell, *m.* Felix Powell/Aubrey Powell, *p.* PUYT Ltd © 1998/Snoo Wilson

Brighton Races (Star of Peace), *l.* Snoo Wilson, *m.* Felix Powell/Aubrey Powell/Nick Bloomfield, *p.* PUYT Ltd © 1998/Snoo Wilson/Nick Bloomfield

Night Comes to Brighton, *l.* Snoo Wilson, *m.* Nick Bloomfield, *p.* Snoo Wilson/Nick Bloomfield

Fast Eddie's Song, *l.* Snoo Wilson, *m.* Nick Bloomfield, *p.* Snoo Wilson/ Nick Bloomfield

I've Got Problems, *l.* Snoo Wilson, *m.* Nick Bloomfield, *p.* Snoo Wilson/ Nick Bloomfield

Love is of the Soul, *l.* Snoo Wilson, *m.* Felix Powell/Aubrey Powell, *p.* PUYT Ltd © 1998/Snoo Wilson

PASS IT ON

Doug Lucie

Doug Lucie's recent work includes *The Ragged Trousered Philanthropists* (Plymouth Theatre Royal); *Believe In* (Plymouth Theatre Royal); and *Hard Times* (BBC Radio 4). His work for TV includes *A Class of His Own*, *Funseekers*, *Hard Feelings* and *Headhunters*; and for radio, *Blind*, *Ghosts*, *The Green Man*, *Gypsy*, *Little Dorrit* and *Small Earthquakes*. His credits for the stage include *Fashion*, *Gaucho*, *Grace*, *The Green Man*, *Hard Feelings*, *Love You Too*, *Progress* and *The Shallow End*.

All professional and amateur rights in this play
are strictly reserved and applications for permission
to perform it must be made in advance, before rehearsals begin,
to Alan Brodie Representation, 6th Floor, Fairgate House,
76 New Oxford Street, London WC1A 1HB

Characters

PLAY ONE: 1971

Sarah
Nev
both seventeen

PLAY TWO: 1982

Monique
fourteen

Kelly
sixteen

PLAY THREE: 1997

Giles
Becky
both seventeen

PLAY FOUR: 2004

Chris
Glen
both nineteen

The Boy
fifteen

Play One

1971

The garden of a smart detached house. Sarah is sitting on a child's swing reading a book. She wears a full-length velvet skirt, flowery top and a crocheted woollen hat. Nev appears from the house. He wears patched flared Levis, a grandad vest, a waistcoat and neckerchief. He stops as he sees Sarah, takes a breath and carries on.

Nev Hi, Sarah.

She looks up.

Sarah Oh, hi, Nev. (*She goes back to her book.*)
Nev What are you up to? (*Beat.*)
Sarah Nothing. (*Beat.*)
Nev What's the book?
Sarah Baudelaire.
Nev *Fleurs du Mal*?
Sarah Yeah. (*Beat.*)
Nev Set text, is it?
Sarah Yeah.

Beat. He pulls a slim book out of his back pocket.

Nev I'm just reading these Yevtushenko poems.
Sarah Yeah?
Nev He's brilliant.
Sarah I know.
Nev Oh yeah, Phil said you liked him. (*Beat.*)
Sarah Are you looking for him?
Nev Who? (*Beat.*)
Sarah My brother. Phillip.
Nev Sort of. We were going to go into town and look at some guitars.

Sarah I think he's already gone.

Nev Shit.

Sarah Colin was round earlier. I think they went in his car.

Nev Oh, right. (*Beat.*)

Sarah So, are you starting a band?

Nev Yeah, maybe. It depends. We've got to get some gear first.

Sarah What do you play?

Nev Guitar.

Sarah Are you any good?

Nev Yeah.

Sarah Oh.

Nev I've been playing since I was about ten. My brother taught me 'Mr Tambourine Man', and I kind of took it from there. I'm no Eric Clapton, but, y'know . . .

Sarah Right.

Nev My brother's in a band.

Sarah Is he?

Nev Yeah.

Sarah What are they called?

Nev Buddhist Monday.

Sarah Right. (*Beat.*) Is he a Buddhist then, your brother?

Nev No. (*Beat.*) He works at the Co-op.

Sarah He could still be a Buddhist.

Nev No, not my brother. My dad would kick him out of the house if he was.

Sarah Why?

Nev My dad's Catholic.

Sarah Oh. Does that mean you are?

Nev No. Well, we never go to church or anything. There was some nastiness when my dad was an altar boy, so he kind of dropped out of it.

Sarah What kind of nastiness?

Nev Dunno. But apparently my gran frog-marched him out of the church while he was still swinging the

incense, and they never went back. He still calls
himself Catholic, though.

Sarah I suppose it's a cultural thing, isn't it?

Nev Probably.

Sarah I mean, he's Irish, isn't he, your dad?

Nev Sort of. He's *Northern* Irish.

Sarah What's the difference? (*Beat.*)

Nev If you're Northern Irish, you're British. If you're
Southern Irish, you're free.

Sarah Aren't they free in Northern Ireland, then?

Nev The Catholics aren't, no.

Sarah Oh. (*Beat.*)

Nev Are you going down The Two Brewers tonight?

Sarah Dunno. Might do.

Nev It was great last Saturday, wasn't it?

Sarah I was only there a few minutes. Me and Alison had
a party to go to.

Nev Oh? I didn't hear about any party. Where was that?

Sarah Over near Latchmere.

Nev We usually hear about it if there's anything
happening.

Sarah It was some guys from the Poly.

Nev Oh, I see.

Sarah There were no schoolkids. Most of the people
there were about twenty.

Nev But they invited you.

Sarah Me and Alison, yeah. (*Beat.*)

Nev Was it any good?

Sarah It was fantastic. There was wine and everything.

Nev Very posh.

Sarah No, it was just really relaxed, y'know? People
lying around on the floor, talking about politics,
listening to music, smoking joints. It was really
mellow. (*Beat.*)

Nev We had a great time down The Brewers, anyway.

Sarah Did you?

Nev Yeah, the new DJ played some great stuff: Spirit, Barclay James Harvest, Yes, Iron Butterfly. And at closing time, he put on 'Out, Demons, Out'. You know? The Edgar Broughton Band?

Sarah Yeah, I know it.

Nev And the strobe lights were going and everything, and we were all jumping up and down, y'know, screaming 'Out, Demons, Out', and two fuzz only walk in, don't they?

Sarah (*laughs*) Really?

Nev Yeah, I think they must have taken it personally, because they backed out pretty sharpish.

Sarah laughs.

Fucking police. They're pigs.

Sarah Yeah.

Nev Hassling us all the time. They're just the state's bully-boys.

Sarah Right. (*Beat.*) I didn't know you were into politics.

Nev Can't avoid it if you're Irish Catholic.

Sarah But you're English.

Nev Not in here. (*He taps his chest.*)

Sarah Well, you're not Catholic.

Nev No, but my dad is.

Sarah Not really.

Nev It's where he comes from. (*Beat.*)

Sarah Don't you think it's more important to worry about where you're going to than where you come from?

Nev Where you come from is what you are.

Sarah But aren't you interested in what you can become, rather than what you are? I mean, isn't the future more exciting than the past?

Nev The past is still crushing Catholics in Northern Ireland, and until that stops, there won't *be* a future there. It's got to be fought for.

Pause.

Sarah I went to a meeting last week, about the
environment. You know, if we go on using up fossil
fuels at the rate we are, they'll run out before a
hundred years are up. Some people reckon sooner.
And if we carry on destroying forests and stuff, they
reckon the temperature will rise and the planet will
become uninhabitable.

Nev What, in a hundred years?

Sarah Yeah. Frightening, isn't it?

Nev But we'll all be dead then, won't we?

Sarah Aren't you worried about it? I mean, what about
when you have kids?

Nev Sarah, one hundred years ago, there were no anti-
biotics, kids still went up chimneys, the toilet was at the
bottom of the garden, houses and streets were lit by gas,
and there were no astronauts landing on the moon.

Sarah So?

Nev So the world's changed beyond recognition in the
last one hundred years. I can't believe that by 2071
we won't have found some other kind of fuel to make
everything work.

Sarah And what if we haven't? What if things just get
worse?

Nev You should have more faith in people.

Sarah It's people that are the problem.

Nev No, the problem is, you want to believe the world
could end tomorrow, because that would justify your
lack of faith and divert people's attention away from
real politics.

Sarah Blimey. Where'd you get that from?

Nev What's important is ordinary people's struggle for
freedom from bigotry and oppression.

Sarah What's the point of being free if you can't breathe
the air and everything's dying?

Nev See? You're just using that as an argument for doing nothing.

Sarah I'm not doing nothing. I intend to fight to save the planet.

Nev (*laughs*) Best of luck.

Sarah Anyway, it *could* all end tomorrow. Have you ever heard of the H-bomb?

Nev Of course I have. That's one of the things we've got to fight to get rid of.

Sarah It's fighting that made us create the H-bomb.

Nev *We* didn't create it. *They* did. It wasn't the people. It was *them*. (*Beat.*)

Sarah Who?

Nev The men with the power. The men who rule the world.

Sarah But the people put them there.

Nev Oh, crap.

Sarah Who put Heath in Downing Street? Who put Nixon in the White House?

Nev Heath, Wilson, what's the difference? What kind of choice are the people given?

Sarah Not a lot, I agree –

Nev The politicians are all part of the same system, just different shades of the same colour.

Sarah And most of the people support them, most of the people support the system.

Nev Because there are no alternatives.

Sarah Right. So we have to provide some.

Nev By running around screaming 'We're all doomed!' I suppose.

Sarah No. By educating people.

Nev Yeah, because people are all stupid, aren't they?

Sarah People don't *know*, that's all I'm saying. They haven't been told the facts, and they're being sold a way of life that's unsustainable. (*Beat.*)

Nev Okay, here's a question: let's suppose you're right –

Sarah I *am* right –

Nev Okay. So the modern world is bound to collapse if things go on as they are, right?

Sarah Totally.

Nev So let's look at the people who are causing this to happen: the oil companies, the industries, the banks. What are they in business for?

Sarah To make money.

Nev Right answer. And how do they make money?

Sarah By buying stuff as cheaply as they can, turning it into other stuff, and selling it for as much as they can.

Nev Yes, by exploiting resources and people. Which is something they've become very good at over the years. And they got good at it by expanding their markets and creating new ones. And to do that, they have to invent new processes and adapt to new situations. It's a massive enterprise. Things have to be planned and financed years in advance; everything's examined down to the last detail, all for one reason: to maximise profit. And they're brilliant at it. But how brilliant would they look if, at the end of it all, they were left with a wasteland? Where's the profit in that? (*Beat.*) Do you see what I'm saying?

Sarah Not really.

Nev Okay. So here's a guy, right? A businessman. He lives in a big house, has a wife, kids, pots of money, foreign holidays, a Jag in the garage, the lot. His whole life revolves around making money: for himself, his company, his company's shareholders, his kids' trust funds, you name it. That's his life. That's his entire existence. Well, just how stupid does he have to be to do this so destructively that in a few years there'll be nothing left to exploit? No money to be made? I mean, do you really believe he's going to sit down and cheerfully sign his own death warrant? (*Beat.*) Do you?

Sarah Maybe.

Nev One man, perhaps. But an entire global system?
I think not.

Sarah But I mean . . . it's . . .

Nev It's a bit more complicated than you think, that's
what it is. (*Beat.*)

Sarah But what if the damage they cause is irreversible?

Nev Such as?

Sarah I dunno . . . what if temperatures rise and the
global ice-cap starts to melt?

Nev Or what if a Martian spaceship landed here in this
garden, right now? It ain't gonna happen.

Sarah Look, the Earth's a unique environment. This one
great big thing, the planet, is made up of millions of
different things all reacting together to create a sort
of balance that makes all life possible. Once you start
fiddling about with it, breaking the connections
between things, disrupting a process that's gone on
for millions of years, you change it totally, in ways that
we can't even begin to imagine. And in the end, you
destroy it.

Nev Hocus pocus. All you're asking is: 'What if?' What
if this happens? What if that happens? Well, my
answer to that is: 'What if it doesn't?'

Sarah So you'd risk the future of the whole planet on the
gamble that the greedy bastards who run things are
always right.

Nev Well, they have been so far!

Sarah Two world wars in living memory and enough
nuclear weapons to wipe us all out in a few seconds?
That's progress?

Nev I'm not saying people are perfect, I'm saying the
opposite. But in the end, they're not as short-sighted or
as stupid as you seem to think they are. (*Beat.*)

Sarah What if they just don't know?

Nev Don't know what?

Sarah What they're doing. (*Beat.*) What if they – we – are so wrapped up in our own lives that we don't see the effects of what we're doing? What if our rational minds have been closed off by our way of life to the consequences of that way of life? Or we see it, but we won't admit our responsibility for what we see?

Nev You make the whole of humanity sound like a psychiatric case.

Sarah Well, maybe we are.

Nev Oh God, that is so simplistic.

Sarah Thanks.

Nev Well, sorry, but it is. There are billions of people on this planet struggling just to earn the basic necessities of life and to stay alive. People who need food, homes, jobs, electricity, transport, schools, hospitals. Poor people, people with no choice. What are you going to do for them?

Sarah I'm going to do what I can to make sure there's still a world for their children to live in.

Nev No you're not. You're going to make sure they stay living in poverty, with disease and oppression there every day to remind them not to get too many ideas about improving their lives. (*Beat.*) You're just a reactionary.

Sarah Crap.

Nev If all you ever say is 'Put the planet first', then you're condemning millions of people to lives of misery and a premature death.

Sarah Does it ever bother you that there might be too many of us?

Nev Oh, here we go.

Sarah Does it?

Nev No.

Sarah Well it should.

Nev Why should it?

Sarah Because over-population is a real danger.

377

Nev Yeah, all these tedious little people demanding their rights and their fair share, it's terrible, I know.

Sarah The more of us there are, the more we consume. The more we consume, the less there will be for future generations. If we just ransack the planet now for a quick fix, the people you say you care about are the ones who'll feel the effects first. Environmental change will hit the poorest hardest.

Nev Ergo, cut down their numbers, stop the buggers breeding.

Sarah No, not quite. The poor aren't the ones doing most of the consuming. They're not the problem.

Nev No. As always, they're the victims.

Sarah Exactly. (*Pause.*) Hey, we agreed on something. (*She looks at her watch and stands.*) I've got to go.

Nev Where are you off to?

Sarah Out. (*Beat.*)

Nev Have you been to that new wholefood café on Market Street?

Sarah No. (*Beat.*)

Nev It's really good. You should give it a go.

Sarah Yeah. (*Beat.*)

Nev If you fancied going there now, I could buy you a coffee or something.

Sarah I'm meeting someone. And I buy my own coffee.

Nev I just meant . . . (*Beat.*) I really like you, Sarah. I think you're beautiful. I was going to ask you out. (*Beat.*)

Sarah Thanks. (*Beat.*) No, I mean it, thanks. But . . .

Nev No thanks.

Sarah Yeah. (*Beat.*) I'm kind of going out with someone already.

Nev Oh. Sorry. (*Beat.*) I did ask Phil, but he said he thought you weren't.

Sarah I don't discuss boyfriends with my brother.

Nev Sure. (*Beat.*) Bummer, eh?

Sarah Look . . .

Nev No, it's alright,

Sarah No, please, I just want to say this. (*Beat.*) You're a nice guy. You're interesting to talk to and everything. And you're pretty cool-looking, too. But I'm just not interested in boys my own age. The guy I'm seeing is twenty, y'know, I mean . . . (*Beat.*) He's got a beard. (*She laughs, embarrassed.*) You live over on the estate, don't you?

Nev Yeah.

Sarah What does your dad do?

Nev He's a milkman. (*Beat.*)

Sarah See . . . (*Beat.*)

Nev What? (*Pause.*) Oh, I see. I live on the estate. My dad's a milkman. Whereas you live out here in splendid seclusion, in your lovely detached house. And Daddy owns a building firm. (*Beat.*)

Sarah Property development, actually.

Nev Whatever it is, I bet it brings in plenty of money. And I bet he doesn't work any harder than my dad ever has. It was just the luck of the draw. (*Beat.*)

Sarah You don't understand.

Nev I do. You're a snob.

Sarah That's bloody rude. (*Beat.*)

Nev What d'you expect? I'm from the estate.

Sarah That isn't what I meant about the estate. I just meant it's a long way to come for nothing. (*Beat.*)

Nev Yeah. (*Beat.*) I still think you're beautiful. (*Beat.*)

Sarah Thanks.

He goes. Sarah goes back to her book.

Fade.

End.

Play Two

1982

A playground. Monique is standing by the swings, drinking from a bottle of cider. Kelly storms on. Monique sits on the swing.

Kelly You vile, rotten cow.

Monique Get lost.

Kelly No way. Who d'you think you are, talking to Mum like that?

Monique She started it.

Kelly No she never.

Monique She was on at me. She's always on at me.

Kelly She asked you to do something, that's all.

Monique She didn't ask me, she told me. Like I'm an idiot or something.

Kelly You *are* an idiot.

Monique Shut your mouth.

Kelly Don't tell me to shut my mouth.

Monique Why? What you gonna do? (*Pause.*) Did she say anything? After I left?

Kelly Like what?

Monique I dunno.

Kelly What d'you expect her to say?

Monique I don't know!

Pause.

Kelly She said your tea's in the oven.

Monique I don't want any tea. (*Beat.*) It'll all be dried up by now, anyway.

Kelly Well, that's tough, innit? It's your own stupid fault.

Monique swigs from the bottle of cider.

And where'd you get that?

Monique Get what?

Kelly *That.* (*Beat.*)

Monique The offie. Where d'you think?

Kelly They wouldn't serve you with that.

Monique Why not?

Kelly 'Cos you're too young. You're fourteen, Monique. (*Beat.*)

Monique I got some bloke to buy it for me.

Kelly So now you're going up to strange blokes in the street and getting them to buy you alcohol.

Monique Er . . . yeah. (*Beat.*)

Kelly I give up. (*Beat.*)

Monique Got any fags?

Kelly Yeah.

Monique Give us one.

Kelly You'll be lucky.

Monique Cow.

Kelly What about the ones you nicked off Mum?

Monique I never.

Kelly I *saw* you. (*Beat.*)

Monique Smoked them all. (*Pause.*) If she's put my dinner in the oven, does that mean she's gone out?

Kelly She's gone down the club.

Monique What for?

Kelly What for?!

Monique Yeah.

Kelly 'Cos she can't bear being in the house with you when you're like this.

Monique I'm not in the house, am I?

Kelly And neither can I.

Monique What you doing here, then?

Kelly Someone's got to try and talk to you.

Monique Why?

Kelly 'Cos otherwise you'll run off again.

Monique So?

Kelly Christ, Monique, you know the answer. You'll get put into care.

Monique It'd be better than living with her.

Kelly No it wouldn't.

Monique Yes it would.

Kelly Why?

Monique 'Cos she's a bitch. I hate her.

Kelly No you don't.

Monique I do.

Kelly You're pissed off at her. You don't hate her.

Monique How do you know?

Kelly Grow up, Monique. (*Beat.*) 'Sides, if anyone's acting like a bitch, it's you.

Monique Must run in the family.

Kelly Mum is not a bitch.

Monique So why'd she kick Dad out if she's not a bitch?

Kelly She kicked Dad out because he hit her.

Monique He hit her because she slept with Terry Wilson.

Kelly Well, maybe he should have hit Terry Wilson. Anyway, she only slept with him because Dad was never here, and when he was he was a bastard to her.

Monique Don't you call my dad a bastard.

Kelly He's my dad too, I'll call him what I like. (*Beat.*)

Monique What was he supposed to do? Leave the army?

Kelly Yeah, he could have, why not?

Monique 'Cos it's his job. She knew that when she married him. (*Beat.*)

Kelly D'you remember when Dean went away on holiday?

Monique Yeah.

Kelly Well, for two weeks you moped around . . . 'What am I gonna do without him? Why hasn't he rung me? Why hasn't he sent me a card?'

Monique That was different.

Kelly Why?

Monique It just was.

Kelly You were in a right state, weren't you?

Monique Only because I knew there were going to be loads of girls there.

Kelly Well, imagine what it was like for Mum, with Dad gone for months on end. And then when he got back, he was like a zombie. Come on, Monique, you know what it was like. All the boozing, all the rows.

Monique He'd been getting shot at by fucking Paddies. How d'you expect him to behave?

Kelly Lots of other blokes did their tour in Northern Ireland without turning into psychos. But he couldn't deal with it.

Monique Two of his mates got blown up.

Kelly Loads of people's mates got blown up. That's what happens to soldiers sometimes.

Monique I know! (*Beat.*)

Kelly But he wouldn't talk to anybody about it. Not even Mum. Especially not Mum.

Monique Why should he have to talk to anybody about it?

Kelly 'Cos that's the only way to get that stuff out of your head. If you just leave it all in there, you go bloody nuts.

Monique Says you.

Kelly Says anybody who knows. (*Beat.*) The trouble is . . . he changed, Monique.

Monique He couldn't help that.

Kelly I'm not saying he could. But he could have helped himself, and us. He didn't have to bottle it all up inside.

Monique He's a soldier. That's what they do.

Kelly Not if they want to stay sane, they don't. And Mum begged him to get help. To save their marriage. But he wouldn't do it.

Monique That's because he's proud.

Kelly Well, he hasn't got very much to be proud of now, has he?! (*Beat.*) Stop making excuses for him.

Monique You stop making excuses for *her*.

Kelly Her? You mean Mum?

Monique Yeah.

Kelly Well, say it. Mum. She's your mum. It won't hurt you to say it.

Monique She's just a bitch.

Kelly Oh, come on!

Monique If she cared about me, she wouldn't be off down the club getting pissed and picking up blokes.

Kelly She's not!

Monique She's a pisshead.

Kelly She is not! She goes there for company. If she didn't, she'd never see anyone except you and me. And then she'd go bloody crazy, too.

Monique Let her. I don't care.

Kelly I don't believe that.

Monique I don't. She's ruined my life.

Kelly How has she ruined your life?

Monique She sent Dad away! And now he's on a boat somewhere, going somewhere else he's gonna get shot at and blown up and I'll probably never see him again!

She's close to tears. Pause. Kelly takes out her cigarettes and sits on the swing next to Monique.

Kelly Here.

She gives her a cigarette and takes one for herself. She lights them.

Look . . . most people reckon the Argies'll leg it as soon as our lot get down there. They're useless, not a real army. You'll see. They're only good at fighting civilians. They'll crap themselves when they see the British Army turn up.

Monique You reckon?

Kelly Easy.

Monique What if they don't?

Kelly If they don't, our boys'll chase them back to where they come from, no sweat. (*Beat.*)

Monique It doesn't seem real. I mean . . . I can't believe they're actually going there. They're actually going to have a war.

Kelly Only if the Argies put up a fight. Which they won't. (*Beat.*) And then Dad'll be home again, and maybe him and Mum can work something out.

Monique She won't, you'll see. (*Beat.*)

Kelly Whatever you think, Monique, it wasn't her fault.

Monique Did someone put a gun to her head and make her drop her knickers for the first bloke who came along?

Kelly It wasn't like that. She's not some slapper like you make out. It was a mistake. She accepts that. But she was lonely.

Monique How d'*you* know?

Kelly Because she talks to me and I listen. She's really unhappy, Mon. That's why she did what she did. It was just one of those things that happen when you're not in control.

Monique She's always in control.

Kelly Yeah, right.

Monique She's always telling me what to do.

Kelly No. She'll ask you to do something. Then she'll ask you again. Then you'll give her some lip, and she'll *tell* you to do it. I've sat there watching you hundreds of times. It bores the tits off me.

Monique Sorry for breathing.

Kelly It's like watching a couple of wind-up toys. Turn the key and watch them go.

Monique All *right*!

Kelly I have to live with it. That's all I'm saying.

Monique Not for much longer.

Kelly What's that supposed to mean?

Monique You won't have to live with it for much longer.

Pause.

Kelly Alright, what you gonna do? (*Beat.*)
Monique I might move in with Dean.

Beat, then Kelly laughs.

What you laughing at?

Kelly laughs.

What?!

Kelly How are you going to move in with Dean? He lives with his mum.

Monique She said it's alright.

Kelly Oh, get off.

Monique She *did*. She's totally cool about it.

Kelly I'll bet.

Monique Not all mums are like ours, y'know.

Kelly I know. Some of them take drugs and ignore their kids. Some of them don't spend nearly twenty years of their lives with the same husband. Some of them don't even know who their kids' dads are. (*Beat.*) Oh, but wait a minute, that's Dean's mum, innit?

Monique You don't even know her.

Kelly I know enough.

Monique You don't know that she takes drugs.

Kelly Well, it's hardly a secret, is it?

Monique You're just the same as everyone else. Got a small mind. (*Beat.*)

Kelly Has Dean ever met his dad? (*Beat.*)

Monique No.

Kelly Does he even know who his dad is?

Monique Dunno.

Kelly You don't know.

Monique No.

Kelly Well, you know who yours is. And d'you know why? Because our mum made sure you did. She stayed this long with Dad for *us*. She could have taken the easy road, and left, any time. But she didn't. She stayed for us. (*Beat.*)

Monique I wish she hadn't. I could have gone and lived with Dad.

Kelly And what about when he was away?

Monique I can look after myself.

Kelly What, when you were ten? You'd have been alright then, would you?

Monique Probably. (*Beat.*)

Kelly Until you realise just what Mum's done for us, you're gonna be a mess. I love Dad, the same as you do. But I'm glad he's gone, and I hope he can get well again and come back. But until he does, *if* he does, I'm gonna give Mum some credit for everything she's done for us.

Pause.

Monique I miss him. I can't help that.

Kelly Course you can't.

Monique It doesn't feel right with him not here.

Kelly But he's hardly ever been here.

Monique But before, you always knew he was coming back. Like he was here even when he wasn't.

Kelly Yeah, I know.

Monique And what if he doesn't come back? (*Beat.*)

Kelly He's coming back, alright?

Monique You don't know that.

Kelly Listen . . . you can pop out for a packet of fags and get hit by a bus any day of the week. Shit happens, yeah? Like Mandy's brother: he gets on his motorbike to go to work, and a couple of hours later, he's in hospital, smashed to bits and in a coma.

Pause.

Monique He was gorgeous, too, wasn't he?

Kelly smiles.

387

Kelly Oh, dead cute.

Monique Out of your league, though.

Kelly You what? I could have had him like that. (*She snaps her fingers.*)

Monique Yeah, right.

Kelly I could. Except I've got Stewart, so I didn't need him.

Monique I thought he dumped you.

Kelly What? He wouldn't dare.

Monique You said –

Kelly I said he was being a pain in the arse and he'd better smarten himself up a bit. So he did.

Monique Yeah. 'Here, Rover.'

Kelly I like a man who does what he's told.

Monique Well, that's Stewart alright. I bet he waits for you to tell him when he can have a crap.

Kelly Eurrgh.

Monique I bet he does.

Kelly I don't let him take liberties, that's all. He doesn't mind.

Monique No, as long as he gets what he came for, he don't mind.

Kelly You watch it.

Monique Well, you have, haven't you?

Kelly None of your business.

Monique You can tell me.

Kelly If I tell you, I might as well spray-paint it up the side of the house.

Monique No, come on, you're my sister. I'm not going to go round making you out to be a slag, am I?

Kelly You better not.

Monique I wouldn't.

Kelly You behave like a right kid sometimes, Monique.

Monique I *am* a kid. That's what you and *her* are always telling me, innit?

Kelly You're fourteen, and no matter how grown up you feel, you're still only fourteen.

Monique You don't know how I feel.

Kelly A couple of years ago, *I* was fourteen. I know exactly how you feel.

Monique But you ain't me. And we're all different, yeah?

Kelly Yeah, different but the same.

Monique Eh?

Kelly We all think we're the only person who ever felt what we're feeling, but we're not. We feel it in our own way, but we're only going through the same as everyone else has gone through.

Monique Not me.

Kelly What, special, are you?

Monique Yeah, I bloody am.

Kelly No you're not. (*Beat.*) I mean . . . you *are* . . . but not like you mean it. You're special, but you're not *more* special.

Monique Why not?

Kelly *Because.* (*Beat.*)

Monique Dean says I'm special.

Kelly Of course he does. Until he finally gets into your knickers, gets what he wants, and moves on.

Monique He's not like that!

Kelly They never are. (*Pause.*)

Monique He's *got* into my knickers. And he ain't moved on yet.

Kelly stares at her.

Oooh, your face. (*She laughs.*)

Kelly Monique . . .

Monique You look just like *her*.

Kelly Don't bring Mum into it. This is between me and you. (*Beat.*) Have you slept with him?

Monique smiles and looks away.

Monique. Have you had sex with Dean? (*Beat.*)

Monique We've made love, if that's what you mean.

Kelly Oh, Christ, you stupid little girl.

Monique Jealous.

Kelly Jealous? Get your head screwed back on, girl. Dean's a no-hope little scrote with no prospects except prison, when he's old enough. And his mum's a junkie wino dope-dealer.

Monique And I'm moving into their house.

Kelly You are not!

Monique Try and stop me. (*Beat.*)

Kelly I won't have to. Mum'll do that. If you leave her house, she'll have you put in care.

Monique Wow. Scary.

Kelly If you get involved with Dean and his mum and the people she hangs around with, you'll end up the same as them.

Monique Maybe I want to.

Kelly Why?!

Monique 'Cos they *do* stuff. They have a laugh. They don't stop and think about everything, they just get on with it and have fun. (*Beat.*)

Kelly Fun.

Monique Yeah. *Fun.* (*Beat.*)

Kelly How many times have you and Dean . . . done it?

Monique Mind your own.

Kelly How many times? (*Beat.*)

Monique A few.

Kelly Five? Ten?

Monique shrugs.

And here comes the silly question . . . did you take any precautions?

Monique What?

Kelly Precautions. (*Beat.*) Contraceptives.

Monique looks away, shyly.

No?

Monique shakes her head.

Oh my God . . .
Monique My period's late, an' all.

Beat. Then Kelly stands, furious.

Kelly You want to break Mum's heart, don't you?
Monique It's nothing to do with her.
Kelly You're stupid. And cruel.
Monique What are you so stressed about? What's it to you?
Kelly I'm your sister!
Monique So act like it!
Kelly What, and tell you everything's alright? Give you a pat on the head for giving your virginity to that maggot? No, I'm not gonna do that. I'm gonna tell you what a fucking mess you've made of yourself. I'm gonna tell you how much that's going to affect the rest of us. And I'm gonna tell you I hate you, Monique. Right now, I hate you. (*Pause.*) Have you done a test?
Monique What?
Kelly A pregnancy test.
Monique Don't know how. (*Beat.*) Doesn't matter, anyway.
Kelly Why not?
Monique Well, if I am pregnant, I'm keeping it.
Kelly Have you got the faintest idea what it'd be like? Have you?
Monique Millions of teenagers have babies. It's not like I'm the first one. Anyway, Dean's mum says she'd help.
Kelly She knows? You've told *her*, but you haven't told your own family?
Monique I'm telling you now. 'Sides, what do you care?

Kelly I care a fuck of a lot more than Dean's mum, I can tell you that. Oh, yeah, she'll love it all for a while, 'cos it means another one like her in the neighbourhood. But that won't last. If she cared about you, she'd have made her son keep his filthy hands off you in the first place, and if she couldn't do that, she should have made sure you took some precautions. But that's not her style. She'll let you make the biggest mistake of your life and she'll revel in it, because without fuck-ups and crises happening all the time, there's absolutely fuck-all going on in her stupid life. It's just a waste, that's all. A big fat waste. (*Beat.*) You can't have a baby, Monique.

Monique Why not?

Kelly Because you *are* a baby!

Monique No I'm not. (*Beat.*) I know what I want. This is what I want.

Kelly Don't you want more?

Monique No, 'cos I'm not gonna get it. All the things I might have wanted are never going to happen. This is the one thing I want that I can have. I'm never gonna have a rich boyfriend or a posh house or any of that stuff. Other people have those lives. People on the telly and in the papers. But I'm gonna be stuck here for the rest of my life with fuck-all.

Kelly It doesn't have to be like that.

Monique It doesn't have to, but it will. (*Beat.*)

Kelly You're fourteen. That's how it looks when you're that age. But you can do something about it.

Monique No, I can't.

Kelly Why not?

Monique Because I don't want to. (*Pause.*)

Kelly I think you should talk to Mum. (*Pause.*) You're going to have to some time. (*Pause.*) You know, if you are pregnant, I think you should have an abortion.

Monique Get rid of it, you mean. Like you all want to get rid of me.

Kelly You are so dumb.

Monique Well, I'm not like you. If I bring a baby into the world, I'm gonna love it and care for it. I'm not going to ruin its life like mine's been ruined. I'm gonna love it, and it'll love me back. (*Pause.*)

Kelly You *are* loved. You're just not old enough to realise it yet.

Monique When are you gonna stop treating me like a kid? (*Beat.*)

Kelly I'm your big sister, so probably never. (*She starts to walk off.*)

Monique Kelly?

Beat. Kelly turns round.

Kelly What? (*Pause.*)
Monique Nothing.

Beat. Kelly goes. Monique rocks a little on the swing.

End.

Play Three

1997

The garden of a large detached house in the stockbroker belt. A rope swing hangs from a tree. On the swing sits Becky, rolling a joint on her lap. At her feet, lying on the grass, are an empty wine bottle and glass. She finishes the joint and lights it as Giles staggers on. He is pretty drunk and swigs from a champagne bottle. He stands by Becky and looks at her.

Giles He's gone. (*Beat.*)

Becky Huh?

Giles He's gone. Portillo's gone.

Becky What d'you mean?

Giles The bastards have voted him out.

Becky No.

Giles Yeah. Our last hope. Gone.

Becky Oh, Jesus.

Giles And you should see the godawful little poof they've elected. Twigg. Looks like a girl. Looks like a bloody girl, with his stupid bloody smirk. (*Beat.*) It's a massacre. We're done for. They're going to have a huge majority. (*Beat.*) Probably nationalise everything now. Tax us till we're in the gutter. God help us.

Becky offers him the joint.

Becky Here, make it go away.

Giles Wish I could. (*He takes the joint and smokes.*) Good stuff.

Becky Yeah, Toddy got it for me. It's home-grown, really takes your head off.

Giles God bless you. (*He smokes again.*) Here, d'you want some of this? (*He holds out the champagne bottle.*)

Becky Too right. Thanks.

She picks up her glass and holds it out. He fills it.

Giles Don't mind a bit of spit, do you?

Becky Don't care.

Giles That's my girl. (*He bends down and kisses her, sloppily.*) Fancy going in the bushes? Cheer me up?

Becky Can do. Smoke that first.

Giles Yeah. (*He smokes and hands the joint back to her.*) Fucking bastards,

Becky Who? (*Beat.*)

Giles Labour. People. Everybody. (*Beat.*) Everybody who isn't us. They're all bastards. (*Beat.*) Envy. Spite. That's all it is. Somebody makes a go of it and they have to drag them back down. (*Beat.*) The old man says he's thinking of relocating abroad.

Becky Yeah?

Giles Says most of his money's there now, so we might as well be, too.

Becky Where's he going to go?

Giles Dunno. Maybe the States.

Becky Whereabouts?

Giles Florida, probably. We've already got a place there.

Becky I know.

Giles Fabulous, it is. Out in the country, miles from any crap.

Becky We have an apartment in New York.

Giles What's it like?

Becky Huge. It's on the Upper East Side.

Giles Great location.

Becky The best. (*Beat.*)

Giles God, if it's a toss-up between this dump and the US of A, I know where I'd go.

Becky The States is just so happening.

Giles Yeah, even with that bloody twerp Clinton in charge it's got bags more going for it than here. The

Democrats may be crap, but at least they're not Socialists.

Becky They don't have Socialists in the States, do they?

Giles No, they got rid of them years ago, like we should have. (*Beat.*) I mean . . . Blair. Have you listened to him?

Becky No, I tune him out.

Giles What a creep! Big smile to hide the lies, that's Blair. We all know what he's going to do. He's going to put taxes up, put the bloody unions in power and run the country into the bloody ground like they always do.

Becky Yeah, and hunting.

Giles How the hell do they think they're going to stop us hunting?! I ask you. They'd have more chance of stopping the sun coming up tomorrow.

Becky They're just a bunch of stupid townies.

Giles Right. They've got no feel for the countryside, for tradition, heritage, all the stuff that made this country great. They just want to concrete over everything and put up ghastly estates full of nasty little boxes for their people to live in, and then they'll tell us what we can and cannot do on the land that's been ours for bloody centuries. I should bloody cocoa. We'll give 'em hell. Class war? We haven't even started yet.

Beat. She hands him the joint.

And the worst thing is, this probably means my career's down the toilet.

Becky How come?

Giles Well, what's the point of joining the army with this lot in power? For a start, they'll probably disarm, ditch the bomb, scupper the subs. Then they'll run down the conventional forces so that we wouldn't be able to fight a war even if we wanted to. They're even talking about making peace with the bloody Paddies! And how the hell do they expect our guys to keep in shape if they do that? (*Beat.*) You want to know the three most pointless things in the world?

Becky Go on.

Giles The Pope's balls, a nun's tits and a peacetime army. (*Beat.*) Can you see that little jerk Blair sending our troops to the South Atlantic to kick the Argies off the Falklands? I don't think so. Or if it kicks off again in the Middle East? Don't make me laugh. All over the world they'd be wiping their arses on the Union Jack and this country won't be worth tuppence. There won't be any wars, so we won't need an army. Bastards.

Becky What are you going to do?

Giles Probably banking.

Becky That's not so bad.

Giles No, they reckon the City of London can look like a battlefield on a Friday afternoon. So, it's not so bad. (*Beat.*) I'd prefer real blood, though.

Becky Oh yeah.

Giles Mind you, if we wind up in the States, I could maybe go to Harvard Business School and do an MBA or something. Everybody does them these days. And then it's a cinch to walk into a directorship back home.

Becky Yeah, and create some serious wealth.

Giles Oh yes. (*Beat.*) You see, that's the bugger about not going into the army. In theory, one does one's time, rises to the requisite high rank, takes retirement and bang, one walks into a job in the private sector: British Aerospace, international security, arms procurement. But I don't suppose Comrade Blair will allow that to continue. (*Beat.*) I thought about joining the intelligence services for a while.

Becky Sex-ee.

Giles Yeah. You know Stevie Jasper?

Becky Don't think so.

Giles Friend of Toby's from Eton. He was at Caroline's bash.

Becky I don't think I met him.

Giles Got it together with Annabel . . .

Becky Oh, in the swimming pool . . .

Giles That's right.

Becky Tattoo on his shoulder.

Giles That's him.

Becky That was *so* wild.

Giles *Well* porno.

Becky Yeah.

Giles Well, Stevie's old man was a spook in the seventies when Blair's lot were last in power. Apparently, they were planning a coup at one point.

Becky Really?

Giles Yeah. The unions, which basically translates as the Communists, were holding the country to ransom and bankrupting the economy, while the government sat twiddling their thumbs. So some of the relevant people got together, you know: spooks, businessmen, soldiers, and worked up a plan to kick Labour out, arrest the militants, send in the troops and set up a new, sensible government.

Becky Wow, that's the stuff.

Giles And, by all accounts, certain members of the royal family were said to be very sympathetic to the cause.

Becky So, did they do it? (*Beat.*)

Giles Don't you do modern history?

Becky Darling, I don't do anything. Don't need to.

Giles No, well, they didn't do it.

Becky Why not?

Giles People got cold feet, that sort of thing, so it never happened. And poor old man Jasper, as one of the main conspirators, got the heave-ho. Kept his pension though, thank God. They should have given him a bloody medal, if you ask me. (*Beat.*)

Becky Did my parents say what time we might be going?

Giles My old man's just broken out the twenty-year-old

Scotch malt, and he only does that when some serious drinking's about to occur. I wouldn't be surprised if you ended up spending the night.

Becky Shit.

Giles It needn't be all bad. I could show you my room.

Becky No, I've got to go up to town first thing. I'm scoring some coke.

Giles Oh, right. Where have you got to get to?

Becky Battersea. Jez Burton's place. He's arranged for his dealer to drop some off.

Giles Is it for a special occasion?

Becky Snort some coke, it's always a special occasion.

Giles Yeah. Mind you don't get ripped off.

Becky No chance. Jez is well in with these guys. They do a really good deal. And there's oodles of cash involved, so they'll behave themselves.

Giles Okay. But be careful. I don't imagine your old man would be too chuffed if you got busted.

Becky He's pretty relaxed about that kind of stuff.

Giles Yeah, but he's got an image to keep up.

Becky He dropped acid in the sixties, you know.

Giles Never.

Becky Yeah. He was good mates with some of the bands, through the gallery. So he got to know them socially. The Stones, Hendrix.

Giles Blimey. Your old man?

Becky My old man.

Giles Bit of a dark horse.

Becky Things were different then, apparently. Everybody mingled.

Giles Eurrgh.

Becky You have to go where the money is.

Giles Yeah, I suppose. (*Beat.*) It'll probably be the same now. They'll all be screaming for equality while the country goes to the dogs. Why don't they ever understand? Some people are born to run things,

others are born to make them run. And it always
worked brilliantly. We ran half the world, for Christ's
sake. But they threw it all away, just so that the bloody
masses could have some of it and feel good about
themselves. And, frankly, who ever cared how they
felt? I tell you, the best thing we could have done
would have been to make life as hard for them as we
could, and if they didn't like it and started making
trouble, great, send in the troops. Maggie showed the
way with the bloody miners, but then those damn
spineless nobodies got rid of her, and look where we
ended up. With the Socialists in power. See, the Yanks
have the right idea. As far as they're concerned, anything
that happens in their backyard is their business. Look
at South and Central America. Chile, Argentina,
Nicaragua, El Salvador. The Yanks weren't about to
let them go Communist, so what did they do?

Becky Search me.

Giles They helped the locals, the decent locals, get rid of
the Socialist bastards and made sure they never had
the chance to take power again. That's the way you do
it. With a gun. If some jumped-up little squirt wants
to start a union and shout about workers' rights, cart
him off somewhere, rip out his fingernails, stick a cattle-
prod up his arse and blow his brains out. Problem
solved. (*Beat.*)

Becky You should go into politics.

Giles No. You have to lie in politics. You can't tell people
the truth.

Becky Pity.

Giles I know. And that's what this country could do
with: a good dose of the truth. Fact: if you want the
economy to work, leave it to us. Get government out
of the picture. Fact: the Welfare State is an outmoded
dinosaur that can't pay its way. Give it to the people
who can make it work. Us. Fact: the country's being

overrun by illegal immigrants and bogus asylum-
seekers. Strengthen the borders and set up bloody
tough camps to house them in before we boot them
back to where they came from.

Becky Hear, hear.

Giles Fact: there's no discipline in schools any more.
Bring back discipline and corporal punishment.

Becky Not so sure about that one.

Giles I don't mean for us. We don't need it. I'm talking
about the inner-city sink-schools. The yobs. Give 'em
a smack. *Pour encourager les autres*, as the old man
always says. Fact: breakdown of discipline leads to
crime. We need more powers for the police. We need
tougher sentences, more prisons, life should mean life
and bring back hanging.

Becky With you on that one.

Giles Fact: there's too much regulation of business. Leave
us to make things work the way we always have done.
Fact: taxes are too high. Let people keep the money
they earn and decide how they want to spend it.
Chances are they won't want to throw it away on
single mothers and benefit-scroungers. (*Beat.*) What
do you think?

Becky Like I said, I think you should go into politics.

Giles If I was to come out with that on *Newsnight*, I'd
be strung up. You'd have Paxman and the Islington
trendies baying for blood. The media have it all
stitched up, you see. The grammar-school boys have
taken over the world, and they're almost all, to some
degree, Socialist. Look what happened when
Communism collapsed: all the Commies suddenly
decided that liberal values were alright after all. And
of course, they don't mean liberal the way *we* mean it,
they mean quasi-Socialist social engineering. They still
want to run the show, they just want to do it under a
different coloured flag.

Becky What about drugs?

Giles How d'you mean?

Becky Well . . . basically, they're a great business opportunity. Face it, everybody more or less takes drugs these days. It's a huge market, and it's left to criminals and lowlifes to deliver the product. Well, why not make drugs legal and hand the business over to *real* business people? You'd take the criminality out of it, at any rate, and the right people would receive the profits. (*Beat.*)

Giles I like your thinking.

Becky It seems so obvious, really.

Giles The trouble comes when you make things available to the bloody masses. Sure, *we* can do a few drugs, get up the next day and make a million, but the ordinary types . . . well, give them a hit of something and the next thing you know, they've become dribbling psychopaths, battering old ladies for fifty p towards their next fix.

Becky But if it was legal, it would be cheaper. I mean, fags are legal, and you don't get smokers robbing people for a packet of Marlboro Lights.

Giles True.

Becky You could have, like, really cool boutique-style shops where you bought your drugs. A properly styled environment like a designer clothes shop, with hip young salespeople, music, a café, the works.

Giles Yeah, on the King's Road or somewhere.

Becky Exactly. Really upmarket.

Giles Well, if it ever happens, and you feel like opening a shop somewhere, I'll back you.

Becky Would you?

Giles Like a shot.

Becky That's sweet.

Giles We'd make a great business couple, actually. I mean, I've got the capital, you know about the marketing side of things . . . we could really clean up.

Becky And I'm sure my old man would invest.

Giles You'd have absolutely no shortage of backers, and I could co-ordinate them into a shit-hot team providing a constant stream of investment. We could be massive, shops everywhere, franchises. Before you know it, you're talking global brand.

Becky What we need are some poiliticians who could make it happen.

Giles And some pretty keen advertising bods. I mean, first of all, you'd have to give drugs a complete image makeover. Forget scrawny bloody addicts and dismal housing estates, think happy, normal people with high-achieving lifestyles. Think smart cars, designer clothes –

Becky And the occasional, recreational toot, or spliff, or whatever.

Giles Yeah. A perfectly natural leisure pursuit for today's high-income achievers. Christ, there'd be money in that.

Becky I can't believe they can't see it.

Giles They still pretend they can make drugs go away. That's another one of their lies. Drugs have always been around in one form or another, but they prefer to pretend they're something only losers do.

Becky Which is such total nonsense.

Giles Absolutely.

Becky I mean, Sherlock Holmes took cocaine, for Christ's sake.

Giles Only the greatest detective ever.

Becky Yeah. In the right hands, drugs can help people do amazing things. Like the Stones, like Jimi Hendrix.

Giles Yeah.

Becky Because, let's face it, they make you feel happier. And who doesn't want that?

Giles That's what life's about. (*Beat.*)

Becky Let's make everybody happy. (*Beat.*)

Giles You wouldn't happen to *have* any coke on you, would you?

Becky I've got a tiny bit in my bag indoors. Enough for a couple of lines.

Giles Oh, that would be nice. I could use some cheering up. This looks like being one of the blackest days in our history.

Becky Didn't you want to go in the bushes? (*Beat.*)

Giles I wouldn't mind.

Becky Well then . . .

Beat. He kisses her sloppily again.

Giles A blow-job would be nice.

Becky I do blow-jobs.

Giles Great. (*Beat.*)

Becky We're not going out, or anything . . .

Giles Course not. We're just comforting one another in our hour of need.

Becky Because I'm too young for anything serious.

Giles Me too. We just want to have fun.

Becky Yeah, fun. You can't beat it. I just want to have some fun!

Giles And who knows? Sometime in the future, when we're in business together, raking in the millions, we could sneak into the boardroom and have some fun.

Becky Why not? People do it all the time, apparently.

Giles Yeah, I've heard that. What a life, eh?

Becky It'll do for me.

Giles And me. (*Beat.*) Unless Blair bans sex.

Becky Isn't he Catholic?

Giles No, that's his godawful wife.

Becky Oh, she is so ugly. And the way she dresses, I mean, who does she think she is?

Giles Mutton dressed as lamb, my dear.

Becky Like she's flipped through a couple of magazines and totally missed the point.

Giles Much like her husband. (*Beat.*) And tomorrow, they're going to be running the country.

Becky Don't.

Giles I don't think I've ever been so depressed.

Becky At least we can get out if it all goes tits up.

Giles *When* it all goes tits up. No 'if' about it. That much is a racing certainty. They keep banging on about stability. Well, Mr Blair and Mr Brown, stability isn't the be-all and the end-all. First law of business: the tree's got to shake occasionally to get rid of the dead wood. Let people have it too cosy and they become complacent and everything stagnates. If you don't understand that, you don't understand anything.

Becky Maybe they do understand it.

Giles No. Trust me, they might be saying all the right things now, but you wait. There'll be a reckoning. Their way of doing things will never work, because it's not natural. Plus, they don't understand the first thing about people. They never have. Their core motivation is envy, and you don't get very far on that. (*Beat.*) Still, look on the bright side: they could provoke a backlash. This time they really *could* find themselves being turfed out by the military. And wouldn't that be nice? Then, we could get a few things done. (*Beat.*) Hey, how are you getting up to town tomorrow?

Becky Train.

Giles You're not driving?

Becky Failed the test.

Giles No.

Becky Yeah. Total disaster. I've got a BMW sitting in the garage doing absolutely fuck-all. Total waste.

Giles Listen, I could run you up there. Drop you off, pick you up and maybe do lunch somewhere. (*Beat.*)

Becky I was going to spend some time with Jez, but . . . you're welcome to come along.

Giles Wouldn't he mind?

Becky Can't think why he should. (*Beat.*)

Giles Okay. And, uh, is it all accounted for, the stuff you're getting?

Becky No. Why? Do you want some?

Giles If there's any going spare. Put me down for a couple of hundred quids' worth.

Becky Will do. Thanks.

Giles My pleasure.

She gets up and goes to the bushes.

Becky Coming?

He smiles and walks towards her. Fade.

End.

Play Four

2004

The rubble-strewn front garden of a house in Southern Iraq. Children's toys are scattered around and a child's swing apparatus lies on its side. From inside the house, we hear shouting and a woman screaming in Arabic, then two armed British soldiers, Chris and Glen, drag a fifteen-year-old Iraqi boy out from inside. The Boy's wrists are bound behind his back; he wears a T-shirt, tracksuit trousers, has bare feet and a canvas bag tied loosely over his head. Chris lets Glen take the Boy and goes back to the house and shouts:

Chris Keep that fucking woman inside! And shut her up! Now!

Silence from inside. Chris turns back to Glen, who is finishing a brief conversation on his headset.

Where's the truck? And the interpreter?

Glen It's gonna be a few minutes. They've found a couple more in the next street.

Chris Oh, fucking marvellous.

Glen Relax. We're okay.

Chris Keep your eyes on the road. I don't want no drive-by happening on my watch.

Glen Chris, we've got roadblocks on every entrance to the village. The only drive-by we're likely to get is the colonel coming to give us a medal.

Chris Vigilance, Glen. At all times.

Glen Jeez . . .

Chris looks at the Boy.

Chris Right. So what do we do with this?

Glen We wait for the truck, we load him in it, and we fuck off back to base.

Chris Yeah. Well, let's make him comfortable.

He grabs the Boy's arm and forces him down.

Sit! Come on! Fucking sit! On the floor! Now!

The Boy squats awkwardly.

Glen Hearts and minds, Chris.

Chris Bollocks. He's a terrorist.

Glen He's a kid.

Chris And kids never plant bombs? They never chuck grenades?

Glen Course they do. But we don't know that this one has.

Chris He's been fingered, mate. He's on the list.

Glen On the fucking list . . .

Chris Problem?

Glen We both know these lists are crap. Someone doesn't like the kid, or his family, so they grass him up as a terrorist, and we settle the feud for him.

Chris We've got good intelligence on this address.

Glen Good intelligence . . .

Chris Problem?

Glen How many lists have we had so far? How many blokes have we pulled in? And how much evidence have we found?

Chris Don't be so naive, mate. It's all hidden somewhere.

Glen Yeah, right.

Chris This lot play for keeps, Glen. They ain't pissing about. They'll slit your throat soon as look at you.

Glen Well, if a foreign army walked into *my* town and started arresting *my* family, *I* might just get the hump.

Chris What you talking about, foreign army?

Glen That's what we *are*!

Chris Only to them.

Glen Yeah, 'cos it's their country!

Chris We're setting them free, you dozy pillock!

Glen looks at the Boy.

Glen You call this setting him free?

Chris Not him, obviously. He's one of the bad guys.

Glen Says some greasy informer who could be lying through his teeth.

Chris No, says a properly accredited intelligence source.

Glen And you've got the cheek to call *me* naive.

Chris These guys with the intelligence know the territory. They know the players. We don't, so we take their word for it.

Glen And if they're wrong, this could be a kid who's never done anything wrong in his life, but tomorrow, or whenever we let him out, he's gonna want to plant a bomb or chuck a grenade.

Chris That's a risk we have to take.

Glen It didn't work in Ulster and it ain't gonna work here.

Chris That's defeatist talk, mate.

Glen I'm just being a realist.

Chris I don't think we've got a lot of room in the army for realists.

Glen No, I've noticed.

Pause.

Chris What's the matter with you, Glen? What's all this about? (*Beat.*)

Glen I never joined up to terrify little kids on the say-so of some sleazy, two-faced grass.

Chris I bet you never joined up to drop thousands of tons of explosives on cities and towns where you knew innocent women and children would be blown to bits or burned or buried alive. But, just in case you hadn't noticed, that's what's been happening to this country for the past few weeks. And that, mate, is warfare. And warfare is what you joined up for. This is just another little part of it. It's your job, so do it.

Pause. He squats down beside the Boy, who flinches as Chris speaks.

Oi! D'you speak English?

He prods him.

You! I'm talking to you! D'you speak English? Come on!

The Boy is terrified. Chris stands.

I'll take that as a maybe, then.

Glen Why should he speak English?

Chris You see that thing on the roof? That's a satellite dish. For watching satellite TV on.

Glen Yeah, they watch Arab stations, not BBC1.

Chris Of course they do. And Saddam Hussein's Santa Claus. Fuck me. You really have got to stop thinking the best of people, Glen. It'll get you killed.

Glen Seems to me I'm more likely to get killed by friendly fire than anything this kid can do.

Chris Heat of battle. Not much you can do about that.

Glen Heat of battle . . .

Chris Problem?

Glen You don't have to go about it like a stormtrooper is all I'm saying.

Chris I'm going about it like a professional, mate, like I'm trained to do. I am doing my job. (*Beat.*) Okay. See if you can do any better.

Beat. Glen squats down beside the Boy, gives him a reassuring pat on the shoulder and speaks to him gently.

Glen It's okay. It's okay, mate, we're not going to hurt you.

The Boy is still tense.

Do you speak English? (*Beat.*) Do you? English? Yeah?

Silence.

Chris Well, that approach certainly yielded fantastic results.

Glen My guess is he doesn't speak English.

Chris And I don't want my life depending on your best guess. (*Pause.*) So what are they, this lot?

Glen How d'you mean?

Chris Religion, politics.

Glen They're Shia. (*Beat.*)

Chris Thanks for clearing that up.

Glen Didn't you read the leaflets? Weren't you listening in the briefings?

Chris No and, er, no.

Glen Bloody hell, Chris.

Chris Far as I'm concerned, if they ain't waving flowers and offering me their sister for a good time, they're the enemy.

Glen They're the religious majority in this country, persecuted for decades by the government we've come here to save them from.

Chris So why are they fighting us?

Glen They're not. Not all of them. The ones that are, they're just doing what almost anyone would do: they're saying this is our country and we'll sort it out, thanks very much. See, the Shia Muslims have more in common with Iran. (*Beat.*) Which is over that way. (*He points.*)

Chris I know where fucking Iran is. Don't get clever.

Glen Blimey, don't tell me you've been paying attention.

Chris It's the axis of evil, innit? They're next on the list.

Glen Axis of evil . . .

Chris Problem?

Glen In the nineteen eighties, Iran and Iraq had a war, right? Their version of World War One. Millions dead. Guess whose side we were on. (*Beat.*)

Chris The good guys.

Glen That's right. Iraq. Saddam.

Whenever Saddam's name is mentioned, the Boy tenses.

Of course, now that Saddam's the enemy, you might expect us to be a bit more friendly with Iran. But, apparently not. Now, suddenly, they're all in it together, even though they've been tearing lumps out of each other since anyone can remember.

Chris So?

Glen So, it doesn't make sense.

Chris Not to you.

Glen Not to anyone.

Chris I got one thing to say to you, mate: 9/11. (*Beat.*) There, that's got you.

Glen You reckon?

Chris Yeah. That's when we turned around and read this lot their horoscope.

Glen But 9/11 wasn't anything to do with this lot.

Chris Oh Christ, get a grip, mate. It's all under-the-table stuff. They finance them, they train them, then they send them out to destroy the West. (*Beat.*)

Glen Chris, they destroyed two buildings.

Chris And three thousand people.

Glen Yeah. And if that's enough to destroy the West, then we must be pretty flimsy to start with.

Chris Three thousand people in the centre of New York. We all saw it.

Glen How many d'you reckon the Yanks have killed up north?

Chris Don't care.

Glen Why not?

Chris It's an eye for an eye. Regrettable, but necessary.

Glen But they didn't do it!

Chris Someone has to be held to account.

Glen Well, try getting the right people!

Chris We've made a start, that's what counts. We've shown them we mean business.

Glen Yeah, business . . .

Chris Problem? (*Beat.*)

Glen What if I said that what we're doing here hasn't got anything to do with 9/11?

Chris I'd do what I always do when you talk crap. I'd move away from the smell.

Glen Listen, when we came here, they told us to expect the lot, didn't they? Conventional weapons, chemical weapons, even tactical battlefield nuclear weapons. We were given jabs, protective suits. Well, maybe I've been in a different war, but all I've seen is a rag-tag gang of badly trained conscripts, a few diehard fanatics and shit-scared little kids like this one here. Sure, they can do a lot of damage, we've seen that, but they're not exactly up to destroying civilisation as we know it.

Chris They've hidden all the stuff and gone to ground, it's obvious.

Glen Not to me.

Chris Of course it ain't to you. You're cleverer than the rest of us. You're cleverer than the combined Western intelligence services, the Prime Minister of Britain, the President of the United States and all their advisers put together. But tell me, if that's the case, why is it you ain't in charge? 'Cos with your superior understanding, it seems to me you ought to be running things. (*Beat.*) Except there might just be one problem here, namely, you ain't always as right as you think you are. You only know a little bit of the picture, but the guys in charge have got the big picture. They see the stuff we don't.

Glen It all depends who drew the picture.

Chris What's that supposed to mean?

Glen We don't know the truth. We're told a load of stuff
by the brass, and because we're soldiers and they're
the brass, we believe it. We don't know if it's true.
(*Beat.*)

Chris This is all beginning to sound a bit dodgy, Glen,
mate. It's all beginning to sound a bit like disaffection.
(*Beat.*)

Glen We're the volunteer army of a free society. If we
can't ask questions, then what the fuck are we
defending?

Chris We're a professional army. We do a job. We serve,
we fight and we obey orders. That's all they ask of us,
and that's all we have to do. No one's interested in
your fucking conscience, least of all me.

*The Boy is shaking and quietly crying. Chris breaks off
and goes to him.*

Shut the fuck up!

Beat. The Boy goes quiet but continues to shake.

And sit still!

*He grabs the back of the bag on the Boy's head and
yanks it.*

Sit still! (*Beat.*) Oh, Christ, he's pissed himself. (*Pause. To
the Boy*) We have a saying where we come from, pal:
if you can't do the time, don't do the crime. Which
means, if you're in the business of killing British soldiers,
you'd better expect something in return. And believe
me, it ain't even started yet. So piss away, boy. There's
a long way to go. (*Pause.*) Look at this. I mean, look
at it round here. Fucking one-horse town in the middle
of nowhere. Who'd fight to hang on to this. Eh?

Glen It's their home.

Chris And they're more than fucking welcome to it. I
mean . . . you call this civilised? It's a dust-bowl, a dump.

Glen Believe it or not, this is actually where civilisation
started.

Chris Yeah, and ended by the look of it.

Glen No. This is where it all began.

Chris So what?

Glen Well doesn't that make you feel something? (*Beat.*)

Chris Such as?

Glen I don't know . . .

Chris I'll tell you what I feel: I feel there's too much
looking back. You want to live in the past? Fine. Me,
I'm looking forwards, 'cos that's where the rest of my
life's gonna happen, in the future, and I'd rather be
there than stuck in a godforsaken shithole like this.

He squats down by the Boy.

You don't know what you're missing, mate. I mean,
wouldn't you rather be like us? Eh? Living somewhere
with proper roads and proper houses? With shops and
cinemas and clubs? And women?

Glen They have women in Iraq, Chris.

Chris Have you seen them, though? Bloody hell. Dogs,
every last one of them. I can honestly say I haven't
seen *one* fit bird since I've been here. Most of them are
built like tanks and look like blokes. And have you
noticed how many of the women have got facial hair,
when you get up close? Fucking freak show, man. And
they stink, some of them. They're totally rank. Like
that one indoors.

Glen His mother.

Chris I don't care who she is. She stinks, mate.

Glen They've had no running water or electricity for
weeks. How d'you expect them to smell?

Chris No, that's just how they are. It's nothing to do
with running water. They're like gyppos. They could

be the same as us if they wanted, but they don't. They want to be different, which is fine, so long as they keep to themselves. But don't let them come into *my* world and inflict their shit on me, 'cos if they do that, they'll get what's coming to them. If they come and start blowing up my world, I'll come and fucking destroy theirs. You got that, Abdul?

He grabs the bag on the Boy's head.

We've taken the gloves off. D'you see who you're messing with now?

Pause. He lets go.

You're stupid, really. You could have what we have. Freedom. If you came to England now, you could have the time of your life, a young kid like you. I mean, let's be honest, it can't be much fun for you living in this toilet, with nothing to do, nowhere to go, and most of all, no fucking pussy.

Glen No fucking pussy . . .

Chris Problem? (*Pause.*) When I was your age, I was having a bit of a laugh, getting pissed on street corners, getting my end away. Great times. Now, when I'm home, I can hit the pubs and clubs, have a bit of a ruck if someone starts, pick up some pussy and have the time of my life. I can walk into any newsagent in the country and buy real porn. I can go to football, eat take-outs, do whatever I like. I can just be a teenager. And that, pal, is freedom. (*Beat.*)

Glen Or you could go and watch a live band, go to a museum, read any book you want, walk in the countryside . . .

Chris Yeah, when you're about eighty.

Glen Face it, Chris, when you're back home, it doesn't matter where you are. You could be anywhere, because you're pissed ninety per cent of the time.

Chris That's not fair. I'm pissed a hundred per cent of
the time. (*Beat.*) Get pissed, get laid, get happy. (*to the
Boy*) Don't you want that? Eh? Wouldn't you trade
this sandpit for some of that? No?

Glen He doesn't understand.

Chris I'm not so sure of that. (*Beat.*) Instead, you're
going to be taken to a facility where you'll be banged
up twenty-four-seven with the lowest of the low, and
I don't mean Two Para. You're gonna be interrogated,
deprived of sleep, possibly beaten, possibly tortured
and who knows, possibly killed. And no one'll ever
know or care. Also, you'll probably be raped by the
other prisoners, a good-looking lad like you. Your
arsehole's gonna be like the M25 in the Friday rush
hour. Even if you survive, you'll come out dead. (*Beat.*)
Unless, of course, you were to tell somebody what you
know. (*Beat.*) Like, who runs the show round here.
Where the weapons are. (*Beat.*) That's your only way
out, mate. Otherwise, you're gonna disappear down a
very deep black hole. (*Pause.*) Course, we could
always take a short cut. You could always try to
escape. In which case I'd have to shoot you. Yeah?
Bang bang?

He puts the barrel of his gun to the Boy's head.

In case you're a bit thick, let me make myself clear. Up
we get.

He hauls the Boy to his feet.

Right. You stand over there.

He places the Boy a few feet away.

I ready my weapon.

He does. The Boy is shaking.

I take aim.

Glen Chris!

Chris puts his finger silently to his lips.

Chris And I fire!

The Boy collapses to the floor, shaking. Pause. Chris turns to Glen.

Now. Don't tell me he doesn't understand fucking English! (*Beat.*)

Glen Feel big do you? Feel good you've terrorised a little kid?

Chris I feel powerful. I feel awesome. (*Beat.*)

Glen Yeah. I was afraid of that.

Chris You handle shit like this with a great deal of care, Glen, 'cos if you don't, you're dead.

Glen The minute you stop respecting the fact that other people are human beings too, the game's over. You've lost.

Chris If my enemy don't respect me, if he creeps up in the night and plants a bomb to kill me when I drive by the next day, then he don't get no mercy. (*Beat.*)

Glen No mercy, no freedom. (*Beat.*)

Chris Twenty-four carat, gold-plated bollocks.

Glen Chris, we're no better than these people. We're just different.

Chris I'd say we were superior in just about every way, actually.

Glen You can't believe that.

Chris I can. I do.

Glen Then I reckon you're a bit funny in the head.

Pause.

Chris Oh, for sure. You're not wrong there, mate.

He laughs and goes and looks down the road.

Heads up, the truck's coming. Let's get this scumbag up.

*He grabs the Boy and yanks him to his feet. Glen takes
the Boy by the arm.*

Glen I'll do it.
Chris He's all yours.

*Glen leads the Boy off to the sound of the approaching
truck. Chris follows, looking through his rifle sights,
tracking round the area. Fade.*

End.

Lobbing Stones at a Skyscraper

Doug Lucie interviewed by Jim Mulligan

Pass It On comprises four plays with very little action and only one piece of furniture: a garden swing. These are not plays in which ideas are discussed; rather they are plays where real characters talk about the things that matter to them. The dates of the action are significant.

> 1971 was just after internment was introduced in Northern Ireland and we were moving from a period that combined political activism and environmental activism. Then the hard left and the environmentalists diverged. 1982 was when we had the Falklands War. 1997 was the Labour landslide and the final scene in 2004 is set in Iraq. When I got to the end I realised I'd written a play to a large degree about war without really meaning to – war in the militaristic sense and the class war. It's a play with small lives but with large reverberations.

Play One is set in the garden of a smart detached house. Sarah is sitting on a child's swing agonising over what we are doing to the environment. The swing in Play Two is in a child's playground. Monique is swigging cider. Play Three takes us to the garden of a large detached house in the 'stockbroker belt'. Becky is sitting on a rope-swing hanging from a tree, rolling a joint. Finally we are in the rubble-strewn front garden of a house in Southern Iraq. A child's swing apparatus lies on its side.

> A swing is a symbol of childhood and the ability to be carefree. By the end of the play it's been smashed. This

isn't physical theatre. I'm just trying to take a tiny segment out of the lives of these people and put it under the microscope. I don't see anything wrong with that. I think there is an internal logic to the way I write that makes it easier to act than it looks on paper. If you understand the emotional rhythm and the rhythm of the language you will get to the rhythm of the ideas. I write musically, and in *Pass It On* we have a series of riffs around a theme that come together to make a whole. The swing helps to give continuity and direction.

The logic that runs through the four plays is that war impinges on all of us and class divides our society.

Nev believes that the past is crushing Catholics in Northern Ireland, and until that stops there will not be a future. It has to be fought for. But that is theoretical when compared to the reality of the class divide between Nev and Sarah. His dad is a milkman and hers is a property developer, so that's the end of that relationship.

The father in Play Two came back from a tour of Northern Ireland a zombie. He beats his wife and neglects his daughters. He is now on his way to the Falklands. The bleak truth is that Monique knows she can never have a rich boyfriend or a posh house and is going to be stuck for the rest of her life with fuck-all.

Just in case we should get too involved in national conflicts, Giles reminds us in Act Three that war has been going on almost without stop since 1945 – in South and Central America, Chile, Argentina, Nicaragua, El Salvador: 'If some jumped-up little squirt wants to start a union and shout about workers' rights, cart him off somewhere, rip out his fingernails, stick a cattle-prod up his arse and blow his brains out.' And Play Four gives us visual and verbal evidence of how war brutalises the participants.

I think everybody agrees these days that the environment, after international terrorism, is the most important
question that faces us. In the second play we see the
knock-on effects of war in the family. The fact is that
if we are violent and brutalise the enemy, we brutalise
ourselves. I don't like the word Brits. It was first used
in the Falklands War. It's a word with a shaved head
and a tattoo on its arm. I believe at that period we were
faced with a choice: were we going to be a skinhead
nation or a peaceful one? We chose to be skinheads,
and I despair of our mass culture. It is superficial,
shallow and manufactured. There is a horrible, violent
viciousness in our society that wasn't there before.
It's as if we feel we have a God-given right to be a
martial nation.

It would be difficult for people to take part in this play
or watch it without having to examine their attitudes to
war and class; to see the dreadful logic that goes from
supporting terrorists in Northern Ireland because you
believe their cause is right to blowing innocent women
and children to bits; to see the connection between the
snobbery of Sarah and the complacency of Giles – 'Let
people keep the money they earn and decide how they
want to spend it. Chances are they won't want to spend
it on single mothers and benefit-scroungers.'

The characters in this play have to give the illusion
that they don't know at the start of a scene where it
will end. And the audience certainly doesn't. So, for
fifteen minutes, everyone finds out where they're
going. Most of the questions are left unanswered.
I have very strong ideas and my plays reflect that.
I know many people who share my ideas and many
more who do not, but that's what theatre is about.
That doesn't bother me. When people say my plays

are a bit one-sided I feel as if I'm lobbing stones up at a very big skyscraper and all those powerful, wealthy people are looking down saying, 'How dare you?' Well, I'm lobbing a few stones in this play. My hope is that people will go in thinking one thing and come out thinking another or at least being prepared to re-appraise what they think. It's a slim hope. But I do my best to make the experience of entertaining a challenging one.

Production Notes

For Doug Lucie, 1971 was something of a watershed year, when he became politically active. Having remembered the year, he went back and did some research and was drawn to connecting with other momentous political and social moments in time. This is how he homed in on the years 1971, 1982, 1997 and 2004.

THE TIME SEQUENCE

In the early seventies, the sixties dream had evaporated, there was a fracturing of left-wing politics, internment was introduced and the political situation in Northern Ireland was escalating. Throughout the country there was a sense of the military doing something dodgy. There are similar situations today and parallels to be drawn. We are part of a quasi-martial nation where our rulers regard it as their right and duty to intervene all over the world.

Doug likes to demonstrate characters' morality by putting them through sexually charged situations. In Play Three, between Becky and Giles, sex has become a kind of transaction. Doug believes that love is missing in today's society. He remembers a progressive, positive time – and wonders if this still exists.

In Scene Four the demhumisation has extended to the treatment of one's fellows. The play looks at the differing views of soldiers. Torture and abuse is taking place. The character of Chris is on the road to dehumanising the situation and the people within it.

Go back to the period in which each play is set and research it thoroughly. Do a complete character life history.

With the exception of Play Four, the play can be set wherever you come from.

THE CONTEXT OF 1971

TV cigarette advertising was banned. • The Open University started. • Strikes in Poland against the Communist Government. • Stabilisation of oil prices. • Charles Manson found guilty. • Britain converts to decimal currency. • The Weathermen, a militant underground organisation, blew up a toilet in the White House. • Lengthy postal strike. • The Israeli ambassador to Turkey was killed. • The 'Pentagon Papers' released. • Detention and internment in Northern Ireland. • Bomb in the Post Office Tower. • Four students protesting against Vietnam War are shot at Kent State University. (Recent parallel: during a US army recruitment visit to an American university, a peace party was beaten up by the National Guard.)

THE CONTEXT OF 1982

The terrorist cell Red Brigade active in Italy. • Falklands War. • The banker Roberto Calvi found hanged. • Israel invades Lebanon. • Post-punk is at its height – Human League, Joy Division. • 'Ghost Town' by The Specials. • After three years of Conservative government, over three million people are unemployed. • Riots occur in Toxteth and Brixton. (In the play, the creation of an underclass as seen in the mentality of Monique, who believes she has so little chance of having a good life that there is no point in trying.)

THE CONTEXT OF 1997

New Labour came into power, challenging Conservative beliefs that were based on historical precedence, the class system and the assumption that they have the right to rule. But all those things that Conservative voters feared Labour would do, did not happen.

THE CONTEXT OF 2004

Hutton report published. • CIA admitted there had been no Weapons of Mass Destruction in Iraq. • Suicide bombers hold hostages in Moscow. • Madrid bombing. • Fighting in Basra. • Last episode of *Friends*. • Abu Ghraib revelations.

SCENES AND CHARACTERS

PLAY ONE – 1971

SARAH Seventeen. Sister of Nev's schoolmate, attends a single-sex grammar school. Her father is a property developer who started off as a builder. She lives in a detached house. A romantic character, she studies poetry and foreign languages. She's interested in environmental issues and is very positive.

NEV Working-class boy, parents in service-type jobs. Northern Irish background, which he is now rationalising. This is something he grew up with viscerally. Visiting this house is a big deal. He fancies Sarah.

When reading through the scene, think about:

The need to communicate the sexual tension.

The power struggle within the scene, and who holds it at any given moment.

Whether Nev is buying into his Northern Irish background in order at certain points to come across as a martyr. Is he taking on an identity to make himself a working-class hero?

PLAY TWO – 1982

KELLY is older, sides with her mother, is more ordered.

MONIQUE is the younger sister, feels less loved and cared for; she was a daddy's girl. She goes out with Dean.

They live on a Military of Defence/army housing estate. They are prototypes of the underclass who drop out from the respectability of being working class. Monique is banging her head against the circumscribed walls of her world. She's very sad. This scene is about learned behaviour and where one fits in in the world.

Remember that sisters often develop a very close way of thinking and talking together. At the end you have the sense that Monique wants to retract her statements but can't.

PLAY THREE – 1997

Its three a.m. in the morning as the election results are coming in. GILES is drunk and stoned, running on empty. We see the effect it has when you see your father defeated, and the bottom falls out of his world: 'It's like your dad has been slapped in the face by a girl.'

BECKY is stoned, disassociated, a little princess, materialistic, there to balance Giles out. A capitalist, nothing impacts on her.

The task with this scene is to make these characters real and likeable. It's hard not to make them two-dimensional, to push the awfulness of what they are saying.

The conspiracy they talk about in the scene did happen and can be read about on the labstarjournal webpage.

PLAY FOUR – 2004

CHRIS His behaviour is learned, his options in life are closed down. He is like an animal penned in. The army is all his life holds, and he doesn't want to know anything that might disturb that.

GLEN has a very different approach to life. He expresses doubts about the situation and feels that someone has to speak up.

The situation is on the verge of becoming a very nasty piece of torture.

The protagonists in this scene can come from wherever you like, but obviously it must be set in Iraq. Look at the shared history of the characters, remember that in the army you are relying on the person next to you. Every day is a life-and-death situation.

FINDING YOUR CHARACTER

This is an easy way of getting people to concentrate on the life history of their character. Take the actors on a journey about their life histories. Ask rhetorical questions that they answer in their heads. Often this ends up running like an internal movie.

Concentrate on the character to be uncovered.

Who are you playing? • Where do they come from? • What town? • Who are these people that will be invented? • In what year were you born? • Where were you born? • Can you picture in your mind's eye the first house you ever lived in? Where was it and what does it look like? • Picture the street it was on. • What does your character's mother/father look like?

Up to five years old:

Is it a noisy or quiet house? • Picture any brothers, sisters, aunts and uncles. • Do you have car, pets, TV, radio? • Who is your best friend? • Who reads to you and tells you stories? • Do you have a nanny or a child-minder? • Picture your grandparents. • How organised is the house? Do you have mealtimes at the same time every day? • Is the house religious? • How are you punished, are you ever hit? • Do you know anyone who has died? • Have you been to any weddings or funerals? • Did you have birthday parties? • Did you go on holiday? • Did you learn to read before attending school? • Any pet? • What was your favourite toy? • Picture your bedroom. did you share it with anyone? • Did you have dreams or nightmares? • Were you ever sick or in hospital? • Younger brothers or sisters? • Did you sing, play the piano or have any hobbies? • What did you watch on TV? What were your favourite programmes?

From five to eight years old, add:

Did you move house? • Going to school, which one, what did it look like? Where was it? How far away? Transport? Friends? • What teachers do you remember? • Favourite and least favourite subjects. • Did you play games or sports? • What was your school uniform? • Did you have an imaginary best friend? • Did you keep a diary? • Did you learn to read and write? • Any great presents? • What houses did you visit, any sleepovers? • Were you in a gang? • What was your nickname? • Were you bullied or the bully? • Were you ill at all or in hospital? • Go to any weddings/funerals? • Did you win any prizes? • Did you talk to God? • Did you see a ghost or a flying saucer? • Did you buy a record, read comics? • Was your name in the paper? • Think of something you did exclusively with mother and then your father. • What was your best Christmas present?

From eight to ten years old, add:

Do you collect stamps? • Do you know the facts of life, if so how? • Do you have a boyfriend or girlfriend? • Who do you know of the opposite sex? • Have you experienced racism? • Do you attend Sunday School? • Do you write poetry? • What do you wear? • Who buys your clothes? • Do you have a bike, watch, tape player, tattoo, pierced ears? • Have you smoked, drunk alcohol or taken drugs? • Who are your heroes and heroines? • Favourite sports and pop stars? • What is your ambition?

From ten to twelve years old, add:

Have you reached puberty? • What physical changes are taking place? • Have you fallen in love? • Do you have a boyfriend or girlfriend? • Have you experienced death? • Have you changed school, what did it feel like? • Do you wear make-up? • Do you get pocket money, what do you spend it on? • Do you know who the Prime Minister is? • Have you experienced racism, demonstrations or been on a march? • Do you use a computer, text or email? • Have you had a snog yet? • Have you questioned your sexuality? • Are you scared of the dark? • What do you spend your holidays doing? • What is your hairstyle? • Who buys your clothes? • What was your twelfth birthday present?

From twelve to fourteen years old, add:

Going into adolescence – think about hair, voice breaking, physical changes? • Are you shy in the changing rooms?

• Have you had sex? • Are you in love? • Have you practical experience of the facts of life? • What is your favourite subject at school? • Do you have a job? • What is your favourite food, what restaurants have you been too? • Who is your best friend? • What is your home life like? • What punishments have you received? • Have you experienced jealousy? • Ever been in trouble with the police? • Are you religious?

From fourteen to sixteen years old, add:

What music do you listen too? • What is your image? • What magazines do you read? • Have you been abroad? • Have you left school? • Have you lost your virginity, been pregnant, had an abortion? • What is your home life like? • Do you go hunting or fishing? • Are you on a team, have you won any prizes, been in a newspaper?

At age sixteen, add:

Are you in a gang? • What is your nickname? • Who is your best mate? • What does your bedroom contain? • Do you own a car or a bike? • Do you go to pubs or go clubbing? • Do you smoke/drink/take drugs? • Do you have any piercings? • Do you wear nail varnish? • Do you go to the dentist? • Do you have any allergies? • Do you have asthma? • What pets do you have ? • What did you do at Christmas?

At age seventeen, add:

Where do you live? • What does your home look like? • What is your relationship with parents/brothers/ sisters? • What music do you listen to? • What do you own? • Are you in love? • What is school/work/job like? • What book are you reading? • What is the image you present to the world? • What are your hopes and fears? • Age now – at the time of the play? • Pick the time of year? • Pick a particular day? • What are you wearing and how do you look? • Have the character look in the mirror – what do you like/dislike about your body?

APPROACHES TO THE PLAYS

Swings are present in every play. You could have a different swing for each one or simply change the seat to give it a different appearance.

PLAY ONE Cast the brother and the boyfriend: who would play them in the movie? • What day of the week is it? • What time and date? • Nev has specifically come to see Sarah. • What has gone on with the boys at the party? • Sarah is 'bigging up' the experience she has had with older boys. • Is Nev a virgin? (Has possibly had a brief unsuccessful dalliance?) • Is Sarah a virgin? • Hard to know how to do the beginning of the play until you get to the end. • This is a mating game and the roles are predetermined. • Sarah is possibly too shy to reject Nev outright.

PLAY TWO It's probable that Monique has run off before. • Their dad has been severely affected by combat. • The sisters are almost acting out the argument the parents never had. • Where do our sympathies lie? • Monique is unable to express her emotions without it consuming her. • The swearing is integral to the piece, it is part of who they are and how they communicate. • Inform the audience in your publicity that the play contains bad language.

PLAY THREE They have had sex before. • Ask what is really going on underneath this scene? • The actors must take it incredibly seriously. • Politics of envy. • Becky – it is very difficult to play bored. • What is Giles's objective? • Something is missing in their level of attraction, they aren't quite human, all is a transaction. • Because she can do anything, she can't do anything.

Here's one way of demystifying the kissing scene. Have the actors sit opposite each other, hands on floor. Focus character into hands, tell the scene with the touching of the hands.

PLAY FOUR At the opening of the scene the soldiers are completely exposed. • There's a sense of '*we* are not foreign, *they* are'. • What does warfare mean? Chris answers the question. • Play with no emotion, let the audience feel it.

We recommend that all the actors in this scene experience it blindfolded

Workshop facilitated by Mike Bradwell
with notes taken by Lisa Spirling

SCHOOL JOURNEY
TO THE CENTRE OF THE EARTH

Daisy Campbell with Ken Campbell

Daisy Campbell was raised in the proverbial theatrical trunk. Her father would direct plays with baby Daisy strapped to his back and her mother would take her on tour. When Daisy was eighteen she directed *The Warp* by Neil Oram, a twenty-four-hour-long play. She translated and co-directed *Makbed* at the Piccadilly Theatre, a Pidgin English version of *Macbeth*. She also has an MA in producing film and TV. *School Journey to the Centre of the Earth*, written as a play when she was sixteen, was based on a story she wrote in primary school, and updated in 2005.

Characters

Stacey

Bee

Miracle

Chrissy

Rab

James

Anna

Tricia

Matthew

Sonny

Jenelle

Sam

Ben

Tom

Louise

Hal

Miss Sheehan

Outside the coach. Chaos: singing, skipping, fighting, dancing, screaming, etc.

Stacey That ain't fair, Bee. You promised me three weeks ago that I could sit next to you on the coach.

Bee Yeah, but I promised Chrissy four weeks ago.

Stacey (*storming off*) That ain't fair. I'm telling Miss.

Chrissy Whatever. (*to Miracle*) See *EastEnders* yesterday?

Miracle (*defensive*) Yeah.

Chrissy I can't believe we're gonna miss it today – What do you reckon Alfie's gonna say to Kat?

Miracle Um, well what is it again? She's doing sex with the –

Chrissy No no no no. She's not doing sex –

Bee (*butting in*) Ohmigod, what about Sonia's little girl? She's gonna get run over.

Anna Ohmigod!

Miracle Hey, maybe there's tellies at Alton Towers.

Rab (*butting in*) Or we could arrange for the driver to run over a baby on the way, then it'll be like bringing *EastEnders* right to yer doorstep!

James Rah, that's bare good, Rab (*doing elaborate impression of a baby getting run over*) Waah waah – splat crunch . . . (*etc.*)

Anna That's not even funny. Babies have feelings, you know. It's not like in *EastEnders* where it's made up. They don't really kill the baby in *EastEnders*, you know. It's made up.

Rab (*doing a der-brain impression*) No! Is it really?

Tricia Oh Sonny! I thought you weren't gonna make it!

Sonny My mum had another party last night. I only got her into bed at, like, past midnight.

Jenelle (*to Tricia*) I'm having the window seat.

Tricia Bloody not.

Jenelle (*doing hip head-wagging à la Jerry Springer*) Girlfriend, put it like this: I don't get the window seat, you don't get to sit next to me. Oh hi, Sonny.

Sonny (*to Tricia*) Is Jenelle sitting with us?

Tricia Yep.

Sonny Can I tell you a huge secret? No, forget it.

Tricia Sonny, you're my best friend. I tell you all *my* secrets.

Sonny Do best-friend shake on it.

They do an elaborate handshake

Sonny You promise you'll never tell?

Tricia Cross my heart and hope to die, stick a needle in my eye.

Sonny whispers in Tricia's ear, her eyes widen at the juiciness of the secret.
   A large crowd of boys bursts suddenly through them, screaming;

The Boys Back of the bus! Back of the bus!

On hearing this, all the kids make a wild dash for the back of the bus.
   They form a bus – popping up for name in register.

Miss Sheehan (*everyone is talking throughout*) Right settle down. Rab? Stop. James! Enough. Okay. Tricia – stop talking please. Rab. That's enough. SHUT UP! Thank you. Right. Sonny?

Sonny Yes, Miss Sheehan.

Miss Sheehan Anna?

Anna Yes, Miss Sheehan.

Miss Sheehan James?

Pause.

Tricia (*doing a der-brain impression*) James!
James What? Oh, yes, Miss.
Miss Sheehan What did you miss?
James What? Oh, yes, Miss *Sheehan*.
Miss Sheehan Miracle?
Miracle Yes, Miss Sheehan
Miss Sheehan Jenelle?
Jenelle Arsenal beat Tottenham two–nil.
Miss Sheehan And what a game it was. Rab?
Rab Here, Miss Sheehan.
Miss Sheehan Sam?
Sam (*loudly*) Yes, Miss Sheehan!
Miss Sheehan Tricia?
Tricia (*even louder*) Yes, Miss Sheehan.

It is now apparent that this is a game. The one who can answer in the loudest voice wins.

Miss Sheehan Chrissy?
Chrissy (*louder*) Here, Miss.
Miss Sheehan Stacey?
Stacey (*louder*) Yes, Miss!
Miss Sheehan Bee?
Bee (*almost screaming*) Yes, Miss!
Miss Sheehan Ben?
Ben (*normal volume*) I am present, Miss Sheehan.
Everyone (*doing elaborate der-brain impressions*) Mr Bean! Mr Bean!

A small boy gets on the coach and looks for a space. Despite the abundance of the free seats, they all appear to be saved.

Rab (*on seeing Tom enter the coach*) Tramp! Incoming, lads.

James You're late, Tom. You Michael Jackson-wannabee.

The register is still going on in the background.

Matthew (*as Tom attempts to sit down*) Sorry, saved.
Chrissy Sorry, saved.
Stacey Sorry, saved.

Many are still waving goodbye to their parents through the window but, beginning to tire of this activity, are chatting to friends at the same time.

Rab Sorry. This is a Clarke's-shoe-free zone.
Miss Sheehan Rab, let Tom sit there, please.
Tom Thank you, Miss. (*He sits.*)
Rab Miss, I'm charging you with the doctor's bill when we all catch lurgy.
James (*to Rab*) Jexies!

Rab and James touch their heads, then cross their arms to touch their shoulders, then touch their waists.

Everyone Lurgies ejected for life!
Miss Sheehan Okay, has everyone got their sick bags?
Everyone (*while holding up see-through plastic bags*) Yes, Miss.
Bee Can't we get the paper sort, Miss? These sort are disgustin'. If anyone's sick you can see right through them.
Stacey The paper ones are worse though. If you're sick in those, they go all soggy at the bottom and burst.
Bee Thanks for that, Stace.
Anna Oh, Miss. I've left my pack-lunch box in the classroom. Can I go and get it?
James No, you can starve.
Miss Sheehan Quickly.
Anna Thanks, Miss. (*She leaves.*)

The electronic sounds of a Gameboy becomes audible.

The are traced to Chrissy. Everyone in the surrounding seats leans in, intent on seeing how badly she's doing.

Sam (*der-brain impression*) No! You've got to go down under that path and switch the lever, then you can get over the bridge. No! Only Puss-in-Boots can climb that wall!

Stacey (*sarcastically*) You don't say.

Sam Jump! Jump! Ah. You missed it.

Stacey It ain't fair. I'm feelin' car sick.

Tom We haven't even set off yet.

Every time Tom speaks he is mocked.

Ben By my calculation we should have left fifteen minutes ago –

Rab Quiet everyone. He speaks. Mr Bean has something he wishes to share. What was it? Mr Bean?

Throughout the following speech Rab is impersonating Ben behind his back.

Ben According to my watch, the accuracy of which is governed by satellite, we should have begun our journey fifteen minutes, twelve seconds and – thirty-two milliseconds ago –

Everyone Shut up, Mr Bean!

The coach revs up, and from the movement of the children and the frantic waving out of the back window, it is obvious that their journey has begun.

*

On three seats of the coach sit Tricia, Sonny and Jenelle. Tricia is still waving frantically out of the back window.

Tricia Bye, Mum. Mummy – (*Cries.*) I'm homesick.

Jenelle Shaaaame! Tricia's crying!

Tricia I'm not cryin' I'm not. Anyway, don't vex me. You're not in the gang. Me and Sonny are a gang and we're well nang. We're the Nang Gang.

Sonny and Tricia do their elaborate handshake.

Jenelle (*kissing her teeth*) You fink I wanna be in your neeky gang?

Tricia Yeah, well, we've got gang secrets. We tell each other everything. Everything. You wouldn't believe some of the stuff Sonny's told me.

Tricia suddenly appears far more pally with Jenelle than with Sonny. Sonny looks left out. He grabs Tricia's arm.

Jenelle Like what?

Sonny You say anything, I'll never speak to you ever again.

Jenelle What sort of secrets 'as he told you?

Tricia I'm sworn to secrecy.

Jenelle Yeah, obviously. What are they?

Sonny I'll break your neck!

Tricia Well. Don't say that I told you, but Sonny well fancies you.

Sonny (*suddenly sitting back in his seat*) That's not – you said – you weren't gonna – anyway, it's not true anyway.

Tricia You love her.

Sonny I don't. In fact, I hate her, see? (*Pulls a disgusting face at Jenelle.*)

Tricia (*singing*)
Sonny and Jenelle up a tree,
K–I–S–S–I–N–G!

Sonny Look! You're the most smelly – (*mouthing*) bitch I ever saw. (*proudly, to Tricia*) See?

Tricia Hold hands! Hold hands!

Sonny I hate her! Look! (*Hits Jenelle.*)

Jenelle Ow!

Tricia You two are gonna get married.

Jenelle I don't fink so.

Sonny I'm never talkin' to you ever again.

Tricia Oh, Sonny. You're my best friend.

James (*popping up*) Oi, do you wanna hear the sickest thing ever?

Tricia James! This is an AB conversation. C your way out of it.

James (*making letter symbols with his fingers, M–W–M*) Your Mum Works in McDonald's.

Tricia You think you're so nang.

James Yep.

Tricia Well, you're not. (*shouting*) Hands up who thinks James is nang.

Rab shoots his hand up. After a glare from James, so does Sonny. Jenelle has her hand sort of halfway. James doesn't even look to see who's on his side.

Tricia See? Three.

James No one else heard you. And anyway, I'm not gonna even ask anyone what they think of you, 'cos you'd be so upset that you'd throw yourself off the coach. And you're so fat that you'd go right through the world and come out at Australia.

Tricia No.

James You would.

Tricia Wouldn't.

James Would.

Ben Actually, she wouldn't.

Tricia Thanks, Mr Bean.

Ben Yes, even weighing 950 thousand, billion, zillion tonnes –

Tricia (*hits Ben*) Thanks a lot.

Ben No no. Just supposing. Well, even then, due to gravity, the furthest Tricia could possibly fall would be to the centre of the Earth.

Tricia Yeah. Well, it's great down there. I've been.

James That's a lie.

Bee Yeah, what's it like, then?

Tricia Well, you go down this tunnel in Staffordshire –

Anna That's where we're going, isn't it?

Tricia Yeah, see, I'm not actually supposed to tell you this, but we're not actually going to Alton Towers at all.

Anna What?

Tricia We are actually going to the centre of the Earth.

Bee (*sarcastically*) Yeah, right.

Bee, James, Anna and Ben try to shout Tricia down.

Tricia No, it's true. Ask my granny. Ask my turtle. We're on a mission, but we don't know it.

Everyone Eh?

Tricia At least, you lot don't know it.

Everyone Eh?

Tricia What I'm gonna tell is very dangerous information.

Everyone Eh?

Tricia In fact, it's probably best that I don't tell.

Anna No, tell.

Tricia No, Anna. It's too dangerous for you to know.

Everyone (*disappointed*) Oo-oh

*

Tricia So, you two. When's the wedding?

Jenelle Shut up. Anyway, Simon might get jealous.

Tricia Who's Simon?

Sonny The pieman.

Sarcastic laughs from Tricia and Jenelle, referring to Sonny's unsuccessful joke.

Jenelle You bricked it, batty boy.

Tricia That's so sad. So who is Simon?

Jenelle He's my boyfriend. He's thirteen.

Tricia *and* **Sonny** *Thirteen?!*

Sonny Older boys are stupid.

Jenelle Older boys are the best.

Tricia That's like your dad, though!

Sonny They only want you for one thing.

Jenelle What do they want me for?

Sonny Well. They only want you for one thing. Like, that thing could be anything, but, thing is, they only want you for that and not for nothing else. My uncle's older than my aunt and she said that's true. I reckon it's her cooking.

Tricia She good?

Sonny Yeah, she made this bare yummy ice-cream cake for my eighth birthday. But she is fat. Like really really fat. She's one of those people you can't imagine on the loo.

Tricia Yeah, 'cos like if she sat on the loo, all her flab would bulge over the edges and touch the floor either side.

Jenelle Gross! You two are so immature.

Sonny Just 'cos you've got an older boyfriend.

Tricia I am eight and three quarters and I am almost nine.

Jenelle I'm nine this week.

Tricia Well, I'm nine last week. I'm eleven. I'm fifteen. I'm seventeen. I work in Sue Ryder. I'm married.

Jenelle Shut –

Tricia I am married.

Jenelle To who?

Sonny Michael Jackson.

Jenelle Urghh.

Tricia No. Robbie.

Jenelle What, so you're Mrs Williams?

Tricia Yeah.

Jenelle But you're not. Oh deeeee-aaaar. You got slewed!

Tricia I am.

Jenelle No. You're Tricia Park. Which means you lied. Liar, liar, pants on fire.

Tricia No, but you see, 'cos you're not s'posed to get married until you're grown-up, I have to have a fake name; 'cos I've got married before I should, and if the police found out they'd hang me.

Sonny Don't be stupid. They don't have the death penalty any more.

Tricia Yeah, they do. But only for treason and getting married to pop stars when you're too young.

Sonny What's treason?

Tricia It's cussing down the Royal Family.

Jenelle Sonny, do you really think I'm buff?

Sonny Yeah!

Tricia (*very loudly*) Woah! Everyone! Sonny's telling Jenelle that he loves her.

Everyone (*getting higher and higher pitched*) Oooooooooooooooooooo!

Sonny No I never.

Jenelle You said I was buff.

Sonny Exactly.

Tricia Sonny, do you actually know what buff means?

Sonny Yeah.

Sonny becomes aware that everyone is listening in.

Tricia What, then?

Sonny (*suddenly unsure*) It's like a mixture between – (*mouthing*) bitch and guff.

Everyone does elaborate der-brain impressions. Sonny is mortified.

James' Voice Who let off a smelly one? Come on, own the stinker. Who ate egg this morning?

Chrissy Anyway, you fancy the driver.

Stacey looks at the driver, then sticks her fingers down her throat.

Stacey (*referring to the driver*) That's disgusting. He is butters. And he stinks of piss.

Chrissy Perfect match, then. You told me the other day that you wet the bed and that your mum got well angry with you.

Rab (*popping up*) Rah. She got yer. Boyage! You got slewed! (*right in her face*)

James *and* **Rab** How do you feel?

James What happened?

Rab She wets the bed.

James O tramp! You live in a cardboard box.

Stacey I didn't. That's not – it wasn't me.

James It wasn't you? What, someone's been crawlin' into your bed at night, pissin' and then crawlin' out again?

Stacey I spilled a glass of water, alright?

Sarcastic, sympathetic nods and chin scratching.

Chrissy An' I feel sorry for your sister who has to sleep in the same bed.

James *and* **Rab** Lesbos.

Stacey That is a lie. My sister – I haven't got a sister.

Chrissy Yes, you do.

Stacey Alright. But she doesn't sleep in the same bed. We've got bunk-beds, and I get the top one's 'cos I'm good.

Rab So it must drip through.

Chrissy Urrrgh.

Stacey I don't wet the bed. I don't wet the bed. I'm not listening. (*hands over ears*) Din din din. I'm not listening.

Rab I wouldn't sleep with you.

Pause.

I mean, in a bed.

Stacey I'm going to the toilet.

She sticks two fingers up at Sonny. He does the same to her.

Rab Yeah, we wouldn't want you doin' it on your seat.

James P'raps you should sleep on the bog. That would solve all your problems.

*

Ben The turbulence is interfering with my digestive tract. By the time we get there I'll be too sick to go on any of the big rides.

Sam Have you been on the big one at Alton Towers?

Miracle The Corkscrew! I've been on that one! It's wicked, innit?

Sam Yeah, I've been on that, like, ten times. I love that bit, you know, when you're slowly goin' up and then –

Tom Oh yeah, an' then you, like, wait at the top for, like, ages –

Sam It's only a couple of seconds –

Tom Yeah, but it feels like –

Sam Yeah, it feels like ages, and then suddenly it dips –

Everyone screams.

Sonny Yeah, an' your tummy gets left behind.

Sam Yeah, your tummy. An' then before you know it you're goin' –

Both have begun to live the ride and, as their audience watches, they too begin to swerve and lurch with Rab and Louise.

Miracle On the upside-down bit –

Tom An' you're 'Waaaah!' and 'Ooooo!'

Jenelle An' then you turn the corner an' –

Miracle You think you're gonna come off the rails and 'Weeeee!' and 'Aaaaaargh!'

All screaming and shouting together.

Jenelle Woooh!
Matthew Aaaaah!
Sonny Excelleeeent!
Sam Help!

Etc.

Ben And then it's the end of the ride.
Everyone Shut up, Mr Bean
Miracle We haven't got to the best bit yet.
Matthew So you start to climb up again –

Everyone is leaning back as they climb the second loop. Then they hang at the top and bomb down.

Sonny An' now we're right upside-down –
Jenelle An' we stop for a couple of seconds –
Sam Yeah, you stop right upside-down –

The children all appear to be hanging upside-down. Suddenly there is a complete silence – a long pause while they hang.

Miracle And then –

Everyone lurches forward and hurtles down the second loop, a look of terror on their faces. All screaming and shouting together.

Sonny Help!
Tom I want to get off!
Sam Wicked!
Sonny Can I open my eyes yet?
Janelle I'm gonna die! I'm gonna die!
Matthew I hate it! I hate it!
Miracle An' we're goin' round the corner –

They lurch to the side as they go round a sharp bend.

Miracle An' we're comin' to the end –

They are all thrown forward as the ride stops. They pant heavily.

What do you think?
Tom (*breathless*) That's excellent.

*

Stacey (*returning*) Out.
James Talk about take yer time on the bog. That bog's for everyone, you know. Not just for people with pissing problems.
Stacey Get out of my seat.
James Urrrgh. Yours, is it? I thought it was a bit damp.
Stacey If you ain't careful I'll piss on you.
James Wow. You've been on the bog all that time and you've still got enough wee left to piss on me? You're amazing, Stace, I gotta say. You're world-class pisser of the year.

*

Anna Please tell me what's going on, Tricia.
Tricia (*super-fast*) Oh, well, Sonny said Jenelle was buff, and I told them about how I'm married to Robbie, then someone guffed, then Stacey said she fancies the driver who smells of piss and then she wet her seat –
Anna No, the secret mission. The centre of the Earth.
Tricia Oh, that. (*Pause.*) Well, I suppose if I tell you what's going on you might be more prepared. We're being kidnapped for – a super-top-secret, mega-scary mission. They're going to watch us to see if we can live down there.
Anna They?
Tricia (*whispering*) Terrorists.

Anna Terrorists?

Tricia Very dangerous men.

Bee And women!

Tricia Bee! I wasn't gonna mention the women.

Anna Worse than the men?

Tricia Much. I wish Bee had kept her mouth shut. I didn't want to frighten you.

Anna Well, what are these women like? How can they be so terrible?

Tricia You know Pat Butcher off *EastEnders*? They all look like her. They're not really humans. They're sort of robots. They're programmed to kill. They've all got really long, sharp red nails like Pat's. If you was to clean out their nails, you'd find dried up flesh and blood under 'em, from where they'd scraped off little children's faces.

Horrified, Anna tentatively touches her face.

Tricia The men give the orders. The women are just sort of like killing machines. The Butcher-bots.

Anna *and* **Bee** No!

Tricia It's an experiment. An evil plot.

Bee They wouldn't pick us. They'd want people who were properly trained.

Tricia No, that's the whole point. They've got to put down people who don't know anything about the experiment. People who aren't gonna grass them up – schoolchildren. It's obvious. People they can 'nipulate.

Anna You mean we're goin' down there for the rest of our lives?

Tricia Yeah. Why'd you think I got homesick at the beginning? D'you think I'd get homesick if I was just going to Alton Towers for the weekend? No, of course I wouldn't. But for the rest of my life –

Anna But I didn't even say goodbye to my mum. I just told her not to forget to record *EastEnders*.

Tricia Ah, well. It's too late now. And you're gonna miss *EastEnders* for the rest of your life.

Bee Doesn't matter anyway. It's ending soon.

Anna Isn't there any way of stopping it?

Bee No, they're gonna blow up Albert Square and that'll be the end –

Anna No, I mean going to the centre of the Earth.

Tricia 'Fraid not.

Anna Well, shouldn't we tell Miss Sheehan?

Tricia She's in on it. So's the coach-driver. There's no hope, I'm afraid.

Anna Miss!

Tricia You could ask her. But she's gonna deny it, 'cos they're not gonna tell us until there's no way out. They can't take the risk.

Anna MISS!

Tricia Miss Sheehan's a terrorist. (*Pause.*) She's trying to find out about the centre of the Earth for Bin Laden so they can burrow underneath and set up camp there, and then spring up from the sewers when we're least expecting it and kill us all and take over the world.

Anna But Miss Sheehan always seemed so nice.

Tricia I know. I'm sorry you had to learn this way.

Bee (*to Tricia*) But wait a minute. Miss Sheehan supports Arsenal.

Tricia All part of the cunning disguise.

Anna How do you know all this?

Tricia Well, it makes sense, doesn't it?

Rab You've been watchin' way too many movies, Trish.

James Yeah, those 'U's that you've been watching 'ave gone straight to your head.

Rab Yeah, like *Tweenies and the Tellytubbies' Big Day Out!*

Rab and James do impression of Tweenies and Tellytubbies.

Tom (*urgently*) I heard Mr Harris and Miss Sheehan talking –

Rab Urggh, Tom, don't come near me with those shoes!

James That's deep.

Rab No, listen, they went out when the dinosaurs came in!

James That's sad.

Rab Yeah, I know – but I just said it to keep in with Tom.

James Oh, you're a joker, bruv. Oh dear, Tom.

Rab *and* **James** How do you feel?

Rab Arrrgh. You gonna beat me up, Tom? No, Tom, please don't beat me up. I'll have to go and find Mumsy.

James Where does your mum shop, Tom? Oxfam?

Rab No, Ultra Oxfam! Tom, did you know?

James Did you know? Did you know?

Rab That cats lay eggs. That's true, actually please.

Tom No, they don't.

Rab Yes they do, 'cos my dad told me actually.

James An' his dad's a scientist.

Rab Did you know that?

Tom Yeah.

Hysterical laughing.

(*desperate*) They don't lay eggs. I meant about his dad. They don't lay eggs. I meant I knew his dad's a scientist.

Rab Vexed. You got slewed.

James 'At was wicked. 'At was wicked.

Tom (*desperately*) They don't lay eggs. I know they don't.

Rab Aw, what a nice Winnie the Pooh lunch box, Tom. Was it part of the Oxfam summer sale? Ultra Mega Oxfam summer sale? Ultra Mega Oxfamopolis.

Tom Please listen! Please listen!

Bee Rab! Let him speak.

Rab Shup, Bee, his mum's a Tellytubby.

Bee Let him speak.

Rab (*mimicking*) Let him speak.

Tom I heard him and Miss Sheehan talking.

Bee What were they saying?

Tom That the school journey might not go quite as planned, and that knowing us we'd all end up lost.

Tricia How did they look?

Tom I don't know. Kind of shifty.

Tricia Mmm. They were talking in code.

Bee Mr Harris is one of them?

Tricia All the teachers are. Those meetings they have. They're all to plan how they're gonna capture us. It was Mr Harris's idea. He's a nasty piece of work is Harris. His wife's one of those Pat-robots.

Bee *and* **Anna** Not a Butcher-bot?

Miracle I've met her. She's nothing like that.

Tricia Obviously not to meet people. By day she's a nice, kind old lady. By night it's all a bit more sinister.

Miracle I met her at eight-thirty in the evening.

Tricia You were lucky then. The change happens at nine. Half an hour more and you'd have no face.

Miracle (*amazed*) Now I think about it she did suddenly run off at about ten to nine. Some meeting or something.

Bee Really?

Miracle Yes.

Bee That is spooky.

Miracle But I still don't understand how come you know all about these terrorists.

Tricia Ah, well, my dear Miracle. That's a bit more cleverer. For a start, Sheehankov is a known terrorist name, but to fool us all she's cunningly missed off the 'kov' bit. And also purple is the terrorist's special colour code, and, as we all know, purple is Miss Sheehan or should I say Miss Sheehankov's favourite colour.

456

They look at Miss Sheehan, astounded.

Tom (*tentatively*) What does the purple code mean?

Tricia It means 'kill the children'. Depending on what colour they're wearing, the chiefs can tell what kind of terrorist department they work for.

Sam You can tell they're terrorists by the colour of their skin. Miss Sheehan isn't dark.

Miracle That's rubbish, Sam. Terrorists can have any colour skin. My mum says so. She says that the worst kind are the ones that pretend to be good people who have smiley families and nice suits and all that and are secretly selling people bombs.

Sam Yeah, well, my mum said that if dark people weren't allowed to come into the country it would never have happened.

Miracle Yeah, but everyone knows your mum's a racialist.

Sam No, she's not. She just says we got enough of them now.

Miracle That is so wrong, Sam. If I tell Miss Sheehan that you're a racialist you'll be in big trouble. Miss!

Sam No, don't! Miss Sheehan's a terrorist.

Tom But I thought terrorists live in cyberspace.

Tricia Yeah, and where do you think cyberspace is?

Everyone Where?

Tricia points down. All look down.

Tricia The terrorists are just a front –

Everyone For what?

Pause.

Tricia That ain't the point. Point is we're on a school journey to the centre of the Earth.

Rab (*popping up*) Cack. Cack. The liar needs a slap.

Sam (*spotting a Mini out the window*) Mini Cooper! No returns.

He punches Stacey.

Stacey (*punching him back*) Mini Cooper!
Sam Oi, you can't do that. I said 'no returns'.
Stacey No you never.
Anna Yeah he did, Stacey.
Sonny Umm. You get a free slap for that, Sam.
Stacey No! That ain't fair.
Rab It's the law, Stace. We can't make exceptions, can we, Sonny?
Sonny No. Put out your hand, Stace.
Stacey No! Please don't!
Everyone (*getting higher and higher pitched*) Ooooooo!

Sam slaps Stacey's hand, hard. She bursts into tears.

James Shut up, Stacey. You better be tougher than that when the terrorists come for us.
Hal (*popping up*) What's this?
Bee Trish reckons we're goin' to the centre of the Earth, wiv purple spies or something.
Sonny Oh yeah, I wonder what the Arabesques are a front for?
Ben (*popping up*) You're getting it all muddled. The Arab culture is ancient and fascinating –
Rab, Jenelle, Anna *and* **James** Shut up, Mr Bean!
Ben They invented the alphabet –
Everyone Shut up, Mr Bean!
Jenelle Nah, he's right. It's not the Arabesques. It's the Funny Mentalists.
Stacey It's the North Koreans what are really behind it all.
Tricia Ah, Stacey. I would never have guessed.
Stacey Guessed what?
Tricia That it was you. I was told someone would be sent to give me vital information. Thank you.
Stacey (*confused, but pleased with the attention*) Oh, that's alright, I mean think nothing of it – comrade.

Jenelle Right, so let's look at the facts.

Tom There are no facts. Only guesses.

Tricia You shut up. How old are you?

Tom (*smugly*) Ten in three weeks. How old are you?

Tricia Yeah, well that don't matter. A few months don't make no difference to anyone. Anyway, clever-arse – where do you think all the terrorists are hiding and making the MWD?

Tom It is too hot for anything to live down there. Science says so.

Tricia I don't know what scientists you've been chattin' with, batty boy, but the one I've spoken to lives down there. So, so much for all your 'science says so' crap.

She sticks her tongue out at Tom.

Rab Murked boy. That was jokes, Trish. Pity you were talkin' outta your little brown star.

Everyone laughs at Tricia. Rab and James slap hands.

Tricia Fine. When you get down there you'll be sorry. You'll wish you listened to your dear old mate Trish when you're trapped by evil terrorists, poking you with needles and pulling your hair out and –

Rab Who's seen *War of the Worlds*?

Miracle Yeah. It's bare good!

James I thought it was crap.

Miracle Yeah, I s'pose it wasn't that good.

Rab What's your favourite bit?

Miracle Oh, urm – I saw it ages ago, so – urm, I can't really remember.

James It's only just come out.

Miracle (*desperate*) Oh. Maybe I'm getting it muddled up with another film.

Rab Which other film?

Miracle I don't know what it's called. I saw it ages ago.

James So you haven't actually seen *War of the Worlds*?

Miracle Urm – no. I don't think I have. I got muddled.

Rab Do you like the bit when the aliens come?

Miracle I told you. I haven't seen it.

Rab No, but that bit's on the trailer. You must've seen it on TV.

Miracle Oh, yeah. Course. (*quickly changing the subject*) So Trish, tell us more about the terrorists.

Stacey How do you get down to the centre of the Earth? I mean, how would you, supposin' we was goin', which I don't believe anyway.

Tricia Ah, well. That's the cunning bit.

James Whoever nicked my Twix had best give it back unless they wanna die a slow and painful death.

Jenelle Vex up! Stress monkey! Watch it, everyone. James might turn nasty.

Tricia You know the rollercoaster at Alton Towers?

Miracle Yeah. The Corkscrew.

Rab Yeah, it's wicked, man.

Jenelle Yeah, that bit when it dips down is blindin'.

Everyone does rollercoaster noises.

Chrissy Yeah, and then you start goin' up slowly –

Rab And then you get to the top bit –

They are all set to take another ride on their imaginary rollercoaster.

Tricia No, not that one. You know the one in the dark? The underground one?

Chrissy Oh, the Blackhole?

They get ready to go down the Blackhole.

Tricia Yeah, whatever. Miss Sheehankov will give –

Matthew Sheehan*kov*?

Jenelle It's Miss Sheehan's secret Funny Mentalist name.

Matthew Oh, right.

Tricia Yeah, well she'll give the signal when the train's filled up with us lot, and the man what works the Blackhole will switch the tracks so instead of goin' back to the beginning, the ground opens up and we go plummeting down into the centre of the Earth.

They all go down the Blackhole.

James Rah, that's sick man.

Miracle Yeah, like the longest rollercoaster ever – straight down –

James Mad.

Tom Wow. Those terrorists are clever.

Jenelle Yeah.

Anna But our parents will notice we've gone.

Tricia For a while, yeah. But you know all these kids that vanish like when they're skiing and stuff?

Miracle Yeah?

Tricia That's where they've gone. We'll probably see them down there.

Matthew They died, didn't they?

Tricia That's what everyone was told. But it's all part of the Spirisy.

 Anna The Spirisy?

Tricia That's what it is. The Spirisy.

Anna What's the Spirisy?

Tricia You know, like Diana.

Chrissy Who's Diana?

Tricia You know, the princess who was killed by the Queen. That was the beginning of the Spirisy. The Queen wanted Diana to marry her son but Diana wanted to marry Saddam Bin Laden so the Queen poisoned Diana's driver –

Matthew Oh, is that why he knocked down the Twin Towers?

Tricia Yes, because Diana had twins in her tummy when she was killed by the Queen, so Saddam knocked down the Twin Towers to get revenge, then Prime

461

Minister Bush smashed up the Arabists, because he's in love with the Queen, who's actually a lizard. That's the Spirisy.

Sonny Oh, is this to do with the Nasties?

Tricia Be careful, Sonny. You're closer to the truth than you know.

James The Nasties?

Sonny You know, the ones who burned loads of people in chimneys and gave out gold stars.

James Oh yeah, they're cool.

Ben You know there is a theory that the Nazis –

Everyone Shut up, Mr Bean!

Sonny No, I want to hear this.

Ben There is a theory that the Nazis were simply one incarnation of a much more ancient and secretive cult, that has emerged throughout the ages to perform genocides.

Rab What *is* he talkin' about?

Ben Apparently a large amount of energy is released during mass murder and if you know the technique you can absorb it and become instantly immortal. That's what the Nazis were trying to do –

Sonny What, so the Nasties never actually went away? We never actually beat them at war?

Tricia No, they just went underground.

James What, so the Nasties are running the Spirisy from under the ground?

Tricia What have I been trying to tell you?

Bee But how did these skiing dead kids get down?

Tricia Similar way to the rollercoaster. Only the chair-lift things suddenly change course and go down.

Miracle So what they gonna say happened to us?

Tricia Oh, we'll probably be one of those 'School Bus off Cliff' tragedies.

Rab You talk the biggest pile of cack ever.

Shouts of agreement.

Tricia No, but no, shut up, right, no, shut up, listen, right. I know it sounds stupid, but I mean, it sounded stupid to me when I first heard it from the Head of the British Intelligence –

Tom You said you put two and two together.

Tricia Ah, well, my dear Tom. I'm afraid it's a bit more complicated than that. I am in fact a spy. Working under cover. Posing as just an ordinary schoolgirl, when actually I am Britain's last hope at exposing the Spirisy. I shouldn't be telling you this. I could be putting you all in mortal danger.

Pause.

James No. (*Pause.*) Carry on.

Tricia No. I mustn't. If the Nasties found out that you knew they'd probably murder you. Pull your heads off with this special new machine that – like – pulls your heads off. It, like, sort of twists it a bit –

James I'm gonna be a torture-and-killing-machine designer when I'm older. I'm gonna design things like what you've never heard of. That like has little stabbing little pins and sucks the jelly bit in your eyes out so they shrivel up and fall out, and like cuts this hole in your tummy and pulls out your guts and plucks your hairs out one by one, and, for like, old men, it would do your nostril hairs as well –

Tom Yeah, but –

James No. Quiet. I'm talking. It pulls your fingers out and sticks sharp points up your nostrils that makes it bleed everywhere and it pierces your brain, and it's red hot – no, white hot, so it frazzles your brain but you don't die yet because your brain's not completely burned yet, and you can still feel pain. And sharp knives dig under your fingernails –

Rab Is that before or after they've been pulled out?
James Shut up!

Eyes widen – a terrifying glare.

Before. And then, when your brain's burned out completely, and your eyes have fallen out, and your fingers have been pulled out, then this claw will come out and it will chicken-scratch your heart until you're dead.

Rubs his hands and grins. Shocked faces.

Rab (*sarcastically*) Nice job.
James Or I might be a doctor.

Pause.

Ben You could be both. (*Pause.*) Being a doctor would give you access to people to test your equipment on.
James (*seeing it, dreamily*) A sick doctor –!
Tricia Has this got anything to do with what I was sayin'?
James You was talkin' about the Nasties' killing machine.
Tricia Yeah, but that doesn't mean that you can just go raving on like something out of *Amityville*. So shut it.
James Yeah, well someone nicked my Twix. I was annoyed, innit?
Tricia You're such a weirdo.
Ben Don't, Tricia. His sadistic tendencies may be useful to us when we get to the centre of the earth.
Tricia Yeah, whatever.

*

Chrissy You ever been to a funeral?
Bee Yeah.
Chrissy I've been to two funerals.
Bee Yeah, I go to funerals every single Monday.
Chrissy Yeah, what happens, then?

Bee They bury people, don't they?

Chrissy Yeah, but –

Bee An' I go to bonfires as well. That's when they put someone in the bonfire and watch them die slowly – and then laugh. And then they get all the ashes and make the relatives eat it.

Sam Doesn't it taste 'orrible though?

Bee It tastes of them. Like, if I were to take a bite out of you now, I'd taste you and remember that taste, right, and then if someone burnt loads of people and put all their ashes in bowls, I could taste each one and see which one was you.

Sam Really?

Bee Yeah.

Sam Shall we try it?

Bee Ain't touchin' you.

Sam I don't mean me.

Pause.

Bee, Sam *and* **Chrissy** Sonneeeee?

Sonny Yeah?

Bee Would you mind if we – urm – if we took a bite out of your leg and then burnt you with loads of other people and then tried you with a small spoon?

Sonny (*after a moment's thought*) Go on then.

Bee You go first.

Sam It was your idea.

Bee No, I've done it so often.

Sam Well, I don't want to lose my appetite. And anyway, they don't burn people.

Bee They do. It's called cremations. Sometimes they give you the ashes to take home in pots, other times people leave it there, and it gets given to cannibal countries. They prefer it to Nescafé.

Tom Cup-a-Soup for cannibals! (*Pause.*) My dad's friend who's a farmer –

Sam Your dad's friend's not a farmer.

Tom He is.

Sam Your dad hasn't got any friends.

Tom He has.

Sam You haven't got a dad.

Tom I have! Like I was sayin', right, my dad's friend
   who's a farmer –

Sam Get on with it.

Tom He got caught under a tractor.

James (*without sympathy*) Did he die? Did he?

Tom No. He was alright.

James Yeah? Which bit of him got mashed?

Tom His legs. He ain't got no legs no more.

Bee What happened to his legs?

Tom They got caught under the tractor, didn't they?

Bee Yeah, but where are they now?

Tom They probably buried them.

Sam Yeah, you go to funerals. Ain't you ever seen legs
   buried?

Bee No, they only bury whole bodies where I go.

James I've just had an idea.

Sam What?

James Wouldn't it be cheaper to bury all your bits, like,
   separate, than buryin' them altogether? And also you'd
   get to have loads of funerals, like, one for your leg and
   one for your head. And you could go to your own
   funeral. Not your head's funeral obviously – or your
   heart's. But you could probably bury a leg or two
   before you died of blood loss. And –

Sam It wouldn't be cheaper because you'd have to buy
   loads of different-sized coffins. And they'd all have to
   be made specially, 'cos they don't normally make them
   different sizes to just ordinary people.

James Yeah. Some rich people get coffins for their cats
   and dogs. I'd need two dog ones, one for each leg, and

two cat ones for my arms. And a small sheep one for my middle bit.

Matthew Buryin' bits separate would be a good idea to find out who really cared about you. It'd be a good idea for my mum 'cos she's always pretendin' to suicide herself to see if we care –

Sam And do you?

Matthew We *pretend* we do. (*with pride*) If you've got a mad mum like me, you have to have a man from the council round every week to check on you.

Sam (*impressed*) Wow.

Chrissy Oh yeah, I get that too, since my dad went to prison.

Sam What's your dad in prison for?

Chrissy Oh, lots of stuff. (*Pause.*) Mainly cos he killed this man.

James Rah! That's so cool.

Sam How did he do it? How did he do it?

Chrissy (*nonchalant*) Strangled him with his bare hands.

Tom Cor. I wish my dad was cool.

*

Anna What's it like down there, Tricia?

Tricia Down there? On the floor of the coach? I dunno. It's sort of –

Anna No the centre of the Earth. Will there be any lights? I can't go to sleep without a light on.

Tricia Well, yeah. Of course the Nasties are gonna make sure that there's some light otherwise they won't be able to see us through the video cameras to watch how we live.

Anna So there will be some light?

Tricia Yeah. There will be light. But wouldn't you rather live a life of darkness than know that you're being watched day after day, night after night?

Anna Er – well, no. You see I can't go to sleep without a light.
Tricia Oh yeah. You said.

*

Stacey (*to James*) I don't think Miracle's got a TV.
Chrissy *and* **Bee** What?
Stacey All that rubbish about *War of the Worlds*. I reckon she hasn't got one.
Chrissy Yeah, and she reckoned the reason Alfie was vexed was because Kat was doing sex with someone!
Stacey *and* **Bee** (*amazed*) No!
Bee (*leaning in to the conversation*) When I went to her house she said it was at the mender's.
Stacey How long ago was this?
Bee About three months ago.
James She ain't got a TV? Oy, Rab. Get this. Miracle ain't got a telly!
Rab Rah! Miracle! Are you a tramp or what? (*in front of the whole coach*) Ain't you got a telly?

Everyone laughs.

Miracle What?
James You ain't got a telly!
Miracle Of course I do.
James Oo yeah.
Miracle I do.
Rab Alright then. How does the Muller advert go then?
Miracle Isn't that the one when – there's the mum at the breakfast –
Everyone NO! Five – six – seven – eight.
Everyone Got my hair, got my head, got my brains, got my ears, got my eyes, got my nose, got my mouth, got my smile. Got my tongue, got my chin, got my bum,

got my boobs, got my heart, got my soul, got my liver, got my sex. I got my freedom, freedom. I got life.

Rab Lead a Muller Life!

Everyone T-E-L-L-Y, T-E-L-L-Y, T-E-L-L-Y. You ain't got a telly!

The chant gets faster and faster and more and more in Miracle's face. All repeat until Miracle breaks down

Miracle (*through terrible sobs*) You don't know what it's like. My mum won't let me have one. She says it rots your brain. She makes me do stuff in the garden and draw and read and play the saxophone instead. She's so horrible. She's like a witch. I hate her so much.

Tricia Miracle, don't worry. It's not that bad. (*Pause, then declares loudly.*) I haven't got one either.

Miracle Really?

James (*to Tricia*) Urggh, you filthy tramp. Get back in your cardboard box.

Everyone starts teasing Tricia.

Jenelle Oh my God! Shut up! Can anyone else hear that ticking?

The paranoia builds up as they search for the source of the ticking, finally traced to – Rab.

Rab Booom!

Screams.

Jenelle That is not even funny, Rab. Now that we know Miss Sheehankov is a terrorist you shouldn't make jokes like that –

Sam Jenelle, don't worry. They need us to be alive – so they can watch us, right, Trish?

Tom Brainwash us, more like.

Rab (*popping up*) Shut up, Tom. Loser!

Tricia No, Rab. He's right. I didn't want to say this. But the experiment isn't to watch us. The experiment is to brainwash us. To turn us into Nasties.

Janelle Why?

Tricia So that we will end up like Miss Sheehankov. Pretending to be a nice teacher what supports Arsenal so that we can capture more kids to brainwash. It's a vikkious cycle.

Miracle What are we gonna do, Trish?

Tricia We'll make a break for it when we're down there and hide out in this cave I know about that the terrorists don't know and keep guard –

Janelle Will we have someone on guard all night for the Nasties?

Tricia Er – yeah.

Janelle Do I have to do it, Tricia? I don't think girls should have to do it.

Tricia No, sorry. Everyone has to do it.

James (*popping up*) I'll do it. It'll be like *Tomb Raider*.

Mimes shooting up Nasties with deadly precision.

Mega-death.

Mimes gore-and-blood splatterfest.

Jenelle Can I be partners with you, James? I think I'll feel safest with you.

James (*suddenly shy and coy*) Yeah, alright. If you like.

Sonny Jenelle? Don't you want to be partners with me?

Pause.

*

Anna Tricia, I've been doing some serious thinking. We've got to try and take control of this situation. We can't let them put us on that rollercoaster. I can't live in the centre of the Earth. I have some tictacs – I mean tactics.

Tricia You? You're scared of the dark!

Anna Well, it's time for me to grow up.

Rab (*whose face has been wedged between the two seats throughout the entire conversation*) Waaaah! I can't believe that you think all this cack is actually true!

Anna It could be true. It could be true. We don't know. Nobody knows.

Everyone is now listening.

We know that terrorists want to kill us and that they live in caves. We know that Harris and Sheehankov were talking in code. We know that purple is the terrorist code to 'kill the children' –

Jenelle – and that the Funny Mentalists are doing bombings –

Sonny – and that the Nasties were never actually killed and are running the whole Spirisy –

Stacey – and that behind them is the North Koreans –

James – and that they have to brainwash us to turn us into terrorists.

Anna Yeah. And Tricia heard it from the Head of the British Intelligence. If you can't trust the Head of the British Intelligence, then who can you trust?

Miracle Exactly.

Tom But who's behind the North Koreans?

Miracle Lets ask Tricia.

Stacey Tricia, who's behind the North Koreans?

Tricia The most terrifying creature you can imagine. Like a jellyfish octopus brain thing with tentacles and massive sharp long teeth. The size of – London. It lives right at the very centre of the Earth and it's tentacles reach all the way through the caves and networks that the Nasties have built and instead of suckers there are cameras all over his tentacles which are watching everyone all the time to see how the brainwashing is going.

Rab (*suspiciously*) What's its name?
Tricia It's name is – Doctor Al Kiyeeder!

Gasps.

Rab So that's who Al Kiyeeder is! Oh my days – it is true.
Ben I think it is true.
James He speaks –
Miracle Shut up, James. Let him have his say.
Rab Shup. You ain't got a telly.
Miracle What d'you think's true, Mr Bean?
Ben I think it is very possible that the terrorists could actually be living in the centre of the Earth. Tricia's accounts have in fact been most accurate.
Rab Tricia's *whats* have been what?
Tricia How would you know? I mean, they have been, but how the hell do you know that?
Ben (*pause*) I've been there.
Tricia Shut up.
Anna How did you get down?
Ben In a chair-lift. Like Tricia said.
Tricia You can't 'ave done.
Anna Is there any light?
Tricia I've already told you that there is.
Anna Well, yes, but, I mean, Ben's actually been there, so he's more likely to know for sure, isn't he?
Ben Don't worry, Anna. There is some light. Things produce their own natural light. Like glow-worms.
Anna Oh, good.
Tricia He doesn't know what he's talkin' about.
Chrissy He's been there. You've only heard about it from the British Intelligence.
Tricia I have been there.
Ben Oh? What is it like then?
Tricia Well, the area I went to, known as – urm – Lower Beemsbry, was made up of these huge caves. Dark, 'cept for when the light from the glow-worms shone

on the bits of jewels in the walls. Lower Beemsbry is like the capital – 'cos it's the most beautiful area. There were dark passages everywhere, like corridors, leading off into different rooms. The floor's soft and sandy – it's actually jewel dust – so it sparkles. When I came back I still had some jewel dust on my shoes –

Rab Let's see.

Tricia It's rubbed off now, stupid. Anyway, there are glow-worms, like Ben said. And glow-maggots. And the Nasties have glow-eels. I slept in one of the small caves – I had a huge, flat rock as a bedside table. I was only there for two days.

Everyone looks at Ben for a confirmation.

Anna Ben?

Ben It's nothing like that. And there's no glow-eels.

Rab Mmm. Nice imagination, Trish.

Tom It's too hot down there.

Ben Not if you wear this stuff called Starlite that a hairdresser in Manchester invented. A suit of Starlite, you could sit on the sun and be okay – on the surface only, obviously. No one believed this hairdresser. The Starlite was mouldable like plastic and yet virtually completely heat proof. Impossible, scientists said. But they tested it, and the laser they tested it with – which burns through slabs of iron in a millisecond – broke due to the reflection of heat. It was on television, but it was on BBC2 so none of you will have watched it. Hairdresser. In Manchester.

Pause.

Anna (*who appears to have been thinking hard*) Miss! Miss! Is Alton Towers near Manchester?

Miss Sheehan's Voice Yes, not far!

The children look at each other for a tense moment.

Jenelle Wow.

Tricia Mr Bean's lying.

Anna Ben is not lying.

When Ben pauses, he looks at his audience through his extra-strong lens glasses and sucks meditatively on his pencil.

Tricia He is. I'm the spy. I know what's going on. Ben's just makin' it up. He's never been there.

Ben Unlike you, I'm not one to boast about my part in such a serious affair as this.

Tricia Just 'cos you can say lots of stupid words that don't mean anything to anyone, you think you're really cool.

Anna What do we sleep on?

Ben Erm – oh, well, when I was there we slept on – erm – rocks –

Miracle How uncomfortable. Was it really bad?

Tricia Don't be ridiculous. They're trying to brainwash us into being like them. And I bet you *they* won't be sleeping on rocks.

Ben That's what I was about to say. I went before the terrorists had set up this experiment. (*Pause.*) I was the first ever person there.

Tricia The brainwashing laboratory was set up in 1936. November. That's before you were born.

Ben Ah, yes. But the west side of the centre of the Earth. Not the bit that everyone goes to. (*Pause.*) If you know so much about all this, tell me the name of the North Korean terrorist spy who is in charge.

Tricia Radkot Flipscoddle.

Miracle That doesn't sound North Korean.

Tricia Obviously. It's a code name. (*Pause.*) Alright then, what's his real name?

Ben hesitates for a moment.

474

Tricia You don't know.

Ben No, I'm just wondering whether it's wise to tell you. (*Pause.*) How do I know you are really who you say you are?

Tricia Oh this is stupid. I know you're lying. You know you're lying. So why bother?

Anna You just wanna have all the attention, Tricia. You just wanna be the one who knows it all. And you can't stand it when someone knows more than you, can you?

Tricia (*shouting*) It's got nothing to do with that! I know he's lying.

Stacey So he's lying and you're not? Is that it? Everything you say goes. Everything he says is cack? Is that it?

Tricia No, that's not it.

Chrissy Well, that's certainly what it seems like, Tricia.

Tricia Piss off, Chrissy. This has got nothin' to do with you.

Anna This has got everything to do with Chrissy and everyone else in class 4S. It's all of us that have gotta face this.

Matthew Maybe it's the time for the revolution!

Stacey What's that?

Matthew It's something they do the whole time in history. My mum's always on about it.

Rab Yeah, but your mum's a loonytune.

Matthew Only 'cos the revolution hasn't come yet.

Stacey Well, how do you do one?

Matthew You just, like, stop doing what anyone tells you. And throw stones and stuff. And like, demand your rights –

Chrissy What's our rights?

James Not to be kidnapped by evil terrorists what are pretending to be nice teachers for a start –

Sam Rah man, I totally believed that she supported Arsenal, you know –

Tricia (*shouting*) Will you all just shut up and listen to me? I know that Ben is lying because – because I made it up.

Rab What about Sheehankov supporting Arsenal?

Tricia No. About going to the centre of the Earth.

Long silence.

Anna Tricia, we all know you're tryin' to protect us from findin' out too much for our own safety – and it's very good of you – but now I think it's time that we all faced facts. Don't you?

Long pause.

Tricia Yes. It's time. You're right. And it was for your protection. I should of known I couldn't fool you lot.

*

Anna So, Mr Bean. Are you a spy?

Ben Well, as a matter of fact – (*Pause.*) – yes, I am.

As everyone crowds around Ben, Tricia sulks in the background.

Stacey Surely you shouldn't say that in case one of us is a terrorist spy.

Ben Yes. (*Pause.*) And I have my suspicions. (*He nods towards the unaware Tricia.*)

Stacey (*whispering*) Tricia?

Anna *and* **Stacey** No.

Ben (*leaning in to his eager listeners*) The name she gave of the terrorist leader?

Anna *and* **Stacey** Yes?

Ben She said it was the code name?

Anna *and* **Stacey** Yes?

Ben The British don't know that code name. It's something we've been trying to discover for years.

Stacey Then how come she knows it?

Ben I wonder.

Anna If it is true, then she'll try and warn Sheehankov. Try and tell her that we know.

Stacey How long till we're there?

Ben (*looks at his watch*) Taking account of the late departure – twelve minutes, seventeen seconds and – twenty-six milliseconds.

Anna Twelve minutes. We have no time to lose.

*

Rab and James can be heard screeching with laughter from behind the seats.

James Look! Look!

He produces one of the see-through sick-bags which appears to be full of vomit.

Rab (*leaning over and pretending to be violently sick into the bag*) I've been sick!

He passes the bag around for closer inspection.

Bee I'm gonna make one too.

She rummages around in her packed lunch, looking for things with which to concoct another bag of sick.

Jenelle I'm actually gonna be sick. Miss! I'm gonna be sick!

Bee and Rab waft the fake-sick in Jenelle's face, while making sick noises.

Miss Sheehan The next one of you to do that will have to eat it.

Everyone Urghh

Tricia Yeah. But it's all mashed up.

Jenelle I'm not jokin'. I'm gonna be sick. Get me a sick bag – quick!

Miracle They're all filled with mashed up pack lunch!

Jenelle Just get me anything! Quick!

Anna (*handing Janelle one of the see-through sick-bags*) Here's one.

Jenelle attempts to open the bag, but it's one of those plastic ones that stick together and you can't tell which end is which.

Anna (*desperate*) I can't get it open!

Eventually Jenelle manages to open it, and is sick – much to everyone's enjoyment.

Rab Look! Look! She 'ad egg for breakfast. She was the one who guffed!

James Oy, leave her alone.

Everyone Oooooooooo!

Rab Excuse me, Miss. But Jenelle's just done exactly what you told us not to. She's put all her packed lunch, all mashed up – into a sick bag!

Chrissy Miss said the next one would have to eat it.

Rab (*triumphantly*) I know.

Bee That is pure jokes!

Sonny *and* **James** Leave her alone!

They glare at each other.

Miracle (*warning*) Sheehankov's coming!

Miss Sheehan Jenelle, did you do what I told you not to?

Jenelle No, it's really sick, Miss.

Chrissy Rab was tryin' to get Jenelle into trouble.

Miss Sheehan Well then, Rab can eat it.

Rab No, Miss!

Everyone has burst out laughing and is pushing the bag of sick towards Rab.

No! Please, Miss. That's not funny. It's not even my sick!
I don't like egg! Please, Miss. I was jokin'. Please, Miss
don't make me, Miss! (*He is almost in tears.*) I'm sorry.

Miss Sheehan Alright, that's enough.

Everyone reluctantly withdraws from Rab.

Rab Thanks, Miss Sheehankov – urm Sheehan. Sorry,
I meant Sheehan.

*Everyone is glaring at Rab when he turns back to face
them.*

I slipped.

Tom You slipped? You slipped? You idiot! You fool.
Now Miss Sheehankov knows that we know. There's
no chance of escape now!

Miracle Look! Look! She's talking to the coach driver.
She's telling him that we know.

Tom There's no hope. You idiot!

Anna We should make plans.

Rab I'm really sorry.

Tom Okay. Apology accepted. Now, come on. Let's
decide what we're gonna do.

Jenelle suddenly bursts into tears.

Jenelle I'm scared.

Sonny (*putting his arm around her*) Don't worry, Jenelle.
It's all gonna be fine.

Anna Jenelle. Keep it down. If Sheehankov hears you
she'll be over here like a shot.

Miracle (*hissing*) She's coming!

Everyone sits back in their seats suddenly.

James (*smiling sweetly*) Hello, Miss.

Miss Sheehan looks suspiciously at James.

Miss Sheehan Are you alright, Jenelle? Do you want to
come and sit at the front for a bit?

Bee shakes her head, scared stiff.

Sonny I'm looking after her, Miss. She's safe with me.

Miss Sheehan So, Anna, what are you going to go on when we finally get there?

Anna stares up at her, terrified.

Miss Sheehan What about the waterslide?

Anna Yes. The waterslide is fun.

Miss Sheehan And the Blackhole? I guess everyone will be going on that.

Anna (*quietly, catching eyes with Ben*) Yeah – I don't think I will be going on the Blackhole – Miss.

Miss Sheehan Oh, I'm sure you will, Anna. I'm going to make it my personal duty to get you all on that rollercoaster. Seeing you all screaming your little heads off will make the whole trip worthwhile.

Anna Oh, right. See you later, Miss.

All look at each other as Miss Sheehan returns to her seat.

Miracle She knows.

Rab (*to Anna*) What's the plan?

Anna We are going to have to get control of the coach.

Ben Five minutes, fifty-two seconds, twelve milliseconds.

Anna Is everyone in agreement?

Solemn nods.

Tricia Don't be stupid. We can't do that. We're only kids. Can anyone drive? I mean, it's stupid. It's impossible. We are just gonna stay calm and see how it goes.

Ben looks at Anna as if to say 'See?'

Anna Tricia, I'm beginning to wonder whose side you're on. First you tell us you're a British spy with nerves of iron –

Tricia I didn't say nothin' about any iron –

Anna And now it seems that you're a terrorist, helping the Nasties to capture us.

Chrissy (*suddenly lashing out at Tricia, hysterical*) You filthy terrorist spy! You traitor! I can't believe I invited you to my birthday party! There's gonna be no traitors at my birthday party!

Chrissy breaks down in sobs.

Tricia Chrissy! I'm not a terrorist spy. I'm not any sort of spy!

Ben As I suspected.

Tricia (*almost screaming*) Shut up! You're the evil one! You deserve to die!

Anna grabs hold of Tricia by the shoulders.

Anna Shut up! You're hysterical! Sheehankov will be here any moment. Now, everyone just stay calm. Jenelle do you need another sick bag?

Jenelle nods.

Sonny *and* **James** I'll get one!

Sonny and James tussle over the sick bag. Sonny wins eventually.

Miss Sheehan's Voice What's going on back there?

Everyone Nothin', Miss.

Sonny A sick bag, Janelle!

Janelle Thank you, Sonny.

She is violently sick.

Anna Now, we need to decide who's in charge of what.

James Rab an' me'll be in charge of the battle tactics.

Rab Now, has everyone got weapons?

Tom Oh yeah. I'll just get my Kalashnikov out of my backpack. You fool. Course we haven't got weapons.

Miracle What do we need 'em for anyway?

Sam This thing has gotta be done using surprise tactics and weapons.

Jenelle Well, none of us got any knives or nothin', so what d'you suggest?

Matthew Packed-lunch boxes? I mean, anything that will hurt if it hits you.

Miracle Satsumas. My mum packed five. Vitamin C.

Miracle passes the satsumas around.

Anna Right, Tom, I'm making you head of communications.

Rab But he's a der-brain.

Anna Rab – it's time to pull together now. We can't afford to be fighting with each other.

Rab has to agree and he and Tom hug manfully.

Anna Right, 4S. Are you with me?

Everyone Sir, yes, sir!

Anna I didn't hear you.

Everyone Sir, yes, sir!

Anna So, James, Rab. How do you suggest we take over the coach?

James Rab an' me'll crawl to the front of the coach an' get ready behind the driver.

Tom Chrissy should go too – her dad's a killer.

Rab Affirmative. Then you lot, after countin' to ten –

Sam Silently.

James Yeah, obviously. Anyway –

Tom If we all suddenly go silent they'll know something's going on.

Miracle Go on, James.

Anna No, Tom is head of communications, and he's right. It needs to be better planned.

Miracle How long have we got?

Ben Two minutes, twenty-one seconds, forty milliseconds.

Anna Tom, what do you think?

Tom I think it would be better, if we sing a song and then arrange a certain point –

James Yeah, whatever. Anyway, when you get to this certain point, we'll all charge to the front and attack Sheehankov –

Tricia NO!

Anna Is there a problem with this plan?

Tricia Yes. What if Miss Sheehankov – I mean Miss Sheehan – isn't a terrorist after all?

Miracle If she's not a terrorist, then why's she taking us the centre of the Earth?

Tricia Maybe she's not.

Tom Forty-two seconds. What are we gonna sing?

Miracle (*to Tricia*) Why d'you think that?

Tricia I made it all up.

Miracle looks at the crowd of excited children and then back to Tricia.

Miracle Why?

Jenelle What about Crazy Frog?

Tricia (*to Miracle*) I s'pose to make you all like me.

Tom Three times through.

Pause.

Miracle Do you really not have a telly?

Tricia No, I do. I just said that so they'd stop picking on you.

Miracle That's the nicest thing anyone's ever done for me.

Tom (*looking at watch, loudly whispering*) Twelve, eleven, ten . . .

The others excitedly join in.

Everyone Nine, eight, seven . . .

Miracle (*suddenly standing*) Stop! Tricia needs to tell us something very important!

A pause. The children look questioningly at Miracle.

Tricia You mustn't do this – there's no terrorists. Miss Sheehan does support Arsenal. I don't know anyone from the Head of British Intelligence –
Anna Yeah, exactly. 'Cos Ben's the spy. Not you.

Pause.

Ben Tricia's right. We're not spies. You can't live in the centre of the Earth, even with a suit of Starlite –
Tricia The Queen is probably not even a lizard –

Pause.

James It's a common problem. I've seen it many times in battle. They're cracking up under the pressure. Don't worry about it. Keep counting!
Everyone Five, four, three, two, one.

They burst into the Crazy Frog Anthem.

Miracle (*panicking*) My mum says that when you're feeling overexcited you should sit down and breathe calmly!
Matthew I thought you said you hate your mum.
Miracle I know – and now I realise that I love her more than anything in the world.

Tricia grabs Sonny's arm as Sonny begins to sing.

Tricia Sonny! You've got to stop them. You know I make stuff up all the time! Tell them! You're my best friend!
Sonny You're not my friend, Tricia. I'll never forgive you for telling Jenelle that I love her.

Everyone continues singing as Rab and James crawl to the front of the bus. They hide behind the driver, each armed with a packed-lunch box and an orange.

As the children get towards the end of the third time through, they begin to sing in loud, excited voices.

Tricia, Ben *and* **Miracle** MISS SHEEHAN!
Anna Stop them!

The children tackle and tie up and gag Tricia, Ben and Miracle.
Tricia and Ben catch eyes and stare at each other. Suddenly the other children charge towards the audience, shrieking. Sonny glances back at Tricia. He pauses for a moment, then continues running.
They attack Miss Sheehan and the driver.

James (*while attacking the driver*) Take that, you North Korean Funny Mentalist Jellyfish Lizard Nastie! Think you could fool us, did you?

Suddenly it seems that the children are back on their imaginary rollercoaster, swerving and lurching. All face the audience, their faces full of fear and excitement.

Rab Waaaaah!
Jenelle Woooooh!
James Wickeeeddd!
Anna Arrrghghhghghgh!

The End.

Unleashing a Dreadful Anarchy

Daisy Campbell interviewed by Jim Mulligan

It is ten years since Daisy Campbell, wrote her stage version of *School Journey to the Centre of the Earth*. At the time Ken Campbell said, as he encouraged his daughter to write, 'I just thought, if Daisy is on her uppers it might be quite handy to know she can write a play.'

> At my primary school we were given a lot of freedom to do the things we wanted. I wrote a story about my class in instalments over a couple of months. I took different character traits and exaggerated them. They loved it. Later on I tried to adapt it for a film script, and then a radio play and finally it became a stage play.

There are remarkably few changes in the revised version, but the language the children use has been updated – which will need to be done whenever the play is staged.

Anyone who has listened to schoolchildren talking will know that their language is a riot of vulgarity, hilarity, jokes, swearwords and insults. Daisy Campbell has very little swearing in *School Journey to the Centre of the Earth*, but there is an abundance of belittling comment, personal abuse and scatological ribaldry (such as the woman on the toilet who is so fat her flab bulges over the sides).

> Of course children use this kind of language, but they know exactly when to switch it off and on. When I paid a visit to my old school recently to learn about the jargon they use, I nearly got bundled in the playground because the kids thought I was writing

down swearwords. No different from when I was
their age.

The only structural change in the play is that, to make for
easier direction, all the lines are given to specific characters.
The children are still the same, but Miss Sheehan, who had
been a Russian spy, is now a terrorist, and the children
refer to the London bombings.

> Children are getting masses of information from all
> over and they filter it through their imaginations.
> News reports and films like *Harry Potter* are tied in
> together. There is this rich cultural world alongside all
> these atrocities. I have to say there is a bit of tension
> in the perceptions of the children. In my mind they
> are eight years old, which is the age I was when I wrote
> the original story. But the eight-year-olds I spoke to
> recently were remarkably innocent, so I have assumed
> they have older brothers and sisters. They are quite
> well-informed without fully understanding things. In
> any case the characters will be acted by older teenagers.

School Journey to the Centre of the Earth is, on the
surface, a light-hearted play. Daisy Campbell has again
captured the voices of the children, and it is possible
that those who see the play will recollect the time when
they were children with imaginations that allowed them
to believe in anything. In Tricia, Daisy Campbell has
created a 'Just William' figure who can put ideas in the
Outlaws' heads so convincingly that they will believe
anything.

> Tricia is a bit like me. I used to go round the playground
> saying I was the Yingo-Yong. I had five layers of skin
> and every time anyone touched me I would lose a layer
> until I became a skeleton. The others really believed it.

Like Tricia, I used to test the limits to see how far
I could take them. But back in the classroom, as soon
as the register was called we were back to a different
reality.

There is an ineluctable logic about a child's imagination.
Once she has accepted something as reality, certain
consequences follow. If that teacher isn't a terrorist why
is she taking us to the centre of the Earth? And 'If you
can't believe the Head of the British Intelligence, then
who can you trust?' Given this eight-year-old certainty,
then the attack on the driver and the coach crash are
inevitable. Children are anarchists. They have a collective
power which they hardly ever use, but once this power is
unleashed, dreadful things may happen.

The children on the coach are typical of any inner-city
community. The families are nearly all dysfunctional in
some way. One mother is a drunk, one father is in prison
for murder and one mother is a hippy who will not let
her daughter watch television. James, for example, is a
character who might be seen as dangerous. He relishes
talking about gory events. He is an expert on horror
movies. He is going to be a torture-and-killing-machine
inventor when he grows up, or he might be a doctor. He
says he goes to funerals every Monday and he speculates
at length on how bodies might be cut up and buried in bits.

I have a soft spot for James. I see him as living in a
council flat with his mother. At home he is very tame,
which is why he lets go a bit in school. I wrote James'
obsession with blood and gore into my play because
it amused me. I am not passing any moral judgements
one way or another. Perhaps the fact that he is so open
about it means he has a perfectly healthy attitude to
violence.

Ten years ago Ken Campbell had the vision to entrust the play he was asked to write to his daughter. Today his role is to listen and, as he is out of touch with young people, if he does not understand the language then it must be right.

I always admire any author who can write for a big cast. It's rare that anyone can bring it off. I live as a kind of hermit now, with two dogs and a parrot, and thinking about more than six people is not in my compass any more. I'd love to see an explicit version of the play, intricate and realistic, with thirty kids actually on a bus with it fully managed as a journey.

Production Notes

The play was written ten years ago when Daisy was
sixteen years old. It was initiated by Ken being asked to
write a play for the National's *Connections* programme,
but Daisy ended up writing most of it, with Ken adding
a few of the jokes here and there. The play was updated
again for the present cycle in the summer of 2005.

IMPROVISATION EXERCISES

Have each person in the group pair up with someone
they don't know and choose whether they are Number
One or Two. Number One has to tell Number Two about
a piece of theatre they went to see that they liked. Number
One should not only describe the play itself, but also
other, smaller details surrounding this visit – what the
weather was like, what the environment of the play was,
and why it made such an impression. Number Two
should listen as carefully as possible. Number One has
precisely three and a half minutes to relay this
information to Number Two.

Next, Number Two has to move to a new Number One.
Number Two then tells Number One the story they have
just heard. So the listener becomes the talker and the
talker becomes the listener. This should also last exactly
three and a half minutes.

Have three people sit in front of the audience and tell
their version of the story they have just been told while
passing it off as their own experience.

This exercise can be useful in allowing someone to listen to a story and then recreating it as their own – i.e., taking on a new character. It can be applied to other situations.

BUILDING A CHARACTER

Decide what a character is. Here are a few thoughts.

A person who inhabits the world of the play.

A person who has a function in a play.

A person who has an objective.

A person the audience might empathise with.

A character has to make a choice under pressure, come to a decision under pressure and take action under pressure. What makes Hamlet such a deep character is the number of decisions he makes. Making decisions under pressure makes the action more dramatic and so more interesting.

How do you create depth of character?

Through the character's backstory.

Through the introduction of change or new revelations.

Through having the character make choices.

APPROACHING THE PLAY

The jargon and slang used in *School Journey to the Centre of the Earth* come from London schoolchildren. Substitute local slang if appropriate, but don't spoil the rhythm or meaning of the piece.

Update the references to films, adverts, etc., as and where necessary. The script should feel immediate and current.

Don't just do the play in one style as it will become boring, but also be selective.

Don't try and do too much. The characters are the most interesting elements in the play, so you should let them develop properly without relying on too many effects and approaches. *Make it interesting.*

Play around with some of the following ideas Daisy and Ken explored with the participants at the Bath retreat.

Get into groups of five and choose different scenes from the play. Have someone read out a selection of the following. Have each group respond to the instruction spontaneously and with minimum discussion. Move from one idea to the next with great rapidity. You'll need a selection of chairs, a sheet and some props. Torches could be useful.

Share all of the parts out. Do each other's lines. • Set the chairs on stage as if on a coach or bus. • Site-specific: stage the play on a coach where both the audience and the cast are on board. • The same, but with the coach moving and actually going somewhere. • Cast in the audience, moving from seat to seat as they do in the script. The auditorium then becomes the coach. To make this happen in the best possible way the auditorium should be extended so that there is no staging area, only raked seating.

Put multiple Sheehankovs in the audience.

Wheelie-chair production: seats on trucks so that they can be moved around. • Complete physical theatre production. No set. The kids have to be everything from the seats to the wheels on the bus. • Physicalise the environment described by the characters. Snapping between reality and fantasy.

Create the journey to the centre of the Earth. Use lighting and movement to visualise the minds of the kids. • Set the play in the future – two centuries ahead could mean they are on a journey through space. • Try out a junkyard production using old bits of coach to represent the coach as a whole.

Have the audience in the middle and the cast performing on raised stages either side, so the audience become the aisle of the coach. • Project images such as the rollercoaster and the journey to the centre of the Earth. • Seat the cast on the aisle seats of the auditorium as if the aisle of the auditorium is the aisle of the coach. • Suspend the coach in the air.

Movie version. As the characters come onto the stage they could freeze and their image could be projected on a screen with their name. • Project images of the centre of the Earth. • Film the action live, and project it while on stage. • Link each scene by doing something physical as an ensemble.

Put chickenwire between cast and audience. Each cast member has a lunchbox with stuff in it that they can throw at the audience, but they can't penetrate the holes.

Give 3D glasses to the audience and have a 3D projection of a rollercoaster. Why not have vibrating/moving seats for the audience?

Set it in a children's playground. • Imagine the whole thing is a figment of their imagination. • Use the classroom environment and construct the coach out of desks and chairs. • Imagine the journey using puppets or dolls.

Revolve the stage to show different parts of the journey. • Use chairs to create the rollercoaster. • Explode the coach. Chairs and props can be placed all over the stage between each scene. Move the chairs to different parts of the stage like a dance. • Use oversized objects. Massive chairs could make older kids play eight-year-olds in proportion.

Introduce newspaper headlines about terrorism and coach crashes. • Use flashback. The play could begin with the bodies dead and the action could be rewound at high speed to start at the beginning. • The theatre programme could be the newspaper describing the coach accident.

Rehearse the kids being animals. • Double-cast. Have one cast of humans and one cast of animals. Experiment with different ways of physicalising the action.

Lighting. Use lighting to reflect changes in the kids' emotions. • Try using shadow puppets. • Find ways for the teacher's voice to appear to come from different parts of the stage. • Suspend the coach on hydraulics, enabling it to slant and move around.

A hyper-real production, using realistic projections and replicas of everything down to the last detail. • Projections of fantasy rather than reality. • Projections of terrorist groups and real news stories. • Snapshot projections. • Teacher represented by a light creating an overbearing presence. • Drawings done by eight-year-olds of what is happening on stage.

Zombie version. • Action takes place in the centre of the earth and the kids re-enact how they got there. • Cast dressed as toys in typical stereotypes such as Action Man, ballerina. • Perspex fourth wall representing the bus windscreen. • Site-specific set in a lift on different floors, as different characters get off. • Site-specific set on a tube. • Site-specific set in a field. Different scenes take place in different areas. • Audience on a coach taking them from scene to scene. • Site-specific set at Alton Towers.

Circus. • Ballet. • Opera. • Melodrama. • Grotesque – exaggerated, stylised movements and sounds. • Masks.

Audience participation. The audience buy a ticket for a day trip including safety talk, a break for lunch – all done in real time.

Tableaux to portray key moments. • Silhouettes to portray key moments through mime.

Prologue and epilogue. A seven-year-old child is playing with a bus at the beginning. Lights go down and the play begins. At the end, lights up on the seven-year-old with the bus broken and the child crying.

Set it as a rehearsal. • Kaos-style. • Dressing-up box. • Communal characters. Anyone at any time might play any character. The character exists but doesn't belong to any one person. • Historical setting. • Nuclear shelter setting. • Picnic production set outside.

McCarthyism and conspiracy theories. • Aeroplane setting. The rollercoaster moments are turbulence. • Boat setting. Rollercoaster is represented by a storm. • Trestle-style. • Pre-record the dialogue and make the action very visual and physical. • Dress kids as adults playing children.

Brecht musical version. • On ice. • *Starlight Express*-style. • Skate park with ramps and graffiti tags for each character. • Roaming minstrels. Mini-epilogues stating what has just happened while the scene changes.

Play the whole thing in reverse. • Age-regressing. Start playing it as seventeen- or eighteen-year-olds and regress as the story takes hold and becomes more and more fantastical.

Coach begins as a graveyard. Chairs have crosses on them, representing graves. • Remote-control play. Option to rewind, fast-forward, pause, etc. • Robotic. • Foreign production with subtitles. • Play it in-the-round. • Choral version. • Crash site. • Radio play with actors making sound effects on stage. • Soundscapes. • Signed version. • Dubbed version in the style of old Japanese movies.

Old people playing children set in an old people's home. • Hallucinogenic trip. • Different culture such as Bangladeshi. • Silent movie version.

DIMENSIONS ON STAGE

The movies of Howard Hartley are plotted by dimension. This demonstrates the range of emotions within the character.

What is the direction of a story on stage?

Direction of the comic is from left to right because that is how we are conditioned to read and that is therefore how our brain works.

Entering from different points of the stage establishes your character and your status.

If a character enters from upstage centre, this is the star entrance and is often used in musicals, or for regal characters.

Upstage right is the main entrance for the protagonist – e.g., Othello: it has a positive energy.

Downstage left is an effective entrance for a character like Iago, or one with negative energy.

AUDIENCE AVOIDANCE
AND COMMUNICATION TECHNIQUES

At a moment of choice the actor can decide where to position and focus to enhance the audience's interpretation.

The use of thinking anchors (looking up or looking down when making a choice) is also a useful tool to make a character appear more interesting.

Dipping technique: as you change eye-contact from one character to the next onstage, drop your eyes and then re-establish eye-contact with the new point of focus.

Arcing technique: as before, but instead of looking down look up as you change the focus of eye contact.

Closing technique: as before but close eyes as the focus changes.

Eye contact with audience: as focus changes onstage, try and make eye contact with at least three members of the audience before re-establishing focus.

All these techniques change audience perception and interpretation of what is happening onstage. Use them to inform your character.

REHEARSAL TECHNIQUES

Instant acting. Record a performance of the script including sound effects. Play this in rehearsal, enabling the characters to create physical images without being constricted by holding a script. This enables the group to explore character, space and staging.

Use of chairs. How many things can you do with a chair?

Chair drills. • Dancing with a chair without making contact with anybody else in the group. • Wearing chairs as backpacks. • Ways of lifting and repositioning chairs effortlessly to music.

Group Exercise: Working in groups of two or three, explore what you can do with chairs.

Creating a drill to the centre of the earth. • Peering through holes in chairs. • Creating monsters by wearing chairs on your heads. • Hanging off chairs upside down for the rollercoaster. • Placing chairs upside down and sitting on them. • Stacking chairs to create different levels. • Using chairs to create a tunnel. • Chairs as guns.

Think about not only what you can create with the chairs but how you can use the chairs to change the environment.

Eight-year-old orchestra. Each participant has a sound with one person conducting. This sound can be a phrase, possibly from the play, or a sound that might feature at some point. The sound or phrase must be able to be repeated continuously. The conductor then creates a soundscape that is reminiscent of a playground with repetitive sounds and voices.

Rollercoaster. Using the same principle as the orchestra, each participant chooses different actions and sounds that you might hear on a rollercoaster, and the conductor controls what it both looks and sounds like – e.g., hands in the air, movements from side to side and screaming at different points as directed. These exercises should eventually lead to a choreographed piece that can be used in the play.

Levels. To help develop the background action and group moments. In the playground, demonstrate Level Five (top level) and then go down to Level One (lowest level). This helps to raise the group's awareness of their energy levels and focus. Think about what happens to the rest of the group when certain scenes are taking place. Does the rest of the group freeze? Does the rest of the group move in slow motion?

Position the group in a semicircle with one person in the centre and the rest of the group staying still but interested in what is happening in the centre.

Another exercise is to have the group mucking about and when one person puts their finger on his/her mouth the rest of the group have to follow suit until all of the group have their fingers on their mouths and are focused on the action onstage.

Using different levels and moving as a group: in a group of five or six stand close together, and whoever is in the front has to lead the group until the direction changes and there is a new leader. This continues as a group exercise. Try to do this exercise through working and moving at different levels.

Play different scenes in different styles and genres. This helps open up further possibilities.

SCENE TRANSITIONS

In groups, think of one or two really good scene transitions in any style.

Very physical scene changes. Lifting characters and moving them into the next scene.

Chair dancing. Choreographed movement of chairs from one scene into the next.

Change formation of the chairs at key moments using different levels.

Play with different speeds.

SUGGESTED READING

Impro by Keith Johnstone.

Impro for Storytellers by Keith Johnstone.

Improvisation for the Theater by Viola Spolin.

Improvisation for Directors by Viola Spolin.

Acting for the Amateur by Seymour Hicks (1934).

Story by Robert McKee.

> *Workshop facilitated by Daisy and Ken Campbell*
> *with notes taken by Imogen Kinchin*

THE SHOEMAKER'S INCREDIBLE WIFE

Federico Garcia Lorca
translated by Lucinda Coxon

Federico Garcia Lorca's first play, *The Butterfly's Evil Spell*, was produced in 1920 at the Teatro Eslava, Madrid, followed by *Mariana Pineda* in 1927 and *The Shoemaker's Wonderful Wife* in 1930. In 1932 he founded La Barraca, a state-funded educational travelling theatre company, and served as its director, composer and playwright. His later plays include *Blood Wedding* (1933), *The Love of Don Perlimpin* (1933), *Yerma* (1934), *When Five Years Pass* (1936) and *The House of Bernarda Alba* (1936). His books of poetry include *Books of Poems* (1921), *First Songs* (1927), *Songs* (1927), *Gypsy Ballads* (1928) and *Poem of Deep Song* (1931). At the start of the Spanish Civil War he was murdered by Nationalist partisans.

Lucinda Coxon's other plays include *Waiting at the Water's Edge* (Bush Theatre), *Three Graces* (University of Essex), *Wishbones* (Bush Theatre), *Nostalgia* and *Vesuvius* (both at South Coast Repertory Theater). Lucinda is currently under commission at South Coast Rep. She also works extensively in film. Her last play for Connections was *The Ice Palace*.

Characters

The Shoemaker's Wife
Red Neighbour
Purple Neighbour
Black Neighbour
Green Neighbour
Yellow Neighbour
First Pious Woman
Second Pious Woman
Sacristan's Wife
The Writer
The Shoemaker
The Boy
The Mayor
Don Mirlo
Young Man with Sash
Young Man with Hat
Red Neighbour's Daughters
Neighbours, Pious People, Priests and Villagers

Prologue

Grey curtain.
  The Writer suddenly appears. He holds a letter in his hand.

Writer Esteemed public . . . (*Beat.*) No – not 'esteemed public', just 'public'. And not because the writer does not hold the public in high esteem – no, on the contrary, I reject the word because it has the taint of fear, it smacks of pleading with the audience, pleading with them to be generous with the actors' performances and the artfulness of the whole concoction.

  No, the poet does not ask for your indulgence, only your attention now he's finally cleared the abyss of terror that all writers encounter when they write for the theatre.

  Because of this absurd terror and because the theatre is for the most part a commercial enterprise these days, poetry has retired from the stage in search of other environments where people will not be mortified if a tree, for example, turns into a burning bush, or if three little fishes – at the wave of a hand and a magic word – turn themselves into three million fishes to feed a great multitude.

  In light of this, the Writer has decided to set his dramatic effort in the everyday thrum of the most ordinary shoemaker's shop. And the poetic creature whom the Writer has dressed as the Shoemaker's Wife is one you will find everywhere – in the proverbs of the past and the soapy love songs of the present.

And the audience should not be surprised if she is
suddenly violent or bitter, because she is struggling all
the time – at war either with the realities of life which
confront her at every turn, or with her longed-for
fantasies when at last they themselves become realities.

The voice of the Shoemaker's Wife is heard.

Wife (*offstage*) I want to come on!
Writer Hold on! Don't be in such a hurry to make your
entrance! Anyone would think you were wearing some
extravagant costume with a long train and feathers,
not the ordinary rags of a shoemaker's wife!
Wife (*offstage*) I want to come on!
Writer Be quiet now . . . !

*The curtain draws back and reveals the set in half-
light.*

Ah . . . look at how day dawns in the city, and people
forget the sleepy world of dreams to come to the
market just like you – about to arrive at your house
on the stage – remarkable little shoemaker's wife . . .

The light grows brighter.

Let's begin . . . you enter from the street . . .

We hear voices offstage, quarrelling.

(*to the audience*) Goodnight . . .

*He takes off his hat and a bright column of green light
shines out of it. He inverts it and a cascade of water
pours out. The Writer looks a little embarrassed before
the audience, backs away, twinkling with irony.*

I do beg your pardon.

He exits.

Act One

SCENE ONE

The Shoemaker's house. A bench and some tools. It is painted white throughout, with a big window and a door. Upstage is a street with some little grey doors and windows. There are doors to the right and the left. The whole scene has an air of optimism and intense happiness, conveyed even in the smallest details. The soft orange light of mid-afternoon floods the stage. As the play opens, the Shoemaker's Wife enters from the street, furious, and halts in the doorway. She wears a dress of dazzling green, with her hair pulled back hard and pinned with large roses. She strikes us as full of wildness and sweetness simultaneously.

Wife You shut your big mouth, you bitch on wheels! Because I'll tell you now: when I did it – when I married him, it was because I wanted to and for no other reason! Oh, if you hadn't got inside your house I would have knocked you down, you poison-tongued snake. Well, make sure you hear what I'm saying now, all of you hiding behind your windows: better to be married to an old man than a blind man like you lot! And I don't want any further discussion on the subject, not with you, not with anyone. Not with anyone anyone anyone!

She slams the door shut.

I know better than to talk to people like that! Never even for a second. No, the blame's all mine – I should have stayed at home with . . . oh, I can hardly believe it . . . with my husband. If someone had told me – me, with

507

this thick and glossy hair, with these bewitching eyes
(come on – credit where credit's due), with this figure
and this exceptionally pretty colouring . . . that I
would go and marry a . . . I would have pulled out all
my hair.

She starts to cry. A knock at the door.

Who is it . . . ?

No answer. More knocking. She's enraged now.

Who is it?
Boy's Voice (*tremulous, offstage*) A friend . . .

*The Wife opens the door, suddenly moved, full of
sweetness.*

Wife Is it you . . . ?

The Boy enters.

Boy Yes, Mrs Shoemaker . . . Have you been crying?
Wife No. It was one of those flies – the ones that go
'iiiiii' – just stung me in this eye.
Boy Would you like me to blow on it for you?
Wife No, my sweet. It's gone now.

She strokes him.

Now, what do you want?
Boy I've brought these patent leather shoes for your
husband to repair. They cost twenty-five pesetas!
They're my big sister's – the one with the fine skin,
who wears two ribbons on her waist every day.
Wife Leave them there, they'll be done in no time.
Boy My mother said to take care with them. Not to hit
them too hard with the hammer because patent leather
is very delicate and they might fall apart.
Wife Tell your mother that my husband knows how to
do his job and that if she knew as much about

seasoning her stews as my husband knows about fixing footwear . . .

The Boy pouts.

Boy Don't get angry with me, it's not my fault, I do my best, get my homework in on time . . .
Wife (*sweetly*) Oh little one . . . Believe me, I'm not angry with you!

She kisses him.

Here – take this doll. Do you like it? You can keep it.
Boy Okay, I'll take it . . . because I know you won't have any need for it.
Wife Mm?
Boy You won't have any children.
Wife Who told you that . . .?
Boy My mother – she said it the other day: 'The shoemaker's wife won't have any kids.' And my sisters and godmother Rafaela all laughed their heads off.
Wife (*upset*) Children? I'll have children – better looking than all hers put together and with more spirit and dignity! Because your mother . . . you might as well know this . . .
Boy Take the doll, I don't want it!
Wife No – no you keep it, my sweet. None of this is to do with you . . .

SCENE TWO

The Shoemaker enters from the left. He wears a velvet outfit with silver buttons, short trousers and a red tie. He takes in his workbench.

Wife Get going and God bless.

The Boy looks frightened.

Boy Take care . . . I'll see you . . . Good luck with everything . . . and God protect you . . .

He runs out into the street.

Wife Goodbye, little one!

The Boy is gone.

If you'd died before you were born I wouldn't have these trials and tribulations! Oh, money, money! The man who invented it ought to have his hands chopped off and his eyes poked out!

The Shoemaker looks up from his bench.

Shoemaker What are you talking about, woman?
Wife None of your business.
Shoemaker Well, nothing's any of my business, of course. My job's just to stand and suffer.
Wife I suffer too! And I'm only eighteen!
Shoemaker And I'm fifty-three! Which is why I control myself and don't completely lose it with you! No, I'm wiser than that. I work hard to keep you, and may God's will be done.

The Wife turns to face her husband, approaches with tenderness.

Wife Oh no, my pet. Don't say that . . .
Shoemaker But if I were forty again or even forty-five . . . !

He beats on a shoe angrily with his hammer. The Wife fumes.

Wife What? Then I'd have to jump when you said jump, is that it? You think I can't be good of my own free will? You think I'm worth nothing?
Shoemaker Wife, give it up!
Wife Aren't my spirit and good looks worth more than all the riches in the world?

Shoemaker Woman – the neighbours will hear you . . .

Wife Oh, damn the day – the dark, dark day – I listened to my friend Manuel.

Shoemaker Would you like some cooling lemonade?

Wife Oh stupid stupid stupid!

She beats her forehead.

With all the fine suitors I had!

The Shoemaker hopes to calm her.

Shoemaker So people say.

Wife 'So people say'? Everybody knows it! The pick of the bunch for miles around! But you know, the one I liked best of all was Emiliano . . . you know him . . . Emiliano, who came riding on that black horse, covered in tassels and little mirrors, that supple whip in his hand and those shining copper spurs. And what a cloak he wore in winter. The finest blue corduroy with silk panels!

Shoemaker I had a cloak too, once . . . a really beautiful one.

Wife You had one . . .? You? Oh, wake up to yourself! A shoemaker could never in his life compete at that level!

Shoemaker But wife, can't you see . . .?

Wife Then there was the other suitor . . .

The Shoemaker furiously hammers a shoe.

He was kind of a rich kid . . . eighteen years old . . . oh, even the *word* is over too quickly – 'eighteen' . . .

The Shoemaker is increasingly upset.

Shoemaker I was eighteen once, myself.

Wife You were never eighteen! Oh, and the things he used to tell me . . . really . . .

Shoemaker (*furiously hammering*) You want to shut up.

You're my wife whether you like it or not, and I'm your husband! Before me you were destitute – no clothes on your back, no roof over your head! Why did you have to choose me? Fantasies, fantasies, fantasies!

The Wife gets up.

Wife Shut up! Don't make me say more than I should, and just remember your obligation to me! Everything you say is lies.

Two Neighbours with mantillas cross in front of the window, smiling.

Who would have believed that I would end up treated this way by an old barrel of a man like you? If that's what you think of me – go on! – swing the hammer.

Shoemaker Oh wife, don't make such a scene! Can't you see there are people? Oh my God . . .

The Neighbours cross back again.

Wife I've ruined myself! Idiot, idiot, idiot! Damn my friend Manuel, damn the neighbours, idiot, idiot, idiot!

She goes out beating her forehead.

SCENE THREE

The Shoemaker takes out a mirror and begins to count his wrinkles.

Shoemaker One, two, three, four wrinkles . . . and another thousand.

He puts away the mirror.

Well, I had it coming, yes sir. I mean, let's ask the question: why did I marry? I should have understood

from the many books I read that all women look good
to a man – but not all men look good to a woman.
I was fine as I was before! My sister – my sister should
take the blame for this – she said: 'You're going to
wind up all alone, and then what?' This has been the
ruin of me! May lightning strike my sister – as she
rests in peace.

We hear voices.

What's that?

*The Red Neighbour appears at the window with great
commotion. She has her Daughters with her, all
dressed in the same colour.*

Red Neighbour Good afternoon.

The Shoemaker scratches his head.

Shoemaker Good afternoon.

Red Neighbour Ask your wife to step outside. Girls,
don't cry any more. Let her come out and say to my
face what she's been saying behind my back, hmm?

Shoemaker Oh, my dear neighbour, for the love of God,
don't bring trouble here! What do you want me to do?
Understand my situation: all my life, terrified even of
the idea of marriage, because I knew what a serious
business it was – and then . . . at the last minute – well,
you can see how things turned out.

Red Neighbour What a sorry sight! Why couldn't you
have taken a wife from your own class – this girl here,
for example – or any other from the village?

Shoemaker My home is no longer a home. It's a
madhouse!

Red Neighbour It's breathtaking. To think – all your life,
such a good reputation.

The Shoemaker checks to see if his Wife is coming.

Shoemaker The day before yesterday, she carved the ham we were keeping for Christmas, and ate the lot. Then yesterday, we ate nothing but egg and parsley soup. Then, because I complained about this, she made me drink three glasses of unboiled milk!

Red Neighbour She's an animal!

Shoemaker Which is why, dear neighbour, I would give anything for you to just go away . . .

Red Neighbour Oh, if your sister was alive! Things would be different then . . .

Shoemaker Of course . . . but take your shoes with you, look, all mended, good as new.

The Shoemaker's Wife appears at the door on the left, spies on the others without being seen. The Red Neighbour turns coy.

Red Neighbour How much will you want for those . . . ? Times are hard and getting worse . . .

Shoemaker Whatever you think . . . it's all the same to me.

The Red Neighbour nudges her Daughters.

Red Neighbour Is two pesetas okay?

Shoemaker It's whatever you say.

Red Neighbour Okay, then I say one.

The Shoemaker's Wife bursts in, furious.

Wife You filthy thief!

The other women screech, afraid.

Do you have the bare-faced cheek to rob this man? And you – will you just stand there and let yourself be fleeced? Give me the shoes. Until you cough up ten pesetas, they stay with me!

Red Neighbour You lizard!

Wife Watch your mouth, lady!

Daughters Oh, let's go please, for God's sake!

Red Neighbour Well, sir, you're doing a great job of handling your wife! And you're welcome to her!

The go off quickly. The Shoemaker closes the window and the door.

SCENE FOUR

Shoemaker Listen a minute . . .

Wife Lizard! Lizard! What . . .? What are you going to say?

Shoemaker Look, my child, all my life I have had gone to incredible lengths to avoid scandal!

The Shoemaker swallows hard.

Wife You dare call it a scandal that I step forward to protect your interests!

Shoemaker All I'm saying is that I run from scandal like a salamander from an ice-cold bath.

Wife A salamander – euch, how revolting!

The Shoemaker summons his patience.

Shoemaker I've been provoked, of course – insulted sometimes, even, and I'm not a coward, as well you know . . . but I swallow my pride and say nothing for fear of being the centre of attention, giving tittle-tattling women and idle men an excuse to discuss my affairs. There – you know how it is now. Have I said enough? Because that's my last word on the subject.

Wife Oh, I don't think so: just what exactly does all this have to do with me? I married you. Don't I keep the house clean? Don't I feed you? Don't you wear collars and cuffs better starched than ever before in your life? Don't you have a beautiful watch with a chain of silver, studded with precious stones, and don't I wind it for you every night? What more do you want? I am a real whole person, my own person. And I'll never give up my God-given right to be that!

Shoemaker Don't tell me that . . . Three months we've been married . . . with me doting on you, and you so cruel with me! It's past a joke . . .

Wife (*serious, as if dreaming*) Doting on me . . .? Doting . . . but . . . (*brusque now*) Where is this doting . . .? I don't see any doting!

Shoemaker You think I'm blind, but I know what I see. I know what you do and don't do, and I'm at the limit! Right up to here!

Wife (*furiously*) You know it's the same to me whether you're at the limit or not, because you don't matter that – (*She snaps her fingers.*) – to me. Got it?!

She cries.

Shoemaker Can't you keep the volume down a little?

Wife It would serve you right for your stupidity if I shouted it in the street!

Shoemaker Oh, it's lucky I don't have too much time left. Because I don't think my patience will last much longer.

Wife We're not eating today. You'll have to find your dinner elsewhere.

The Shoemaker's Wife hurries out, furious.

Shoemaker Tomorrow – (*He smiles.*) – maybe you'll have to do the same.

He goes to his bench.

SCENE FIVE

The Mayor appears at the main door. He wears a dark blue suit, with a big cloak and carries his silver-topped cane of office. He speaks slowly and with some sarcasm.

Mayor Busy working?
Shoemaker Busy working, Mr Mayor.
Mayor Are you making much?
Shoemaker Enough.

The Shoemaker continues working. The Mayor looks around the place.

Mayor You're not yourself.
Shoemaker No.
Mayor The wife?

The Shoemaker nods.

Shoemaker The wife!

The Mayor sits down.

Mayor It's because of your age. At your age you ought to be a widower – of one wife, at least. I've buried four: Rosa, Manuela, Visitacion and Enriqueta Gomez, the last. Beautiful young things, all of them. Expert dancers and models of virtue. And all, without exception, had a taste of this cane on occasion. In my house, the rules were clear: you sew and you sing.
Shoemaker Well you can see for yourself the life I lead. My wife . . . she doesn't love me. She talks through the window with any man that passes, even old Don Mirlo, and it makes my blood boil.

The Mayor laughs.

Mayor She's a carefree young thing, it's only natural . . .
Shoemaker No! I'll tell you what I think – that it's all to torment me. Because I've no doubt she hates me. At first I thought I would reform her with my gentle character and my little gifts . . . Coral necklaces . . . rings . . . shell combs for her hair. Even garters! But she . . . she's always *herself*!
Mayor And you're always yourself: God in Heaven!

Come on – I sit here and it seems impossible to me that a man – if he calls himself a man – can't get a woman under control. Or eighty women, even! If your wife talks at the window with everyone and anyone, if your wife is angry with you, it's because you want it, because you don't stop it! All a woman needs is a squeeze around the waist, and to see your foot stamp down hard and hear your voice raised, and if she still wants to strut and squawk, the cane – there's no other way. Rosa, Manuela, Visitacion and Enriqueta Gomez, who was the last, they would all say the same from the other side – if that's where they happen to be.

Shoemaker But if I'm honest, I've left something out.

He looks around, afraid. The Mayor speaks firmly.

Mayor Tell me.

Shoemaker I know it's an outrage . . . but . . . I don't love my wife.

Mayor God above!

Shoemaker Yes indeed, sir. God above!

Mayor In that case, you great lump, why did you marry her?

Shoemaker Oh that's the question! I can't explain it. My sister, it's my sister's fault. 'You're going to wind up all alone, and then what?', always ringing in my ears. I had a little money, had my health, and so I said: okay! But oh my blessed and long lost solitude! May lightning strike my sister, RIP.

Mayor It's quite a drama.

Shoemaker Yes sir, quite a drama. But now I can't stand any more. I didn't know about life with a woman. You've done it four times! But at my age I can't stand this fuss and kerfuffle!

The Shoemaker's Wife is heard, singing forcefully.

Wife
Let's dance a fandango
Now that we've finished the fighting,
Let's dance a fandango
Now that we've finished the scrap!

Shoemaker Do you hear her . . . ?

Mayor What are you going to do?

The Shoemaker points, off.

Shoemaker Head for the hills.

Mayor Have you lost your mind?

Shoemaker The shoemaker and his shoes are over and done with as far as I'm concerned. I'm a man of peace, not used to this racket and being the talk of the town.

The Mayor laughs.

Mayor Reconsider what you're planning. Of course you could do that, but don't be an idiot. It's a pity when a man like yourself can't find the courage to do what needs doing.

The Shoemaker's Wife enters, stage left, putting blusher on her cheeks and smoothing her eyebrows.

SCENE SIX

Wife Good afternoon.

Mayor Very good. (*to the Shoemaker*) What a beauty, really stunning!

Shoemaker Do you think?

Mayor What beautiful roses you have in your hair, and such a scent . . .

Wife You've got lots of them on the balconies of your house.

Mayor Indeed. You like flowers?

Wife Do I . . .? They enchant me. I'd have flowerpots on the roof, the doors and the walls. But he . . . him . . . he doesn't like them. He's spent all his life mending shoes. What can you do?

She sits by the window. Looks out and flirts.

Good afternoon.
Shoemaker See that?
Mayor A little fiery, but . . . that's a handsome wife. What a perfect figure!
Shoemaker You don't know her.
Mayor Pish!

He sweeps out in a majestic manner.

Until tomorrow. And see if you can't clear your head. Relax, my sweet. What a waste of a beautiful woman . . .

He leaves, still looking at the Wife.

Oh, the waves in that hair . . .

He is gone.

SCENE SEVEN

The Shoemaker's Wife sings.

Wife
If his Lordship disappoints you,
Don't come crying to me:
There are plenty more pebbles out there on the beach,
There are plenty more fish in the sea . . .

The Wife takes a chair and sets it down by the window. Begins to spin round on it. The Shoemaker grabs the other chair and begins to spin round in the opposite direction.

Shoemaker Stop spinning – you know I take that
superstition so seriously you might as well shoot me as
carry on like that! Why are you doing it?

The Wife stops.

Wife Aren't I allowed to move?

Shoemaker I am sick of reasoning with you . . . it's
pointless.

*He goes to leave but the Wife begins to spin her chair
again. The Shoemaker rushes back and spins his own
chair in the opposite direction.*

Why don't you let me leave, woman . . . ?

Wife Dear God! That's all I want – for you to leave!

Shoemaker Fine – I'll go!

Wife Good. What are you waiting for?

*Outside, we hear a flute accompanied by a guitar
playing an old polka tune with a comical rhythm.
The Wife begins to mark the rhythm with her head
and the Shoemaker goes off, stage left.*

SCENE EIGHT

The Wife sings.

Wife Da-dum, da-dah . . . oh, I've always loved the flute –
I have – I've always had a passion for it . . . it makes
me want to cry . . . Such beauty! Listen – I wish he
could hear it . . .

*She gets up, begins to dance as if with an imaginary
suitor.*

Oh, Emiliano! What precious rings you offer . . . No,
no . . . I'm embarrassed . . . it's too much . . . But
Jose Maria, can't you see they're watching? Take a

handkerchief . . . I don't want to spoil my dress . . .
Oh, it's you, I love . . . you . . . Oh, yes . . . tomorrow
bring the white mare, the one I like.

She laughs. The music stops.

Oh – damn my luck! The moment I taste the honey on
my tongue . . .

SCENE NINE

*Don Mirlo appears at the window. He's dressed in a
black tailcoat and short trousers. His voice trembles and
his head shakes like a wire doll's.*

Mirlo Pssst!
Wife (*without turning to look at the window behind her*)
Chirp, chirp, cheep, cheep, cheep.

Coming even closer.

Mirlo Pssst! Little shoemaker's wife, white as the heart of
an almond and just as bitter. Little shoemaker's wife . . .
a reed of burning gold . . . little shoemaker's wife . . .
beautiful temptress of my heart.
Wife Well here's a turn-up for the books – Don Mirlo.
I didn't know crows could talk. But if there's a bird
flapping away there, old and black, tell him I can't
listen to his song until later – much later. Chirp, chirp,
cheep, cheep, cheep . . .
Mirlo When the shadows of evening pull their webs
across the world and the streets are all deserted, I'll
come back.

He takes some snuff and sneezes on the Wife's neck.

Wife Aaaagh! Make sure you don't, you old obscenity!
You scarecrow, you soot-stain. Go. Go on. Do you

know you just sneezed on me? God help you. You make me sick.

SCENE TEN

At the window, a Young Man appears in a sash. He has his hat pulled low over his face and seems deeply sad.

Young Man with Sash Are you taking the air, little shoemaker's wife?

Wife That's right, just like you.

Young Man with Sash And always alone . . . Such a shame.

Wife And why a shame?

Young Man with Sash A woman like you, with such hair and this ample bosom . . .

Wife But why do you say it's a shame?

Young Man with Sash Because you ought to be painted on a postcard, not caged up here!

Wife Really? I like postcards very much . . . especially the ones sent by suitors on their travels . . .

Young Man with Sash Oh, little shoemaker's wife, how I burn for you!

They continue talking. The Shoemaker enters, hangs back.

Shoemaker Talking to anyone who passes – and at this hour! What will they be saying over their rosaries in church? What will they say at the club? They'll have me under the microscope! In every house – they'll have me down to my underwear!

The Wife laughs.

Oh, dear God! I have reason to leave! I wish I could hear the sacristan's wife. And the priests . . .? What are the priests saying? That's what I wish I could hear!

He goes off in despair.

Young Man with Sash How can I put it? I love you . . . I
love thee like . . .

Wife Oh – that 'I love you . . . I love thee', it's like
someone tickling my ear with a feather. 'I love thee . . .
I love you . . .'

Young Man with Sash How many seeds has a sunflower?

Wife How would I know!

Young Man with Sash As many as I give out sighs of love
for you every minute. For you . . .

He draws closer.

Wife Stop right there! I'll listen to you talk all night,
because I like it . . . but nothing more. You hear?
Behave yourself.

Young Man with Sash But that can't be. You can't mean
you're spoken for elsewhere . . .?

Wife Look – go.

Young Man with Sash I won't move from here until you
say 'Yes' to me. Oh, my little shoemaker's wife. Give
me your word!

He goes to embrace her. She shuts the window hard.

Wife What impertinence! What lunacy! Well, let him
suffer if he must. As if I were here just for that! Can't
a woman talk to anyone in this town? As far as I can
see, in this town a woman can only be one of two
things – a nun or a dishcloth to wipe the floor. That's
all I needed!

She sniffs the air, starts to run.

Oh, now the dinner's burning! Absurd woman!

SCENE ELEVEN

The light is fading. The Shoemaker enters wearing a great cloak with a bundle of clothes in his hands.

Shoemaker Either I am another man entirely or I do not know myself! Oh my little house! Oh, my little workbench! Wax, nails, calfskin . . . Well.

He heads for the door, then holds back, so as not to collide with two extremely pious women passing right outside.

Pious Woman 1 Relaxing, are you?
Pious Woman 2 It's good to relax.
Shoemaker (*in a bad humour*) Goodnight!
Pious Woman 1 You relax, sir.
Pious Woman 2 Relax, relax.

They go.

Shoemaker Oh yes, relax. While they've got their eyes glued to my keyhole! Old bats, get lost! And watch that sarcastic tone when you speak to me! Well, it's clear – there's no other topic of conversation in town now. Just me, her and those young men. Oh let lightning strike my sister, may she rest in peace! So – better to be all alone than be pointed at by all the rest!

He quickly departs, leaving the door open. His Wife appears stage left.

SCENE TWELVE

Wife Dinner . . .! Did you hear me . . .?

She goes to the door, stage right.

Did you hear me? Oh, don't tell me he's had the nerve to
go off to the café, leaving the door open, and without
finishing the boots? Well – when he gets back he'll
certainly hear me. I'll have something to say then! Men
are all the same. They can't help taking advantage!

She shivers.

Oh, it's turned cold.

*She lights the lamp and hears from the street the calls
of sheep returning to the village.*

What magnificent sheep. But the best of the lot for me –
the ones I love most, are the little lambs. Hey – that
horrible big one's crushing the little one . . . (*She
shouts.*) Shepherd! Look, you stunned mullet! Can't
you see the newborn lamb being trampled . . .?

Beat.

Well, certainly it concerns me! Why wouldn't it concern
me! . . . You nasty brute! . . . And the same to you
twice over!

She leaves the window.

Just how much longer is my husband going to be? I'll tell
you now – if he's not back in two minutes, I'll go right
ahead and eat alone. After I made this delicious dinner,
too. My casserole – with best potatoes, two green
peppers, white bread, a little lean pork-belly, and all
topped off with sweet pumpkin and lemon rind! I took
a lot of care over it, a lot of care, all prepared by this
hand.

*Throughout this monologue she is very agitated,
moving from side to side, rearranging chairs, picking
lint off the curtains and her clothes.*

SCENE THIRTEEN

The Boy appears at the door.

Boy Are you still upset?

Wife Oh, my sweetest little neighbour. Where are you going?

Boy You're not going to be cross with me? Are you? You know my mother beats me black and blue, but I still love her twenty times over. You I love thirty two and a half.

Wife How did you get to be so charming?

He comes in and sits on her lap.

Boy I came to tell you something no one else wants to tell you. 'You go,' they said . . . 'No – *you* go,' 'No – you go,' they called, but no one did. 'Send the boy,' they said then. Because it's the sort of news no one ever wants to give.

Wife Well tell me quickly . . . What's happened?

Boy Oh – don't be frightened – no one's died . . .

Wife Tell me now!

Boy Look . . . little shoemaker's wife . . .

But a butterfly flutters in through the window and the Boy jumps down to chase it.

Oh – a butterfly, a butterfly! Do you have a hat? It's golden, with blue and red markings . . . wonderful . . .

Wife But what were you about to say . . . ?

Boy Be quiet – you have to whisper. You don't want to frighten it away. Hey – give me your handkerchief!

She's caught up in the hunt now.

Wife Take it.

Boy Shh . . . don't stomp about!

Wife You nearly managed to let it escape.

The Boy sings softly to the butterfly.

Boy Butterfly up high,
How beautiful you are,
Butterfly up high,
Fluttering there
Like a candle flame.
Butterfly up high,
Stay right there, there, there . . .
Butterfly up high,
How beautiful you are,
Butterfly up high,
Fluttering there
Like a candle flame.
Butterfly up high,
Stay right there, there, there . . .
Stay there . . .
Are you there . . . ?

The Wife plays a trick.

Wife Here I am . . .

The butterfly flutters away.

Boy Oh, that's no good . . .
Wife Now – finally –

The Boy runs happily after it with the handkerchief.

Boy Don't you want to stay a while? Aren't your wings
tired?

The Wife runs to the other side.

Wife It's escaping, it's escaping . . .

*The Boy goes running out of the door, following the
butterfly.*

Where are you going?

The Boy halts – suspended.

Boy It's true.
Wife What?
Boy (*quickly*) But I don't want the blame!
Wife Get on and tell me what's happened. Come on now!
Boy Well, here's the thing . . . your husband. The shoemaker. He's gone as far away from this place as he can and he's never coming back.
Wife (*terrified*) What?
Boy It's true – he said so at the house before getting on his way. I saw it all myself . . . and he gave us the message to give to you and now the whole village knows too.

The Wife is on the verge of collapsing.

Wife It's not possible . . . it's not possible . . . I don't believe it . . .!
Boy Yes – it's all true – please don't tell me off!

She becomes furious, stamping her feet on the ground.

Wife This is how he repays me? This is how he repays me?

The Boy hides behind the table.

What will become of me, all alone in life? Oh, no no no . . .

The Boy runs out. Neighbours appear at the window and the door.

Oh yes! Come and have a good look, you gossiping godmothers! This is all down to you . . .
Mayor Look, now, you be quiet. If your husband has left you, it's because you didn't love him and he couldn't stand it any more.

Wife Oh. you think you know more about this than I do? I loved him! How I loved him! All the rich handsome suitors I had, and I never said yes to one of them! Oh, my poor deceived love, what stories have they told you . . . ?

The Sacristan's Wife enters.

Sacristan's Wife Woman, control yourself.
Wife I'll never accept this! I won't!

At the door, Neighbours enter wearing harshly bright clothing, bringing tall glasses of cold drinks. They spin and rush, coming and going with the rhythm of a dance around the Shoemaker's Wife, who sits shouting. The Neighbours' long skirts swirl out when they spin. They all affect an attitude of comic anguish.

Yellow Neighbour Have a cool drink.
Red Neighbour A little cool drink.
Green Neighbour For the blood.
Black Neighbour With lemon.
Purple Neighbour Sarsaparilla.
Red Neighbour Mint is best!
Purple Neighbour Neighbour.
Green Neighbour Little neighbour.
Black Neighbour Shoemaker's wife.
Red Neighbour Little shoemaker's wife.

The neighbours make a terrible racket. The Wife weeps and screams.

Curtain.

Act Two

SCENE ONE

The same set. To the left, the toolbench, banished to a corner. To the right, a bar with bottles and a bowl of water in which the Shoemaker's Wife washes glasses. The Wife is behind the bar. She wears a loose-fitting flame-red dress and has bare arms. There are two tables. At one sits Don Mirlo, enjoying a soft drink; at the other, the Young Man, with his hat pulled down over his face.

The Wife washes wine glasses and tumblers with a vengeance, and sets them on the bar. Then, the Young Man with the sash and the wide-brimmed hat from Act One appears at the door. He is sad. Physically limp. He looks tenderly at the Wife. If the actor playing the part exaggerates in the slightest, the director should take a stick and give him a sharp thwack on the head. Nothing must be overdone. Farce requires a natural manner at all times. The author has drawn the character and the costume designer has dressed it. Simplicity. The Young Man waits at the door. Don Mirlo and the other Young Man turn their heads and see him. It's like a scene from a film – the looks and the expressions of the group. The Wife stops washing up and fixes her eyes on the Young Man. Silence.

Wife Come in, why don't you?
Young Man with Sash If you want me to . . .
Wife Me? I couldn't be less interested, but you're blocking the entrance, so . . .
Young Man with Sash Well, if you want . . .

He settles at the bar, mutters.

Here I go again . . .

531

Wife What can I get you?

Young Man with Sash Whatever you recommend.

Wife I recommend the door.

Young Man with Sash My God – times have changed!

Wife Don't expect me to burst into tears over it. Now what do you want? Wine, coffee or something soft?

Young Man with Sash I'll take a soft drink.

Wife Don't look at me like that while I'm pouring the syrup.

Young Man with Sash Pardon me – I'm only dying here!

At the window, two young women with large fans look in, scandalised, make the sign of the cross, cover their eyes with their fans and hurry away with tiny dainty steps.

Wife Your drink.

Young Man with Sash (*looking at her*) Oh!

Young Man with Hat (*looking at the ceiling*) Oh!

Mirlo (*looking at the floor*) Oh!

The Wife turns her head towards the three 'Oh's.

Wife 'Oh, oh, oh'? What is this, a bar or a hospital ward? God, it's outrageous! If I didn't have to earn my living with this wine and all the rest, now I'm alone since my dear little husband left – all because of you – I'd never put up with it. D'you hear me? I'd throw you out into the street!

Mirlo Very good. Very well said.

Young Man with Hat But as it is, you run a bar and we can stay here all we want.

Wife (*furious*) What? What?

The Young Man with the Sash gets up to go and Don Mirlo stands, smiling, as though he's in on some secret and will return.

Young Man with Hat You heard what I said.

Wife Well I'm saying this now – and you can hear all
about it and the rest of the village as well: it's four
months since my husband left, and in that time I've
not yielded an inch to any man. Because I'm a married
woman and I conduct myself in accordance with God's
will. And I'm afraid of nothing, do you hear? I have
the blood of my grandfather in my veins, he who rests
in glory now, a man who broke wild horses, a man
you could really call a man. A decent woman is what
I was and what I shall stay. I am promised to my
husband, till death do us part.

*Don Mirlo bolts for the door, making gestures that
imply a relationship between himself and the Wife.*

Young Man with Hat (*getting up*) I have such heart,
I could grab hold of a bull by the horns, drive its head
into the sand, tear out its brains with these teeth, and
then chew on and on until the job was good and done!

*He hurries off and Don Mirlo escapes off left. The
Shoemaker's Wife holds her head in her hands.*

Wife Lord in Heaven, so help me!

She sits down.

SCENE TWO

*The Boy appears at the door, approaches the Wife and
covers her eyes.*

Boy Who am I?
Wife My little boy, my little shepherd of Bethlehem.
Boy The very one!

They kiss.

Wife Have you come for a treat?

Boy If you really want to give me something . . .

Wife I have a little chocolate.

Boy Oh, I love to visit you.

Wife Ha! Cupboard love.

Boy I didn't get this bruised knee banging into any cupboard!

Wife Show me.

She sits on a low seat, takes the Boy in her arms.

Boy I got that from Cunillo because he was singing that song they made up about you. I smacked him in the face and he pitched a stone back at me – bam – see?

Wife Does it hurt?

Boy Not any more, but I cried when it happened.

Wife You take no notice of the things they say.

Boy But they were disgusting things. Disgusting things that I could tell you, except I don't want to repeat them.

Wife (*laughing*) You do, and I'll rub a chilli on your tongue till it bursts into flame!

Boy But why should you take the blame if your husband's upped and left you?

Wife They should take the blame, those who ruined my life.

Boy (*sadly*) Don't say that, Mrs Shoemaker.

Wife I saw my true self reflected in his eyes. When he came riding up on his white horse . . .

The Boy interrupts.

Boy Hey – hang on. You're pulling my leg – the Shoemaker never had a white horse.

Wife Have some respect, boy! He had a white horse alright . . . but it was . . . it was before you were born.

She strokes his face.

Boy Oh . . . okay.

Wife You see . . . we met for the first time when I was washing my clothes in the village stream. Half a metre deep the water, and the pebbles in the bottom laughing as the water tickled by them. He was wearing a fine black fitted suit, a beautiful red-silk tie, and four gold rings that shone like four suns.

Boy He looked good!

Wife I looked at him . . . . He looked at me . . . I lay back on the grass. I can still feel the cool breeze from the trees on my face. He steadied his horse, and the horse's tail was so white and so long that it trailed in the water of the stream.

The Wife is on the verge of tears. A song is heard, faintly, off in the distance.

I was so flummoxed I let two little handkerchiefs slip into the stream.

Boy That's funny.

Wife And then . . . he said to me . . .

The song is coming closer. Pause.

Shh.

Boy The song.

Wife The song.

They listen together.

You know it?

The Boy gestures with his hand.

Boy Half-know it.

Wife Sing it to me. I want to hear it.

Boy But why?

Wife So I can know finally what they are saying.

Boy Really?

He sings and follows the rhythm.

The famous Mrs Shoemaker
Whose husband would not stay
Has opened up a tavern
And the men can't keep away.

The Boy marks the rhythm with his head and his hands.

Oh, half her clothes are trimmed with lace –
D'you see that silken sash?
And the question on the whole world's lips
Is 'Who put up the cash?'
With Mr Mayor enthralled by her
And poor old Don Mirlo
The shocking cobbler's missus
Really puts on quite a show!

The voices are clearer and closer, accompanied by tambourines. The Wife takes up a delicate shawl and wraps it around her shoulders.

Boy (*amazed*) Where are you going?
Wife To buy a gun!

The song begins to fade. The Wife runs to the door but falls over the Mayor, who looks full of himself, beating his stick on the ground.

Mayor Who's on duty at the bar, then?
Wife The Devil.
Mayor Why? What's happened?
Wife Something you should have known about days ago, something you, the Mayor, should not have allowed! People singing songs about me, the neighbours laughing in their doorways, and me with no husband to defend me! Well then, I'll have to do it myself, the authorities in this village are a barrel of rotten apples, useless pap through and through.
Boy Well said.

Mayor (*annoyed*) Zip it, shorty. Do you know what
I just did? Had two or three of those songbirds thrown
into jail.
Wife I'll believe that when I see it!

A voice calls outside.

Voice O-o-o-o-oy!
Boy My mother's calling me.

He calls out of the window.

What!? Goodbye. If you want, I can bring you my
grandad's big sword, the one he fought with in the war.
It's too big for me, but I think you could handle it.
Wife (*smiles*) Whatever you want.
Voice (*offstage*) Bo-o-o-o—o-o-oy!

The Boy's already on his way.

Boy Whaaaaat?

SCENE THREE

Mayor As far as I can see, that devious little know-all's
the only person in the village you treat with any regard.
Wife Can't you say anything without insulting
somebody? What are you smiling about up there on
your high horse?
Mayor You there, so beautiful and all going to waste.
Wife I'd take a dog over you.

She serves him a glass of wine.

Mayor What a stupid world. I've known many women –
women like poppies, like scented roses . . . dark-haired
women with eyes full of fire, women whose hair has
the scent of valerian, women whose hands are always
hot, women so slender these two fingers could encircle

their waists, but a woman like you . . . ? No. None of
them could hold a candle to you. The day before
yesterday I was weak from dawn till dusk, all because
I saw two slips of yours, embroidered with blue ribbon,
laid out on the grass to dry, and it looked just like you
lying there, my darling Mrs Shoemaker.

Wife (*furious*) You shut up, old man, you shut up. A
man with young daughters and a family shouldn't
conduct himself in this obscene and outrageous way!

Mayor I'm a widower.

Wife And I'm a wife.

Mayor But your husband's left you and he won't come
back, I'll tell you that for sure.

Wife I mean to live as though he were still with me.

Mayor For the record: he told me himself that he no
longer loved you, not even a little.

Wife For the record, you've had four wives, damn each
of them, who hated you to death.

Mayor (*banging his stick on the ground*) Well, there we
have it.

Wife (*throwing a glass*) There we have it.

Mayor (*under his breath*) If I took you on, I'd soon tame
you!

Wife (*mocking*) What did you say?

Mayor Nothing . . . I was thinking . . . you ought to
understand that . . . if you were to behave yourself,
then it is well within my power to sign over, in front,
a solicitor, the deeds to a beautiful house.

Wife Yeah – and?

Mayor With a sideboard that cost five thousand, with
candelabra, brocade curtains and full-length mirrors.

Wife And what else?

Mayor (*in the manner of a Don Juan*) This house has a
bed, its headboard adorned with birds and lilies in
shining copper, a garden with six palm trees and a
gushing fountain . . . but wait, to be happy it needs the

person who within its rooms would be . . . (*to the Wife*) Imagine, you would be a queen!

Wife (*mocking*) I'm not used to life in the lap of luxury. It's better you enjoy the sideboard, and tuck yourself up in the bed, and look at yourself in the mirrors, and sit open-mouthed beneath the palm trees catching dates, because you'll get no date with me. I'm the shoemaker's wife and that's what I'm going to stay!

Mayor And I am the Mayor. You might want to come to your senses before you reject an offer as good as this.

Wife And you might want to remember that I don't like you or anyone else in the village. What a sad old sack you are!

Mayor (*indignant*) I'm going to see you end up in jail!

Wife You do that!

They hear a resounding trumpet tune, comically elaborate, far off.

Mayor What's that?

The Wife is amazed, delighted.

Wife The puppet show!

She drums on her knees. Two women cross by the window.

Red Neighbour The puppet show!
Purple Neighbour The puppet show!

The Boy calls in through the window.

Boy You think there'll be monkeys? Let's go!
Wife (*to the Mayor*) I'm going to close up . . .
Boy They're coming to your house.
Wife Really?

She goes to the door.

Boy Look for yourself!

SCENE FOUR

The Shoemaker appears in disguise at the door. He has a trumpet and a poster rolled up on his back. People crowd round him. The Wife looks full of anticipation and the Boy jumps in through the window and clings on to her skirts.

Shoemaker Good afternoon.
Wife Good afternoon to you, Mr Puppeteer.
Shoemaker Can I rest here?
Wife And drink too, if you'd like.
Mayor Come in, good man. Tell me what you would like – and I'm paying.
Mayor (*to the Neighbours*) And you lot, what are you hanging around for?
Red Neighbour How can we be bothering you out here in the street?

The Shoemaker sees all without anyone noticing, places his roll on the table.

Shoemaker Leave them, Mr Mayor . . . I assume that's what you are . . . they are, after all, my living.
Boy Where have I heard this man before?

Throughout the scene, the Boy watches the Shoemaker with intense curiosity.

Hey – where are the puppets?

The Neighbours laugh.

Shoemaker Once I've had my glass of wine.
Wife (*happily*) You mean you'll do the show in my house?
Shoemaker If you permit it.
Red Neighbour Then can we come in?

540

Wife You can come in.

She gives the Shoemaker his drink.

Red Neighbour (*sitting down*) We can enjoy ourselves a little.

The Mayor sits down.

Mayor Do you live far away?
Shoemaker As far as possible.
Mayor Seville?
Shoemaker Add a fair few miles.
Mayor In France?
Shoemaker A few miles more.
Mayor In England then!
Shoemaker The Philippines.

Gasps of wonder from the neighbours. The Wife is ecstatic.

Mayor So have you seen the rebels?
Shoemaker As well as I'm seeing all of you here today.
Boy What are they like?
Shoemaker Appalling. And can you imagine, they are almost all shoemakers.

The neighbours are amazed to hear it.

Wife (*stung*) Aren't there any other occupations?
Shoemaker Not one. In the Philippines, only shoemakers.
Wife Well, the shoemakers in the Philippines don't sound up to much, but here, in this region, they're very smart. Extremely smart, actually.
Red Neighbour (*full of flattery*) That's very well spoken.
Wife (*brusque*) No one asked you.
Red Neighbour My child!

The Shoemaker interrupts energetically.

Shoemaker What fabulous wine! (*He redoubles his enthusiasm.*) Quite outstanding wine! (*Beat.*) From grapes black as the souls of some women I've known.
Wife If they even have souls!
Mayor Shush. What does this great work of yours consist of?

The Shoemaker empties his glass, snaps his tongue and looks at the Wife.

Shoemaker It's a little show with a lot of wisdom. I'll teach you about the life within. There's *The Tale of the Henpecked Shoemaker*, and *The Life of Don Diego Corrientes*, *The Wild Woman of Alexandria* and *The Adventures of the Handsome Francisco Esteban*, and – above all – *The Art of Putting the Bite on Chattering Cheeky Women*.
Wife My poor little husband knew all these things!
Shoemaker May God forgive him!
Wife Hey – listen you . . .

The Neighbours laugh.

Boy Shush!
Mayor (*authoritative*) Be quiet! Every creature here has something to learn from this. When you're ready . . .

The Shoemaker unrolls the poster on which the story is painted, divided up into little squares and painted in violent colours. The Neighbours begin to close round the Shoemaker, and the Wife sits the Boy on her knees.

Shoemaker If I could have your attention . . .
Boy Oh – it's fantastic.

He hugs the Wife. The crowd whispers.

Wife Make sure you pay attention in case I don't understand it all.
Boy It can't be harder than the Bible stories.

Shoemaker Esteemed public, hear now the grave and
true tale of the red-faced wife and her long-suffering
husband, and let it serve as a lesson and an example to
the world. (*a dark tone*) Open your ears and your
minds, now.

*The Neighbours lean forwards and some of the
women grip one another's hands.*

Boy Doesn't the puppeteer sound just like your husband
when he talks?
Wife He had a much sweeter voice.
Shoemaker Are we ready?
Wife It's giving me the shivers.
Boy Me too!

Pointing with a stick.

Shoemaker
In a farmhouse in Cordoba
Where the rosebay sheds its seeds
Lived a man who worked in leather –
And a wife to meet his needs.

Expectation . . .

Now the cobbler was a peaceful man
But angry – always – was his wife.
Mind you, she was only twenty,
He was . . . into middle life.

Good God, how that couple fought!
You should have seen the witch,
Lashing her husband with eyes and tongue
To a terrible fevered pitch.

*We see on the scroll a comically childish looking
woman. The crowd murmurs.*

Wife What an awful woman!

Shoemaker

An empress would have envied this
Young cobbler's wife's fine hair,
And when she shook her skirts in springtime
Mint and lemon filled the air.
Oh,the lemons of the lemon tree,
Mouthwatering tree of life.
Oh, the lemons of the lemon tree,
What a tasty cobbler's wife.

The Neighbours laugh.

See now how her suitors came
On horses white as milk,
Elegant men on prancing beasts
Wearing tassels of finest silk.
Such handsome individuals
Who entered at her door,
Shining the gold of their watch chains
Till they couldn't have shone any more.
The wife could hardly choose between
These gents that she would greet,
As they clattered their horses' hooves so hard
On the cobbles under their feet.
Look at her talking to one of them,
Her hair all coiffed and fixed,
While her poor neglected husband
Pines and hammers his leather to bits.

Very dramatically, his hands joined . . .

Oh, husband old and virtuous,
Wed to this thorny young rose –
Watch out as these flashy, prancing fops
Steal her love out from under your nose.

The Wife, who has been racked with sighs, now begins to weep. The Shoemaker turns.

What is it?

The Mayor bangs down his stick.

Mayor Buck up, girl, stop crying!
Red Neighbour Perhaps she has some nasty secret to cry about!
Purple Neighbour Please go on!
Wife You've stirred up more tears in me than I can hold in, do you see? I can't contain them.

She cries on, then begins to hiccup in a hilarious manner.

Mayor For goodness' sake!
Boy Do you see?
Shoemaker I'll thank you to refrain from further interruption. It's hard enough to remember all this as it is.
Boy (*sighing*) And that's the truth!

The Shoemaker's in a bad mood now.

Shoemaker
On Monday – it was in the morning,
Around half eleven or so,
When the sun shone without any shadow
On the reeds and flowers below.
When the breeze rushed up on the mountain
And asked the thyme to dance
The green leaves fell from the strawberry bush
As the shrew wife watered her plants.
Then up on his white mare rode lover boy,
And he whispered between his sighs,
'Tomorrow, at your place, and all alone,
Can I feast at your table and thighs?'
'But what if my husband finds us there?'
'Your husband won't spoil our fun.'
'He might.' 'He won't – I'll kill him first.'
'He's quick – you'll need a gun.'

'Oh, I can go one better,' says he.
'But what can you mean, my dear?'
An icy death lies in wait for him,
From this cut-throat razor here.'

The Wife covers her eyes and clings onto the Boy.
The Neighbours are in a state of rapt anticipation,
their faces tense, expectant.

'And I don't mean just a scratch,' he said.
'Are you sure you can do it?' 'No fear!
He'll get ten well-aimed blows in this elegant style,
Four back, two more head, then some here.'
'And will you kill him soon?' she asked.
'Tonight, when homeward he tends,
With his leather and horsehair, he'll wind up dead
In the ditch where the wide road bends.'

Suddenly a loud cry of distress is heard offstage. The
Neighbours get up. Another cry, much closer. The
Shoemaker drops his poster and his stick. All tremble
in a comical manner. The Black Neighbour appears at
the window.

Black Neighbour They've drawn their knives!
Wife Oh my God . . .
Red Neighbour Holy Mary!
Shoemaker What a ruckus!
Black Neighbour They're carving each other up and all
  because of that woman!

She points to the Wife.

Mayor (*nervous*) Let's go and see.
Boy I'm frightened to pieces!
Green Neighbour Hurry, hurry!
Voices (*off*) That evil woman!
Shoemaker I can't stand this. I can't bear it!

He runs around with his hands on his head. Everyone else hurries out, with looks and cries of hatred for the Wife. She quickly closes the door and windows.

SCENE FIVE

Wife Have you ever seen such infamy? I swear on the most precious blood of our Saviour Jesus that I am innocent. Oh – what's happened? Look – look how I'm shaking. (*She shows him her hands.*) My hands are trying to make a quick getaway from the rest of me.

Shoemaker Calm down, dear. Is your husband out there in the street?

Wife My husband?

She starts to cry again.

Oh, sir!

Shoemaker What's happened?

Wife My husband left me because of these people, so now I live all alone with no one to care for me.

Shoemaker Poor little thing!

Wife Oh, how I loved him. How I adored him.

Shoemaker (*blurts out*) You didn't!

The Wife suddenly stops crying.

Wife What's that?

Shoemaker I said . . . you didn't . . . you couldn't have . . . have just told me this terrible story. It just seems impossible.

He's rattled.

Wife You're so right. But it surely happened and since then I can't eat, I can't sleep, I'm barely alive. He was all my happiness, you see, my security.

Shoemaker If you loved him as much as all that, and he abandoned you, your husband couldn't have been very bright.

Wife Keep your tongue in check if you don't mind. I don't remember asking for your opinion.

Shoemaker Forgive me, I didn't mean to . . .

Wife Let me tell you, he was exceptionally bright.

Shoemaker (*entertained*) Really?

Wife (*forcefully*) Absolutely. You know all those romances and things that you sing and perform for the villages? That's a fraction of what my husband knew. He knew three times as much!

Shoemaker (*seriously*) That can't be.

Wife (*forcefully*) Four times! He used to tell it all to me when we went to bed. Ancient stories you've never even heard of . . . and I would sometimes get frightened . . . but he would say to me, 'My precious darling, it's only a made-up story!'

Shoemaker (*indignant*) Made-up indeed!

The Wife is confused. He quickly corrects himself.

(*bitter*) Your husband was right. These stories we spin are pure lies, nothing but fantasy!

Wife (*bitter*) Of course they are. You think I'm that soft in the head? But you can't deny that they're very impressive.

Shoemaker Well, that's a different bag of flour! They're impressive if you're an impressionable soul!

Wife Everyone has feelings.

Shoemaker You may say so. But I've known many people without feelings. Why, in my very own village there lived a woman . . . a while back now . . . with a heart so cold she would flirt with her gentlemen friends at the window while her husband mended boots and shoes from morning till night.

The Wife gets up, grabs hold of a chair.

Wife Are you talking about me?

Shoemaker What?

Wife If you've got more to say, spit it out! Come on, be brave!

Shoemaker (*meekly*) Miss, what are you saying? How could it be you? I never meant to offend you. Why are you so angry with me? (*He is almost in tears.*) But that's my fate.

Wife (*firm but moved*) Look, you're a good man. I spoke that way because I am forever being accused! The whole world besieges me, criticises me. I'm always braced, waiting, for the least provocation, ready to defend myself. Yes, I'm alone, and still young – yet with nothing but memories to look forward to.

She cries, and he starts to cry also.

Shoemaker I understand, dear girl. I understand much better than you can imagine, because . . . there's no doubt that your situation is – in almost every detail – the same as mine.

Wife (*intrigued*) Is that possible?

He falls down on the table.

Shoemaker Well, you see my . . . my wife abandoned me!

Wife And she wasn't struck down dead?!

Shoemaker She dreamed of a life that was not my life, she was a domineering fantasist, obsessed with mindless chatter and with treats I couldn't afford. And then one desperate whirlwind of a day, she blew away from me for ever.

Wife And what are you doing now, travelling the world?

Shoemaker I'm searching for her, to tell her I forgive her and I want nothing but to spend whatever remains of my life with her. At my age, it's no fun living in a B&B.

Wife (*quickly*) Have some hot coffee. It'll perk you up after all this hullabaloo.

She goes to the bar to pour the coffee, turning her back on the Shoemaker. He crosses himself in an exaggerated manner and closes his eyes.

Shoemaker God bless you, my little red carnation!

She gives him the cup, holds the saucer in her hand as he sips the coffee.

Wife Is it good?
Shoemaker (*sweetly*) Made to measure!
Wife (*smiling*) Thank you!

The Shoemaker drains the cup.

Shoemaker Oh, how I envy your husband!
Wife Why?
Shoemaker (*gallantly*) Because he married the most wonderful woman on earth.
Wife (*melting*) The things you say!
Shoemaker And now I'll be happy to get on my way, because . . . with you alone and me alone, you so attractive and me letting my tongue run away with itself . . . it would be better to avoid any further provocation . . .
Wife (*reacting*) For God's sake! What are you imagining? I keep all my love for the man who's out wandering the wide world, the man to whom I owe my love, my husband!

The Shoemaker is delighted, throws his hat onto the floor.

Shoemaker Oh – beyond wonderful! That's what an honest wife sounds like – that!

The Wife's surprised, a little entertained.

Wife Okay – now I think you're a little . . .

She points her finger at her head.

Shoemaker You think what you like. But I must assure you – I love no one but my wife, my lawfully married wife.

Wife And I love no one but my husband. I've said it so many times the deaf have heard it! (*with her hands clasped*) Oh my precious shoemaker!

Shoemaker (*aside*) Oh, my dear little shoemaker's wife!

There's a knock at the door.

SCENE SIX

Wife Jesus – it's one thing after another! Who is it?

Boy Open up!

Wife Why what is it? What have you come for?

Boy I ran all the way to tell you!

Wife What's happened?

Boy They've cut each other up, two or three of them, and you're said to be at the bottom of it. Blood's spurting everywhere. The women have all gone to see the judge to get him to kick you out of town . . . oh! . . . and the men asked the priest to ring the bells so they can sing your song . . .

The Boy is breathless and sweating. The Wife turns to the Shoemaker.

Wife Do you see?

Boy The square is packed, like when there's a fair on – but today you're the main attraction!

Shoemaker The swine! I am going to defend her!

Wife What for? They'll just throw you in jail. No, I'm the one has to make the big gesture.

Boy You can see the crowded square from the window, look.

Wife (*quickly*) I want to see these devils for myself.

She goes quickly.

Shoemaker Yes, yes, you swine, but I'll soon change your tunes, and pay you back for this! Oh, my little house, what warmth from all your doors and windows. Oh, those awful hotels with the terrible food. All the rough dirty sheets you lie in, in a life lived on the road. What a stupid thing I did when I suspected my wife was anything but the purest gold, the purest gold on this earth! It makes me want to cry!

SCENE SEVEN

The Neighbours rush in.

Red Neighbour Good man.

Yellow Neighbour Good man.

Red Neighbour You've got to get out of this house! You're a decent person and you shouldn't be in here!

Yellow Neighbour This house belongs to a lioness, a hyena!

Red Neighbour There's bad blood in her, she's not what she seems.

Yellow Neighbour She'll leave this village or we'll chase her out of it, we locals.

Red Neighbour I'd like to see her dead.

Yellow Neighbour Yes – in her shroud – her flowers on her breast.

Shoemaker (*upset*) Enough!

Red Neighbour Blood has been spilled!

Yellow Neighbour Not a single white handkerchief left!

Red Neighbour Two men, like suns –

Yellow Neighbour – cut open with knives.

Shoemaker (*angry*) I said that's enough!

Red Neighbour And all on account of her.

Yellow Neighbour Her at the bottom of it all.

Red Neighbour We came looking for you –

Yellow Neighbour – to tell you in time!

Shoemaker Of all the lying slanderous hags! I'll tear out your hair!

Red Neighbour (*to the other*) Another one she's made her own!

Yellow Neighbour Broken with kisses, look!

Shoemaker Get out, you devils! Snakes! Liars!

The Black Neighbour appears at the window.

Black Neighbour Neighbour, run!

She runs away. The two Neighbours do the same.

Red Neighbour Another one in the trap.

Yellow Neighbour Another!

Shoemaker Harpies, trolls! I'll put razor blades in your shoes! I'll come after you in your dreams!

SCENE EIGHT

The Boy runs in.

Boy Now a group of men've gone into the Mayor's house! I'm going to see what they're saying!

He runs out. The Wife comes in.

Wife (*valiant*) Well, here I am, if they want to come looking! And with my ancestors' blood in me, people who never feared to ride their horses bareback over the steepest mountain ranges!

Shoemaker Will your strength of spirit never weaken?

Wife Never, while it's sustained, as I am, by love and honour. No, I'll keep going till every hair on this head has turned white!

The Shoemaker is moved, approaches her.

Shoemaker Oh . . .
Wife What's wrong?
Shoemaker I'm very moved.
Wife Look – I've got this whole village on me, wanting to come and slaughter me, and still I'm not remotely scared. A knife can be met with a knife and a stick with a stick, but when it's night and that door's locked and I go to bed alone . . . that's when I suffer! Oh, such suffering! I can hardly breathe! There's a creak from the chest of drawers – I get such a fright! When the rain rattles at the window – another fright! When I accidentally rustle the curtains round the bed – a double fright! And all this is just terror of loneliness and all its ghosts – ghosts I've never seen because I've never wanted to, but which came to my mother and my grandmother and all the women in my family who had eyes in their heads.
Shoemaker But why don't you change your life?
Wife Have you lost your mind? What would I do? Where would I go? No, here I am, right where God wants me.

Offstage and far away, they hear voices and applause.

Shoemaker I'm really sorry, but I've got to get on the road before nightfall. How much do I owe you?

He rolls up his poster.

Wife Nothing. A fair exchange is no robbery.
Shoemaker Thank you.

Sadly, he packs the poster on his back.

Shoemaker Well then, it's goodbye. And probably for ever – I mean at my age . . .

He is moved. She responds.

Wife I don't want to part this way. I'm a much happier person than this. (*in a clear voice*) Good man, may God restore your wife to you and with her the life of comfort and respectability you once enjoyed.

She is moved.

Shoemaker I wish you just the same with your husband. And, you know, it's a small world. What would you like me to say to him if I chanced to bump into him on my travels?

Wife Tell him that I adore him.

Shoemaker (*coming closer*) And what else?

Wife That although he's fifty-odd years old – fifty blessed years – he's got more spirit and vigour than any other man in the world.

Shoemaker Oh, my child, that's wonderful! You love him every bit as much as I love my wife!

Wife No – much more!

Shoemaker Impossible. I'm like a lowly dog that my wife orders around from her castle. But such orders! She's smarter than I am.

He is close to her, looks adoringly at her.

Wife And don't forget to tell him I'm waiting for him, and that the winter nights are long.

Shoemaker So you'd welcome him home with open arms?

Wife As if he were King, Queen and country all in one!

Shoemaker (*trembling*) And if, by chance, he was here right now?

Wife Oh, I'd be blissfully happy!

Shoemaker You'd forgive his madness?
Wife I forgave him that so long ago!
Shoemaker Do you really want him right here right now?
Wife If only he would come!
Shoemaker (*cries out*) Well here he is!
Wife What are you . . .?

The Shoemaker throws off his glasses and his disguise.

Shoemaker I can't stand it any longer! My dearest,
darling wife!

*The Wife looks stunned, her arms adrift from her
body. The Shoemaker embraces her and she fixes her
gaze on him unwaveringly in the middle of this crisis.
A sound can be clearly heard striking up offstage.*

Voice (*offstage*)
The famous Mrs Shoemaker
Whose husband would not stay,
Has opened up a tavern
And the men can't keep away.
Wife (*reacting*) Rascal, scoundrel, idiot, swine! It's all
your fault!

*She throws chairs around. The Shoemaker goes to his
bench, moved.*

Shoemaker Oh, that's my beloved wife alright!
Wife You tramp! Oh I'm so happy to have you back!
What a life I'm going to give you! Better than the
Spanish Inquisition it'll be!
Shoemaker (*at his bench*) Bless this happy house!

*The voices get closer, the Neighbours appear at the
window.*

Voices
Oh, half her clothes are trimmed with lace
D'you see that silken sash?

And the question on the whole world's lips
Is 'Who put up the cash?'
With Mr Mayor enthralled by her
And poor old Don Mirlo,
The shocking cobbler's missus
Really puts on quite a show!

Wife Oh, the shame of it! That God should saddle me with such a man!

She goes to the door.

I'll stop your long tongues from flapping you red-faced losers! Come on, come on if you want some! There are two of us now to defend this house! Me and my husband!

She points to her husband.

This idiot, this scoundrel!

The sound of the singing fills the stage. A bell starts to ring furiously, far away.

Curtain.

Beckett Performed by Groucho Marx

Lucinda Coxon interviewed by Jim Mulligan

Lucinda Coxon was scrupulous about her role as translator of *The Shoemaker's Incredible Wife*:

> When you translate you have to slow your blood down. It's an incredibly slow process, but it was a great labour of love. It became a meditative exercise. I decided I would leave in the loose ends and the murky, messy bits because they are the play and it's not for me to tidy up Lorca's work. He had revised it many times and it is his play. It was my job to serve the play and release it.

The plays of Lorca are usually set in the rural Spain of the time when he was writing, in the nineteen twenties and thirties, but since that society had scarcely changed for generations the plays feel as if they are set far back in time and in a society that is nothing like ours today. But Lucinda Cozon thinks *The Shoemaker's Incredible Wife* is relevant to young people:

> Lorca is very much a writer of the twentieth century. Although he was friends with Dali and Buñuel, we do not see him as a modernist, but you could talk about Sartre and Beckett in the same breath as this play. It's a play that champions the imagination. Lorca himself often played the Writer when he was touring the show. It's a fantastic opening, full of disingenuous charm. 'Ladies and gentlemen, do relax. We won't frighten the horses. No need to be anxious. There'll be no

surprises. You're in for a lovely quiet night at the theatre.' And then he pulls the switch. It's a great act of theatrical bravado. And it's very funny. Young people love this play.

The Shoemaker's Incredible Wife is a play about relationships and how we constantly reinvent ourselves and each other and the world around us in a way that transcends a narrow political reading, such as claiming that it is a play about the role of women. The wife is young, in some ways still a child who is afraid of the dark and eager to play games with a boy not much younger than herself. She lives in a town where she has a limited set of options. She has no money and nowhere to go. And she has made a marriage of convenience to a much older man.

> You can tell that Lorca is passionate about the Wife. Even though she's insufferable for a lot of the time, he loves her. She is intelligent, but she is not in control of herself. She can't figure out how to get her husband to love her. She's amazed and shocked when he leaves, but when he comes back in disguise they manage to express their love for each other in a way they could never do face to face. You sympathise with him. He never has a quiet moment. Every time he sits down, she comes in. She's provoking him, trying to engage with him.

The Shoemaker is a fifty-four-year-old boy. He has been looked after by his mother and then his sister, and he is astonished to find himself in a house with a woman who does not want to mother him but instead wants a peer relationship with him. He is incapable of responding to his wife, and in the end he leaves in order to find himself. When he returns, they realise they need each other, and he desires her in a way we certainly do not see in the first act. Their declaration, however, can only take place in the context of a play.

> When the husband returns he puts an audience on the stage and we have a play-within-a-play. The whole town comes to watch the puppet show, so we as the audience are able to watch an audience experiencing what it is to be an audience. We are able to see the puppet show bring about a great cathartic realisation that raises the emotional temperature of the town and brings about an act of violence in the street. The power of this theatrical performance is such that it changes things materially in the world and we are able to watch that. I think that's glorious.

Roughly speaking, Lorca has given us the 'seven ages of man', ranging from the Boy through the middle-aged Shoemaker to doddering Don Mirlo – all characters in a play that is completely circular. It ends as it began but not precisely where it began. People are changed, but there is a very strong sense that the society Lorca depicts requires people to fulfil certain roles: the unattainable beauty looking out of her window; the man of authority who has to go for a lie-down when he sees a petticoat hanging out to dry; the neighbour with all the children; the pious, judgemental women; the henpecked husband; the sexually frustrated young wife. Those were the constraints on two people trying to find themselves. That they realise they need each other, love each other and desire each other for the first time is a triumph for them and a triumph for Lorca as a writer. But is all this relevant to young people today?

> Any relationship is partly a performance. It's how we conduct our lives in public. If you are a teenager, the

stuff you show the world is something you think about quite a lot. You are vulnerable and self-conscious. You are in fear of your emotions. The world will narrow you and shut you down if it can, but this farce can teach you to reach out in all directions without toppling over. Keep it simple; keep it in the moment; keep the shifts fast and simple – and this extraordinary play will be like Beckett being performed by Groucho Marx. It has a wild dynamic about it, but you have to have a very steady centre to pull it off.

Production Notes

When touring, Lorca would often add songs and ad-libs to his script, but this translation is based on what is now regarded as the standard version of the play. Don't be tempted to cut the Writer's introduction at the beginning as it would be defrauding the audience. His direct address is an introduction to the play, giving the audience equal status to the characters in it. This signals that it's going to be a different kind of piece. Originally, Lorca would have played the part himself.

Lucinda Coxon translated directly from the Spanish, though she isn't a Spanish speaker. She found the vocabulary very simple, unlike Shakespeare's – it's what Lorca does with it that's remarkable. She tried to stay close to the text, but it had to be playable. The play is full of Spanish colloquialisms that have to be appropriately translated for a language of today or they simply wouldn't make sense. The action must be energetic and the characters equipped with the language to achieve this.

The play is often called *The Shoemaker's Prodigious Wife*, but Lucinda thought 'incredible' suggested a show, a billing, and that the Wife isn't a credible witness. Lucinda worked in pencil between the lines of Spanish. The opening speech is full of long sentences and she didn't want to change that.

The play presents a choice between security, and freedom and adventure. It asks how in life we can manage to marry these things. Lucinda thinks the answer is through imagination – it's the only thing that keeps the Shoemaker's

Wife sane. Her only freedom is in her head. Her husband goes away and finds imagination. In some ways it's very simple, in other ways very complicated. You need to take a simple approach to directing it – moment to moment.

There are many plays inside this play. There are stock types from *commedia*, a play-within-a-play as in *Hamlet* or *A Midsummer Night's Dream*, but it's also modernist to the point that at the conclusion we ask whether it is all going to start again.

You'll need to consider the practicalities of the butterfly scene, the old man and the puppets. The biggest challenge, though, is how you ride the emotional journeys. Direction must be specific about where the emotions come from – the fear, the anger. These shifts in emotion create the vibrancy of the play. Sometimes it's like *Tom and Jerry*, at other times like *Who's Afraid of Virginia Woolf?*

You need to build a world that is coherent and cohesive, but not be afraid of potential stylistic inconsistencies. Things are changing all the time, so the performances and physical design need to be delicate sand not to inflict limitations. Handle it as if it were a dream, a fractured reality. That's the idea of the butterfly – the power of illusion and the suspension of disbelief.

Performing this play in-the-round might add to the sense of storytelling – you could make the street feel busy through the possibility of numerous entrances. The Neighbours should seem predatory and appear to be invading the space, creating an energy that makes the audience feel they're being caught in a whirlwind.

The worst thing that can possibly happen in the community of this play is not to have a husband. Is the Shoemaker's Wife an outsider? Lucinda believes that she was destitute, living up on a hill with no family, but managed to broker a marriage deal through the Shoemaker's sister.

FINDING CHARACTER THROUGH EXERCISES

Have the actress playing the Shoemaker's Wife imagine trying to undress with all the men standing at the edge of a circle looking at her. Have the actor playing the Shoemaker try to protect her. Ask the men to circle round the Wife as if in a bar and as if she were for sale. Now have the women stand at the edge of the circle and consider the Shoemaker's Wife's choice of clothing. Ask them to move around the circle in a censorious manner. Get the Shoemaker's Wife to get rid of them by touching them and signalling for them to leave the circle.

Have all the men use the Shoemaker's Wife as a sofa on which to have a snooze while the Shoemaker addresses the audience. Have all the men act the Young Man with Sash while the Shoemaker watches from the side of the circle. The Shoemaker should then get rid of the men, getting them to melt away from the circle.

These exercises should help the cast explore the Shoemaker's paranoia and help define the Wife through his eyes. It can convey the idea that the Shoemaker saw reflections of his wife's infidelities.

Now have the Shoemaker's Wife take on the role of director and deliberately heighten the Shoemaker's sense of powerlessness. The Shoemaker's Wife's objective is to excite the Shoemaker by encouraging the Young Man in the Sash. The Shoemaker's Wife can suggest romantic poses the Young Man might make while the Shoemaker walks the circle.

This exercise should heighten the farcical elements of the play and put the focus on the Shoemaker and his Wife's relationship.

Get the Shoemaker to stand in the centre of the circle and speak his story while imagining visual representations of the story to be flying around the space. The exercise can be repeated with him looking in a different direction with the introduction of each character. And repeated again, but this time with people playing 'dumb' characters and the Shoemaker using them to point at throughout the story.

The relationship between the Boy and the Shoemaker's Wife is intriguing. He could represent the Shoemaker's youth; he could be the child she will never have. The Boy is her only connection to the outside world; and he has a connection with the Writer because he gives important plot information. He is an innocent who is constantly being poisoned by the community; he reveals another side to the Shoemaker's Wife and is the only character who doesn't demand things from her. She herself is a kind of child: is this why she gets on with the Boy?

Look at the scene where the Writer releases an imaginary butterfly for the Shoemaker's Wife and the Boy to follow. Repeat it, but this time have four more people play the Boy simultaneously.

Using multiple Boys might suggest these are the fantasy children the Shoemaker's Wife will never have. It could be interesting if the actress playing the Shoemaker's Wife is conscious that the butterfly represents the last moment of peace she will have.

Look at the fundamentals of the relationship between inside and outside the house and what they represent. Arrange your space so that the action can be played end-on. Decide if the outside threat is real or imagined.

Read the opening of the play with the Writer talking directly to the audience end-on, placing a door frame in the background. It might be good if the door frame is constantly moving and the Writer dominating the stage. The audience should be unsure whether or not to trust the Writer. It's as if the Writer is saying 'I'm going to dress her down – you're going to get kitchen-sink realism, forget poetry,' and then at the end of his speech we witness something spectacular.

The Writer is disingenuous from the word go. He is looking to reassure the audience by saying, 'Don't worry if you're uncertain when outside the comfort of the *EastEnders* box,' and then, 'Oops, sorry, something different did happen.' The Writer is very important. Lorca wrote a play-within-a-play-within-a-play, like a hall of mirrors, and it is important that the audience accept the artifice from the beginning. This is a play that refuses to be defined.

Explore the idea of the Writer. Have the actor playing the Writer make as much contact with the audience as possible. Repeat this with the Writer in control of introducing all the elements of the play. For example, he could introduce a door frame into the space, then click his fingers and the Wife could appear, being chased by villagers. Or he could click his fingers before a fight ensues. Repeat the exercise, but this time have the Wife get into an argument with the Villagers situated in the audience. The Writer can introduce the Boy into the scene by moving the door frame into the space with the Boy standing on it. This time, have the actor reading the Writer, and dress an actress as the Wife in the way that he describes her. She could be dressed down from diva to housewife.

This exercise might help create a tension and relationship between the Writer and Shoemaker's Wife that could be explored throughout the play – perhaps mirroring Prospero and Miranda's relationship in *The Tempest*.

Think about the world of the Shoemaker's Wife in relation to the community. Look at her first speech. Firstly, using a moveable door frame on castors, have her move the frame from downstage to upstage instead of simply shutting the door on the Neighbours. Ask her to imagine that the Neighbours are in the audience and to find a way of shutting the Neighbours/audience out by pushing the door frame from upstage to downstage. Decide what positions are most useful for the door frame.

Try an alternative exercise and shut the Neighbours outside the Shoemaker's Wife's space. Get her to shout at the Neighbours in the direction of the audience and have someone else – a kind of offstage Foley artist – create the sound of doors slamming at certain points in the text. This might give the impression that the Neighbours are growing tired of the Shoemaker's Wife's rants and are slamming their doors in her face.

This exercise might help show the difference between the public and private image of the Shoemaker's Wife. It could suggest that she is the one being locked out by the Neighbours rather than the other way round.

Look at the moment when the Red Neighbour appears. Find a way of locating the Red Neighbour outside, and defining the Shoemaker's territory. Start by asking what the Red Neighbour's objective is. It might be to get cheap shoes. The Shoemaker's objective could be to defend his 'castle'. Ask all the many children to follow their mother (Red Neighbour) everywhere in a close ball behind her. The Shoemaker's workbench should be located in the centre of the space, and he needs to move his workbench wherever he goes. If the Shoemaker feels pressured or threatened he should stay behind the bench in relation to the Red Neighbour.

Emotionally the Shoemaker has no territory; his sister has previously taken care of everything, and now he is being asked to be a man – sexually and emotionally – by his wife. It's inevitable that he leaves – it's his time in the chrysalis – in order for him to transform.

Place the bar in different positions on stage – in the centre, upstage and downstage centre, and with the Shoemaker's Wife on different sides of it. Each position will significantly shift where the focus of attention is for the audience. It's important to try different options before making a final decision. Avoid having the Wife serving drinks on a tray – she might look like a waitress.

THE FINAL SCENE

Look at the final exchanges between the Shoemaker and his Wife. The space should reflect the dynamics of their verbal sparring. Change the position of the actors playing the two parts as they are speaking: look at finding the point that reveals the tension inherent in this 'epic' conversation.

Ask whether the Shoemaker is pretending when he claims to be leaving the Shoemaker's Wife as the lynch mob is coming for her. It could be a moment of transition where the puppeteer leaves and the husband returns – he might be cowardly, or he might simply be testing his wife.

Direct the final scene using the following instructions to the actors:

The entire group should be a ferociously excited mob once the decision is made to seek out the Shoemaker's Wife (but only vocally).

Both the Shoemaker and the Wife should hear the rabble in the direction of the audience. They should look out, look at each other, and then the Shoemaker should be businesslike in preparing to leave.

The Shoemaker's Wife should explore the idea of losing the puppeteer by putting all focus on him.

They should embrace after 'My dearest, darling wife.' Then they should hear the singing crowd from the direction of the audience.

The Shoemaker and the Wife should focus on the idea that they have to argue for social reasons, to meet public expectations. The Wife should curse the Shoemaker, while he starts joyously back at his workbench.

Repeat the scene, but think about the Wife recognising the Shoemaker earlier – at the moment she offers him some coffee? This might be, for example, because he stirs his cup in a particular way or dances a little jig.

Repeat the final scene again. This time ask the group as Neighbours to gossip about the Shoemaker's Wife rather than sing, and for the Shoemaker to treat his workbench like a drum-kit. Underscore the reunion with an accordion. It's important to cast the villagers as a group of grotesque individuals and necessary to decide on the class and status of the Shoemaker's Wife within this community.

MUSIC

The text is like a musical score – it's good to play with rhythms. Lucinda likes the idea that the music isn't beautiful – maybe like the percussion of the Shoemaker's hammer and nails. The notion of something terrible happening offstage could be powerful – and could be unsettling if it builds in the music. Keep it simple, maybe with a single penetrating note, maybe some whistling and rustling when the Shoemaker's Wife is on her own in the house. Listen to an album by Enrique Moriente called 'Lorca'. Avoid underscoring.

SET

You could build a massive white box, with a square floor, entirely on wheels. It could rotate and resemble a prison, which would make it easy to define the relationship between the public and private space. The bench could become a bar on wheels.

Look at the extent to which the threat from the outside world is real or imagined. You could explore the use of shadow and use a minimal set. Consider setting the play in-the-round, with a net curtain dividing the audience from the action, but also implicating them as voyeurs.

COSTUME

In terms of social isolation and repression, think through how important costume could be – the exposure of the Wife's flesh, whether she is self-conscious or not. Maybe it would be useful to think about ignoring the primary colour coding of the Neighbours in terms of costume – they could all be monochrome, and the only character with colour the Shoemaker's Wife. Colour suggests imagination.

Workshop facilitated by Phyllida Lloyd
with notes taken by Martin Constantine

SHUT UP

Andrew Payne

Andrew Payne's plays include *Mugged* for Connections 2005, *The Plan*, *Squash* and *Then What*. His TV credits include *Malice Aforethought*, *Dead Gorgeous*, *Midsomer Murders*, *Pie in the Sky*, *You Me and It*, *Love After Lunch* and *Minder*.

Characters

Dexter

Mum

Dad

Teacher

Tatiana (Tats)

Chloe

Ben (Bins)

Richie

Anthony

Johnny Smith

Doctors

Jack

Jill

Shrinks

SCENES

HOME SWEET HOME
SCHOOL
BREAK
HOME AGAIN
DOCTORS, SHRINKS, WEIRDOS
IN THE PARK
HOME AGAIN
BACK IN THE PARK
THE PRESENTATION
VISITING TIME

*Sets should be minimal: a few chairs and tables
which can be quickly rearranged to suit
the various settings.*

*A whiteboard should be on stage,
somewhere or other, in every scene.*

*Better if the screen of the TV is not visible
to the audience. If that is not possible,
the screen should be blank. Or showing
one unchanging image. And no sound.*

ONE

Mum and Dad sit side by side, watching television.
A table with a bowl and spoon on it. The whiteboard.
Dexter enters, bag over his shoulder. Mum and Dad
don't notice him. Mum shouts without looking away
from the TV.

Mum DEXTER! IT'S GONE TEN PAST! (*pointing at*
TV) Ooh look, it's whatsername. I like her, she's
lovely!

Dexter writes HOME SWEET HOME *on the whiteboard.*
Watches Mum and Dad.

Dad Look at the state of her!
Mum She's lovely. I loved her in that thing. (*shouting*)
DEXTER!
Dad She's had her tits done.
Mum No!
Dad And her lips. Lips, tits, bum, she's had the lot done.
Mum No!
Dad It said in the paper.
Mum (*shouting*) DEXTER! (*to Dad*) You call him. Be
nice.
Dad GET DOWN HERE, YOU LAZY LITTLE GIT!
Mum I said be nice! Today of all days!
Dad Why? He's a lazy little git, isn't he?

Dexter drops his bag on the floor, sits at the table. The
noise alerts Mum.

Mum There you are, sweetie!

Mum gets up, goes over to the table. Dad doesn't take his eyes off the TV.

Eat your breakfast, it's your favourite.

Dexter looks at the bowl. Doesn't touch it.

You've got to eat some breakfast today, 'cos it's a big day. It's a big day for all of us, isn't it, Dad?

No response from Dad.

Now, sweetheart, I'm just going to say this once, alright? Because I don't want to go on at you, I know you think I go on at you, but it's because I'm your mum, and mums care, don't they, so all I'm saying is, please, Dexter, please please please will you *try* this time, try and get on at this new school, will you, sweetheart?

Dad Talking to yourself, darling.

Mum What I'm saying is, I don't think I can go through this again, Dexter, I can't take the stress, not after the last time. So make an effort, will you, darling, because we've worked really really hard to get you into this new school, haven't we, Dad?

No response from Dad.

Are you listening, Dexter? (*Beat.*) Dexter?

Dad Wasting your time, darling.

Mum (*to Dad*) Will you be quiet, just for one second, I am trying to talk to our son. (*to Dexter*) It's a very good school, Dexter, we're very lucky get you in, so you will make an effort, won't you?

Dad That'll be the day.

Mum Will you please turn the telly off, I'm trying to talk to Dexter!

Dad I'm waiting for the weather!

Mum What do you need the weather for?

Dad Because I'm driving around all day, aren't I? I need to know what the weather's like, don't I?

Mum You're in the van, what difference does the weather make?

Dad It affects the driving conditions, doesn't it?

Mum Well, I'm trying to talk to Dexter.

Dad Wasting your time, darling.

Mum So you see what I'm saying, Dexter? Will you please try? For our sake?

Dad What he's got to do is, is *talk*, like a normal human being! 'Cos if he gets kicked out of this school, he's toast! He's history!

Mum (*to Dad*) If you can't say anything positive, just shut up, will you?

Dad I'm being realistic, aren't I? He gets kicked out this time, he's on his own, he can't come on the van with me, not till he's sixteen.

Mum Why would he want to come on the van with you?

Dad He's got to earn a living hasn't he?

Mum Not in your van, not if I've got anything to do with it.

Dad Why, what else is he going to do? After-dinner speaker?

Mum What your dad's trying to say is, please make an effort, will you, Dexter? We'll give you all the support you need, but you've got to think of us as well, haven't you? You've got to think of the stress we're under. Promise me you'll try, will you, sweetheart? (*Beat.*) Dexter? (*Beat.*) Sweetheart?

After a long pause, Dexter nods.

Good boy! (*to Dad*) He says he's going to try!

Dad I didn't hear him.

Dexter stands, picks up his bag.

Mum Bye, darling. Give us a kiss. Love you loads, sweetheart.

577

Mum kisses Dexter.

Be a good boy. And *talk* to people. Make some nice new
friends. Dexter's off now, Dad.

Beat. Dad watching TV.

Did you hear what I said? Dexter's off now.

Beat.

Dad She's not in that thing any more.
Mum Who isn't?
Dad Her – (*Points at TV.*) Who's had her tits done. She's
not in it any more.
Mum That's a shame, I loved her in that.
Dad She's in this new thing.
Mum We'll have to watch that. It's new, is it?
Dad Course it is. Makes sense, doesn't it? New tits, new
series.

Dexter exits.

TWO

*Richie, Anthony, Ben (Bins) and Chloe (rearranging set if
necessary).*
    Tatiana (Tats) cleans whiteboard, writes SCHOOL *on it.
The Teacher enters with Dexter.*

Teacher (*weary*) Alright, back to your places, pay
attention everybody. This is Dexter, who's joining us
today. I want you all to make Dexter feel at home and
help him settle in. Sit over there, Dexter.

The Teacher points at an empty desk next to Tats.

Richie Sir, excuse me, sir, why is Dexter starting term
late?

Teacher That's neither here nor there, Richie.

During the above, Dexter walks to his desk. Richie sticks out a leg and trips him.

Richie, I saw that.
Richie I was just stretching my leg, sir.
Teacher Apologise, Richie.

The Teacher turns to wipe the whiteboard clean.

Richie (to *Dexter*) Sorry, geeze.

Richie leans across from his desk and holds out his hand. Dexter hesitates, then extends his hand. Richie withdraws his hand at the last moment, gives Dexter the 'loser' sign, to the amusement of Bins, Anthony and Chloe.

The Teacher turns back from the whiteboard.

Teacher Anthony, you can show Dexter round at break –
Anthony Can't, sir, got a meeting about the school trip.

Tats sticks her hand up.

Tats I'll show him round, sir.
Teacher Alright, Tatiana, thank you very much.

Lascivious noises from Richie, Bins, Anthony and Chloe.

Shut up! Now then –

The Teacher turns to the whiteboard.

William Blake . . .

The Teacher writes on the whiteboard: WILLIAM BLAKE 1757–1827.

Who knows anything about William Blake?

579

Richie sticks his hand up.

Richie His name was William Blake, he was born in 1757 and he died in 1827, sir.

Teacher Not amused, Richie. Anyone else?

Tats sticks her hand up.

Tatiana?

Tats He was a poet, sir.

Teacher Very good.

The Teacher writes POET *on the board.*

He was a poet and an artist.

The Teacher writes ARTIST *on the board. Then* MYSTICAL.

He is known as a 'mystical' poet. Anyone know what that means?

Tats sticks her hand up.

Tats It's about religion, sir.

Teacher Very good. Blake was very interested in religion and spirituality, and we're going to study two poems he wrote which illustrate this. One is called 'The Little Boy Lost' and the other is called 'The Little Boy Found'. They're on page fourteen . . .

They all turn to a page in one of their textbooks, except Dexter.

Tats Sir, Dexter hasn't got a book.

Teacher Use this.

The Teacher hands Dexter a book.

Okay, Ben, read the first verse of 'The Little Boy Lost' please.

Bins stands.

Bins (*incredibly fast*)
  'Father, father! Where are you going?
  O do not walk so fast –'
Teacher Properly!
Bins (*a bit slower, monotone*)
  'Father, father! Where are you going?
  O do not walk so fast!
  Speak, father, speak to your little boy
  Or else I shall be lost.'
Teacher Next verse, Anthony.

Anthony stands.

Anthony
  'The night was dark, no father was there;
  The child was wet with dew;
  The mire was deep, and the child did weep,
  And away the vapour flew.'

*Various mocking 'aahs', 'wuss', 'wimp' and giggles
from Richie, Bins, Anthony and Chloe.*

Teacher Shut up!

They take their time quietening down.

Now we'll read 'The Little Boy Found'. First verse please,
  Tatiana.

Tats stands.

Tats
  'The little boy lost in the lonely fen,
  Led by the wand'ring light,
  Began to cry –'

'Aaahs' etc. from Richie, Bins, Anthony and Chloe.

Teacher Shut up!

Tats

        '– but God, ever nigh,
  Appear'd like his father in white.'

Teacher Right, thanks, Tatiana. Last verse, Richie.

Richie Sir, why can't Dexter read it?

Teacher Because I'm asking you.

Richie I'm just being *inclusive*, sir –

Teacher Shut up and read it, Richie!

Richie gets to his feet with great reluctance.

Richie
  'He kissed the child –'
Yeuch!

*'Pervert!', 'Gross!,' ''Sgusting!' etc., from Bins,
Anthony and Chloe.*

Teacher Shut up! Get on with it, Richie.

Richie (*melodramatic*)
  'He kissed the child and by the hand led,
  And to his mother brought,
  Who in sorrow pale, thro' the lonely dale,
  Her little boy weeping sought.'

Amusement from the usual suspects.

Teacher Okay, a week today you'll do a presentation
    about these poems –

Groans and moans.

Here are some of the things you should think about while
    you're preparing your presentation, things I shouldn't
    have to tell you because we've done it all before. (*The
    Teacher turns to the board.*) MEANING. (*Writes the
    word.*) What are the poems about? LANGUAGE. (*Writes.*)
    Why does Blake use certain words? What is the effect
    he's trying to create? VOCABULARY. (*Writes.*) Find out
    what words like 'mire' and 'fen' mean. (*Writes.*) FORM,

RHYME and RHYTHM. (*Writes*.) Then *contrast and compare* the two poems. Alright? Got that? That's next Monday, then. Dexter, is that okay? You did presentations at your last school, I presume?

No response from Dexter.

Dexter? Any problems?

No response from Dexter.

Dexter?

Tats holds her hand up.

Tats He said it's fine, sir. No problems.
Teacher Okay, fine . . .
Richie I didn't hear him. (*to Bins*) Did you hear him?
Bins I didn't hear him. (*to Anthony*) Did you?
Anthony Not a thing.
Chloe Me neither.
Teacher That's it, then. Dexter, would you stay behind for a moment, please?

Richie, Bins, Anthony and Chloe get up, file past Dexter as they exit.

Tats (*to Dexter*) I'll wait for you outside, okay?

No response from Dexter.

Right, I'll wait for you outside then.

Tats exits. The Teacher comes and sits near Dexter.

Teacher Now then, Dexter me old mate, what are we going to do about you, eh? I believe there's a bit of a problem – okay, not a *problem*, let's call it a *situation*, shall we? A situation whereby you don't talk very much. Yes?

No response from Dexter.

Would I be right in thinking that?

No response from Dexter.

'Cos the thing is, I'm not a special . . . whatever you want
to call it, I'm not a *special* teacher, I'm just an ordinary
teacher, okay? I mean, I'll do anything I can to help,
obviously. Shyness? Tell me about it! When I was your
age, wow, are you kidding? (*Beat.*) So, the presentation
thing, getting up in front of the class and talking, is
that going to be okay, old mate? I could let you off this
one, as you've just started. I could do that, no probs.

No response from Dexter.

But you're going to have to do it sooner or later, aren't
you? You know, stand up and *say* something. Because
I can't go on making exceptions, can I? Because this is
a tough class, and I'm doing my best, okay? I really
am, but there's always this pressure, day after day, and
nobody really understands. (*emotional*) My partner,
she works in IT, I mean, come on, are you *kidding*?
What does she know about pressure? Sod-all, that's
what!

A beat as the Teacher recovers his composure.

So what do you reckon, Dexter? Will you do the
presentation?

Beat. Then Dexter nods.

Great stuff! Top man!

THREE

Tats writes BREAK *on the whiteboard, then sits next to Dexter.*

Tats (*pointing*) The Townies hang out over there, and the Grungers hang out by the science block. The Druggies are mostly over there, under the trees.

Dexter looks where's she pointing but says nothing.

I don't hang out with any of them, not much anyway. My friend Dora and me, when we were in year nine, we were Townies, okay, but Dora's a Druggie now, sort of Goth-Druggie, she's on the cusp. We're still friends, okay, but I don't hang out with her so much. Goths, God, they're such a stereotype. I don't want to be a stereotype, it's so boring. You're not a stereotype. I'm not going out with anyone at the moment. My boyfriend, okay, he left after GCSEs. He's gone to stage school. He's really talented. He's already been on telly. Actually, you remind me of him. He didn't talk much either. He was a very good listener. Like you. You're a very good listener, Dexter. Everybody else is just like blah blah blah, all the time. You really remind me of him. Except you're cuter. Would you like to come round to my house? It's a really nice house. My parents are musicians. My dad's on tour with his band, he's in America. It's a comeback tour. They weren't cool for a bit, but now they're cool again. My mum's a singer. She's got a fantastic voice. Her career is going *really* well. So would you? Come round to my house? Am I going too fast? I do that sometimes.

Pause. Tats looks at Dexter.

Would you?

Dexter nods – and Richie, Bins and Chloe enter.

Richie / Bins / Chloe (*to Tats*) Alright, Tats? Hi! (*etc.*)
Richie (*to Dexter*) Alright, Dexter?

No response from Dexter.

Tats shown you round, has she? Shown you the many
   delights of our lovely school, has she?
Chloe Asked him out yet, Tats?
Tats Shut up!
Chloe You have, haven't you? You're so bad, Tats.
Tats Shut up!
Bins (*to Dexter*) You want to watch her, bruv. She's
   desperate.
Tats I am not.
Chloe He's quite cute, actually. I might ask him out. Hey,
   Dexter, fancy going out with me?
Richie (*to Bins*) You see how it works? The man of
   mystery. Never says a word and they all want to shag
   him.
Bins (*to Chloe*) You'll have a great time with this one,
   Chloe. Great *conversations*.
Chloe Who wants cònversations?
Richie Hey, Dexter. How come you're here? What's the
   story?

Dexter doesn't respond.

Bins Come on, geeze. Talk!
Richie Yeah, talk to us, Dexter. You're starting to do my
   head in.
Bins Come on, where was your last school?
Richie Yeah, share the fascinating story of your life with
   us.
Bins (*waving a hand in front of Dexter's face*) Hello!
   Anyone there?
Chloe The lights are on but no one's home.

Richie He's starting to stress me out.

Tats Leave him alone.

Richie We're making conversation, and he's not replying, it's very bad manners.

Tats He's shy, okay?

Richie Shy? I don't think so.

Bins (*to Tats*) He told you he was shy, did he?

Tats Yeah, he did.

Chloe You are such a liar, Tats.

Richie He actually uttered the words 'I am shy', did he?

Tats Yes.

Bins When?

Tats When we were talking.

Chloe Well, *duh*!

Richie When you were *talking*?

Tats Yes, Richie. Just now. Before *you* turned up.

Bins And he confessed to being shy.

Tats Not exactly in those words.

Bins Aha!

Chloe Aha!

Richie Not exactly in those words, eh? Well, what words, Tats? What words *exactly*?

Bins I'll tell you – none!

Richie Exactly! No words at all! Because you're lying, Tats. He never spoke. And I'll tell you something else – he isn't shy. You're not shy, are you, Dexter?

Tats Leave him alone!

Richie He's not shy at all. Are you shy, Dexter?

Bins Answer the question, bruv.

Richie Send us a sign, that we might be enlightened.

Bins Come on, Dex! What is your answer?

Pause. Dexter shakes his head.

Richie I knew it! You know how I knew?

Bins How, Richie?

Richie Because I have seen this before!

Chloe Seen what before, Richie?

Richie The Look.

Bins What Look?

Richie The Look on his face. The Look of the Nutter!

Bins Johnny Smith!

Richie Yes! Johnny Smith!

Chloe Ohmygod, you're right! Johnny Smith!

Bins The love of your life, eh, Tats?

Tats Shut up!

Chloe He so was, Tats.

Tats He so was not.

Chloe Face it, Tats. You love weirdos.

Tats He is not like Johnny Smith!

Richie Let's hope not, for his sake. (*to Dexter*) You want to know what happened to Johnny Smith, Dexter?

Bins Tell him.

Richie I'll tell you what happened to Johnny Smith –

Anthony enters.

Anthony Alright?

Richie / Bins / Chloe Alright? (*etc.*)

Anthony (*to Dexter*) Alright?

No response from Dexter.

(*to Dexter*) I've been hearing all about you.

Richie You've been hearing all about Dexter?

Anthony Yes, there's a kid in year ten, his brother was at school with Dexter.

Bins What did he say?

Anthony What *didn't* he say!

Chloe What? What?

Richie Come on, *what*?

Anthony (*to Dexter*) Do you want to tell them, or shall I? Oh, alright. If you insist.

Richie Let's hear it then.

Anthony He only attacked a teacher, didn't he?

Bins I knew it.

Anthony And he beat up a couple of kids.

Richie Perfect!

Anthony One of them was a *girl*!

Richie Nice!

Anthony Anyway, he was excluded.

Chloe Great. And now *we've* got him. A woman-beater.

Tats You don't know if it's true though, do you?

Anthony Of course it's true!

Richie It's true alright! He's a div, he's a psycho like Johnny Smith!

Chloe He's a weirdo.

Richie (*to Dexter*) You know what happened to Johnny Smith? They locked him up!

Bins They sedated him.

Anthony He was unconscious for a month.

Chloe In a straitjacket. Handcuffed to the bed.

Richie He beat someone up and you know what they did? They *sectioned* him!

Bins Do you know what that means, bruv?

Richie It means you're a loony. It means they can take you away and bang you up for as long as they want.

Anthony Johnny Smith never said a word either.

Richie And they *sectioned* him, the div!

Tats Stop it! Leave him alone! He is not like Johnny Smith! He is not a div! Tell them, Dexter!

Richie Yeah, tell us, Dexter! Speak! Are you or are you not a div?

Bins He's a div, believe me.

Anthony Psycho!

Chloe Special Needs!

Richie Yeah, Special Needs! Is that it, Dexter? Do you have Special Needs?

Anthony If he's Special Needs, I'm complaining. I'm writing to the governors. I shouldn't be taught with a Special Needs kid. It could hold me back.

Richie Come on, Dexter. Speak to us!

Chloe Tell us about this *girl* you bashed up!

Bins Say something, you freak!

Richie Hey! Special Needs!

Tats Go on, Dexter. Say something. It doesn't matter what. Just say something, then they'll leave you alone. Please, Dexter!

Richie I can't hear you!

Dexter stands.

Bins Hey! We have lift-off!

Richie Come on, loser boy, we're waiting!

Richie pushes Dexter.

Tats Richie, don't!

Richie Say something, you freak!

Richie pushes Dexter again. This time Dexter lashes out at him. He misses but Richie lets out a melodramatic howl of pain. Richie doubles up, trying to protect himself as Dexter flails away at him.

Bins Fight, fight!

Anthony (*calling off*) Sir, sir!

Bins Fight! Fight!

Richie Get him off me, get the psycho off me!

Richie lets out melodramatic howls of pain. Bins tries to kick Dexter while keeping his distance.

Bins Do him, Rich! Do the nutter!

Anthony (*calling off*) Sir, sir! Over here!

Chloe Get off him, you freak!

Chloe grabs Dexter's arm and hangs on, kicking out at him. Dexter pulls himself free. Chloe reels away, screaming in pain.

Bastard! Did you see that? He attacked me!

Anthony (*calling off*) Sir, sir, Dexter's gone berserk! He's attacking all of us!

Dexter lashes out once more at Richie, who collapses whimpering. Dexter exits. Tats goes to Chloe, who's lying on the ground.

Tats He didn't do anything!
Chloe He attacked me, the psycho!

Bins and Anthony help Richie to his feet.

Bins Rich? You alright, bruv?
Richie Did you *see* that?

Tats turns to the boys.

Tats He didn't do anything!
Anthony I've never seen anything like it! He's totally out of control!
Bins He's a nutter!
Chloe He's a psycho!
Richie He's a total maniac, that's what he is!

FOUR

Dexter writes HOME AGAIN *on the whiteboard, then sits at the table with Mum. Dad is watching TV, a can of beer in his fist. Silence for a beat or two.*

Mum Dexter?

Dad laughs at the TV.

Dexter?

Beat.

Why did you do it, Dexter?
Dad What?

Mum I was talking to Dexter.

Dad Good luck.

Mum Why, darling?

Dad *Why*? I'll tell you why!

Mum And on your first day, Dexter!

Dad What difference does the day make?

Mum What are we going to do?

Dad I'll tell you something – he's not coming on the van with me!

Mum What happened, Dexter?

Dad Talking to yourself, sweetheart.

Mum I'm sorry, Dexter darling, but I've got to say it – I'm very, very, very disappointed.

No response from Dexter.

You know what this means, don't you? It's going to start all over again! Your father and me, we can't cope. We don't know where to turn. You see what I'm saying, Dexter? We need help. To find out what's wrong with you.

Dad How many times? There's nothing wrong with him!

Mum Well, they've got to sort it this time, whether there is or not. I can't go on like this! The stress is killing me! Headache, backache, *and* I'm putting on weight! You're making me *fat*, Dexter! Someone's got to do something!

Dad What's the point? He's seen them all. Therapists, counsellors, doctors.

Mum And now we've got to go through with it all over again!

Dad We've even had him tested for allergies. They all say the same thing – there's nothing wrong with him!

Mum Will you shut up for one second, please, I am trying to have a serious conversation with our son!

Dad I could've told them that. I could've saved them the trouble.

Mum Will you be quiet?

Dad He's not even allergic to wheat!

Mum What do *you* think we should do, Dexter?

Dad He used to talk, didn't he? I can remember him talking. He's a troublemaker, that's all, a selfish little git. Making our lives a misery and having a good laugh, that's his game!

Mum Your dad's right, Dexter –

Dad Course I'm right!

Mum – it is a little bit selfish, what you're doing.

Dad A *little* bit selfish? Joking!

Mum Because you *can* talk –

Dad Oy! It's starting!

Mum – you can talk and hear and everything, we know you can, because you've had all the tests –

Dad Oy!

Mum *What?* I'm *talking*!

Dad It's starting! (*pointing at TV*) You wanted me to tell you when it's starting!

Mum It's starting now?

Dad Jesus, how many times? Yes, that's why I'm telling you!

Mum stands, glancing at the TV, then back at Dexter.

Mum It's not much to ask, Dexter, is it? *Talk* to people. Please, darling. Like a normal person. For your own sake. For our sake.

Dad It's starting!

Mum edges nearer the TV. Still looking at Dexter.

Mum Do you understand, Dexter? Do you see what I'm saying?

Dad It's starting now!

Mum Do you, Dexter?

Dexter finally nods.

Oh thank you, darling! You're a good boy really, I know you are!

Mum runs to Dexter, gives him a hug, then goes over to sit next to Dad in front of the TV.

Dad Look, it's him, I didn't know he was in this.
Mum He's funny, I love him!
Dad Yeah, he's alright.
Mum Dexter said he understands.
Dad I didn't hear him.
Mum He does really, deep down, I'm sure he does.
(*Laughs at TV.*) Oh, look at her!
Dad (*laughing*) Look at the state of her!
Mum Oh, I love her! She's lovely!

FIVE

Dexter enters, writes DOCTORS, SHRINKS, WEIRDOS *on the whiteboard, sits, paper and pen in front of him.*

Doctor 1 enters and peers into Dexter's eyes and ears with one of those torch things, yanking Dexter's head this way and that as he does.

As Doctor 1 finishes, Doctor 2 enters and listens to Dexter's chest with a stethoscope. Listens to his head, whatever.

As Doctor 2 finishes, Doctor 3 enters and takes Dexter's pulse.

As Doctor 3 finishes, Doctor 4 enters. Holding a wooden spatula.

Doctor 4 Open!

Dexter opens his mouth. Doctor 4 inserts the spatula, peers into Dexter's mouth.

Say 'aaaarh'.

Dexter doesn't respond.

SAY 'AAAARH'!

Dexter writes something on a piece of paper, holds it up: a big 'R'.

(*peering*) And again. Louder.

Dexter writes a bigger 'R'.

Thank you.

Doctor 4 exits. Shrink 1 enters, puts a sheet of paper in front of Dexter.

Shrink 1 Answer the following questions, please. Do you have dreams (a) 'a lot', (b) 'sometimes', or (c) 'never'? Tick the appropriate box.

Dexter writes. Shrink 2 enters, puts a sheet of paper in front of Dexter.

Shrink 2 Do you ever wonder if there's life on other planets? Tick the appropriate box, please.

Dexter writes. Shrink 3 enters, puts a sheet of paper in front of Dexter.

Shrink 3 Do you ever wonder how mountains are formed?

Dexter writes.

Shrink 1 Do you play practical jokes?
Shrink 2 Do you like being the centre of attention?

As the Shrinks speed up, their questions overlapping, Dexter ticks away frantically, going from one form to the other.

Shrink 3 Do you get into fights?
Shrink 1 Do you eat vegetables?
Shrink 2 Do you watch violent movies?

Shrink 3 Do you prefer animals to human beings?

Shrink 1 Do you sometimes wish you were an animal?

Shrink 2 A little fluffy animal or big, hairy animal?

Shrink 3 Would you rather eat a bag of crisps or a nice rosy apple?

Shrink 1 Do you have violent fantasies?

Shrink 2 A burger or a nice big carrot?

Shrink 3 Do you have violent fantasies about little fluffy animals?

Shrink 1 Would you rather –

Shrink 2 – see a movie with your girlfriend –

Shrink 3 – see a violent movie with your girlfriend –

Shrink 1 – or look after a sick fluffy animal? Tick the appropriate box, please!

A beat while Dexter catches up.

Shrink 3 That's all for now, Dexter.

Shrink 2 Thank you, Dexter.

Shrink 1 Good boy, Dexter.

The Shrinks take the pieces of paper from Dexter and exit. Dexter slumps, exhausted. Shrink 4 enters, sits opposite Dexter.

Shrink 4 Hiya, Dexter! How's it going?

No response from Dexter.

Not too good, from what I hear. Got yourself in a spot of bother, didn't you?

No response from Dexter.

Again.

Beat.

Don't you remember me, Dexter?

No response from Dexter.

Don't you remember our little talks?

No response from Dexter.

No? Don't remember our little chats?

No response from Dexter.

Well, I do! You know why? Because you were a teensy bit difficult, weren't you? A teensy-weensy bit difficult. (*Beat.*) Yes, you caused me quite a lot of trouble. You know why? Because I'm supposed to be the best! I'm supposed to be the tops! I've written a book! In the end, Dexter, everyone talks to me! *Everyone!* (*Beat.*) Except you.

Beat.

So I spent a lot of time thinking about it. Why did I fail with this boy? Where did I go wrong? Then it came to me in a flash! It wasn't me that failed, it was *you*! It's not *my* problem, it's *yours*! What a revelation that was! It changed my life! *You* changed my life, Dexter! I might even write another book! Thank you! Thank you from the bottom of my heart!

Shrink 4 exits. Shrinks 5 and 6 (Jack and Jill) enter. Carrying clipboards.

Jack Hi, Dexter! I'm Jack, this is Jill!
Jill Good to meet you, Dexter!
Jack How's it going? Can we get you anything? Latte? Mineral water?

Dexter shakes his head.

Okeydoke, let's see what we've got here.

They refer to their clipboards.

Jill (*reading*) 'Facial expressions and body language good . . .'

Jack (*reading*) 'Maintains good eye contact . . .'

Jill (*reading*) 'Reads social situations well . . .'

Jack (*reading*) 'Personal hygiene excellent . . .'

Jill And look at the fluffy animal results! Fantastic!

Jack It's a classic case, isn't it?

Jill Absolutely!

Jack VWS!

Jill Verbal Withdrawal Syndrome!

Jack Congratulations, Dexter!

Jill He's a good-looking boy, too. (*She takes out a camera. To Dexter*) Do you mind?

Dexter shakes his head. Jill stalks Dexter with her camera.

Jack Dexter, which do you want to hear first? The good news or the good news?

Dexter shrugs.

First, we think we can help. Interested?

Dexter nods.

Okay, second. Second one's a biggy. Ready?

Dexter nods.

How. Would you. Like to be. On television!?

SIX

Dexter and Tats enter. Tats writes IN THE PARK *on the whiteboard. They sit.*

Tats I told them what happened, Dexter. I told them you didn't start it. (*Beat.*) But it was me against them. They all lied. Richie and Bins. And Anthony. I thought Anthony was alright, but he does whatever Richie

says, he's such a wuss. They are such wankers. And
Chloe. She is such a bitch. I hate them all. (*Beat.*)
Richie was practically *crying*, and you hardly touched
him. What a pussy. What a freak. I wish you had hurt
him. *Really* hurt him. If they tried it again –

*Tats jumps to her feet, furiously kicks and punches the
air, karate-style.*

I do kick-boxing. I'm a black belt.

Tats does more kicking and punching.

Hi, Richie, how are you today? Bam! In the balls, Richie!
Bam! Bam! Hi Chloe! Bam! Bam! In the throat, Chloe!
Bam! Chloe the bitch! Bam! Bam! Bam!

Tats sits.

Tell them what really happened, Dexter. Maybe they'd
believe you. Then they'd let you come back to school,
I know they would. It would be so great if you came
back to school. (*Beat.*) Then we could hang out
together. We wouldn't have to hang out with anybody
else, we wouldn't need to, would we? Would you like
that, Dexter?

Beat. Then Dexter nods.

Say 'Yes'.

No response from Dexter.

Go on. (*Beat.*) I won't tell anyone you talked. (*Beat.*) Say
my name. Not Tats. Say 'Tatiana'. Go on. 'Tat-eee-
arna'. Just once.

Dexter doesn't respond.

I'm going to ask you something, okay, and if you answer
me, you don't have to say anything else. (*Beat.*) For a
year, okay? A whole year. We'll have an anniversary,

okay? On the . . . whatever it is, on this same day, every year, I ask you something and you answer me, and then you don't have to talk for another year. Okay?

No response from Dexter.

Okay? So here's this year's question. The first one ever. Okay? (*Beat.*) Okay? (*Beat.*) Do you like me, Dexter?

Long pause. Dexter doesn't respond. Tats watches him. Then runs off.
    Dexter sits motionless for a beat or two, then stands, goes over to the whiteboard and writes LATER *under* PARK. *As he writes, the light fades.*
    Dexter sits down again.
    Enter Johnny Smith. He's dressed in white – hat, T-shirt, jeans, trainers – from head to foot. Maybe he seems to glow a little in the gloom.
    He stands some distance from Dexter, watching him. Then walks over.

Johnny Smith Alright, Dexter?

Johnny Smith holds out his hand.

Johnny Smith.

A beat. Then Dexter shakes his hand.

Good to meet you, bruv. You've probably heard them talking about me at school, yeah? Course you have, I'm a celebrity, aren't I? And if you're a celebrity, people talk about you. It's all crap, but what can you do, it's out of your control, know what I mean? The trick is not to mind. You're a smart kid, you know what I'm saying. I know you're smart, 'cos I know all about you, Dexter. That's the good thing about my current situation. I hear all the stories. I know everything. That's why I wanted to talk to you. 'Cos

I got to give you respect, Dexter. What is it, almost a year without talking? Major respect for that, man, really. I only did six months and three days and that's not strictly accurate, 'cos I swore at that teacher before I decked him. I used the 'C'-word, right, but it was under duress. I don't swear any more, it's not appropriate in my situation, but if you're only going to say one word in six months and three days, it might as well be 'cunt', right? (*Beat.*) Then I decked him. I did a lot of that when I stopped talking. I decked people. People would go, 'Hey, I'm talking to you!' and whack, I'd deck 'em. And what I want to say to you, Dexter, is this: it doesn't work! It won't cure the anger! 'Cos that's what you're full of, bruv! Anger and guilt and shame!

Johnny Smith raises his arms.

And the only way to get rid of it, Dexter, is *talk*! Join us, Dexter, join the talkers! Stop hating yourself and come back to the world of words! I did, and look at me! Me, Johnny Smith! Hear my words! They're full of love, Dexter! Hear the words of Johnny Smith!

No response from Dexter.

You'll come back to us in the end, Dexter. The words will pour from you in a veritable torrent, and you will be loved and you will be forgiven!

No response from Dexter.

You're going to be alright, bruv. I know it. (*Beat.*) Talk to you later.

Johnny Smith goes to exit, pauses.

Hear the words of Johnny Smith!

Johnny Smith exits.

SEVEN

Dad watching television. Mum sitting at the table with Jack and Jill.

Dexter enters, writes HOME AGAIN *on the whiteboard and sits.*

Mum (*to Dad*) Will you turn that off? This is important!

Dad I'm waiting for the weather, aren't I?

Mum (*to Jack and Jill*) He's waiting for the weather. He wants to know the driving conditions.

Dad I've got to go out in the van, haven't I? Some of us have got to work for a living, you know.

Mum Just ignore him. What was it you wanted to talk about?

Jill Dexter. We're interested in making a programme about Dexter.

Mum A what?

Jack A film.

Jill About Dexter.

Jack For television.

Mum For the telly? You want Dexter to go on the telly?

Jack That's the idea, yes.

Mum You hear that, Dad? They want to put Dexter on the telly.

Dad They what?

Mum They want to put Dexter on the telly!

Beat.

Dad On the telly?

Mum Yes!

Dad gets to his feet for the first time.

Dad They want to put Dexter on the telly?

Jack With your permission, of course.

Dad I thought you were shrinks.

Jill We are, but we're moving on.

Jack We're rethinking our approach.

Jill It's the stress.

Jack (*to Mum*) I'll be frank with you. I'm burnt out.

Jill So am I.

Jack Knackered.

Jill Totally.

Jack So we're moving into the private sector.

Jill We're moving into the media.

Jack Where we can be so much more effective.

Jill Where we can really *help* people.

Jack *Young* people.

Jill Young people who have no *voice*!

Jack Like Dexter!

Jill That's how we can really help Dexter.

Dad By putting him on the telly?

Jack / Jill Exactly! / Yes!

Mum What about the help me and his dad need? Will we get that if he goes on the telly?

Jack There's a very good chance.

Jill A *very* good chance.

Jack You see, the problem is, Dexter's ahead of his time.

Jill His condition isn't recognised.

Dad What condition?

Jack VWS.

Mum Vee what?

Jill Verbal Withdrawal Syndrome.

Mum A syndrome? He's got a syndrome?

Dad Are you saying my son is a nutter?

Jack No, no, no!

Jill He's just ahead of his time, that's all.

Jack VWS is the next big thing.

Jill And Dexter is a textbook case.

Jack Except there isn't a textbook yet.

Jill Until we write it.

Jack There's a boy in the south who hasn't said a word in six months.

Jill And a boy in Scotland who hasn't spoken since Christmas.

Jack And there's Johnny Smith!

Jill Johnny Smith! Classic case!

Jack Poor Johnny Smith.

Jill If only we'd got to him sooner.

Jack Apart from that, there's only Dexter.

Jack So Dexter here is a bit of a pioneer.

Mum You hear that Dexter? You're a pioneer.

Jill And he's a good-looking kid.

Jack He'll look great on TV and imagine, just imagine, if he spoke for the first time – on camera!

Jill Just before the last ad break! What a perfect TV moment! What a cliffhanger! With a sequel guaranteed. You'll be famous, Dexter.

Mum Will me and Dad be on telly?

Jack Well, as Dexter's parents, we'll want you to tell your story too.

Dad What about money?

Jack I'm sure there'll be some money, yes.

Jill *Some* money –

Mum Isn't that marvellous, Dad? There's money *and* we'll be helping Dexter.

Jill There is one thing I wanted to ask. Can you remember the last time Dexter spoke to you?

Beat.

Jack Either of you?

Beat.

Jill No recollection of when your son last spoke to you?

Beat.

Dad Does it matter?

Jack It's an important part of the story. People will want to know.

Beat.

Mum Yes, I remember. (*Beat.*) It was almost a year ago. (*Beat.*) Wasn't it, Dad?

No response from Dad.

I remember exactly. It was Dexter's birthday.
Jill And the last conversation you had with Dexter, can you remember what it was about?

Beat.

Mum We were watching the telly. Dexter wanted to go round to a friend's. It was a bit late, so we said no, didn't we, Dad?

No response from Dad.

Jill And that was it?
Mum Well, there was a bit of an argument. Just a normal family argument.

No response from Dad.

He was grounded, you see.
Jill Grounded?
Mum He wasn't allowed out.
Jill Why not?
Dad He was mouthing off.
Mum Boys will be boys, won't they?
Dad He was lippy. He was disrespectful. So he wasn't allowed out. Birthday or no birthday.
Mum Just a normal family argument.
Jill And do you remember what the last words he said were?

Long pause. Dexter stares at Mum. She looks away.

Mum (*upset*) No, I don't remember.

Dexter stands up, starts to exit. Mum gets up, grabs him, holds him tight.

No, sweetie, don't go! Please don't go! Everything's going to be alright now, you're going to be on the telly, isn't that brilliant? It might get you into a special school, with special teachers, and we'll get some money and we'll be back to normal, just a normal happy family, wouldn't that be lovely, Dexter? And if we had a bit of money, we could go on a holiday, we haven't been on a proper holiday for ages, wouldn't that be nice? We could go somewhere hot, I'll go on a diet and this time I'll stick to it because it's easier when you're happy, isn't it? If we were all happy, everything would be easier, wouldn't it? There wouldn't be all this stress. That's what I'd like, Dexter, I'd like to live without all this stress.

Long pause.

Dexter Because you deserve it, Mum.
Mum Yes, I do! I –

Then a long pause as the penny drops. Everyone is looking at Dexter, including Dad.

Dexter! You're talking!
Dexter Hair as soft as silk, because you deserve it.
Mum What do you mean, Dexter?

Dad walks over to Dexter.

Dexter How can colour look this natural?
Dad It's a shampoo ad off the telly.

Silence for a beat or two. Jill and Jack stand.

Jack (*to Jill*) It was worth a try.
Jill Could've been great.

Jack Back to the drawing-board.

Mum Wait! Don't go!

Jill Sorry. Out of our hands now, I'm afraid.

Mum What am I going to do?

Dexter Just add a splash of sunshine, Mum.

Mum What? I don't understand, Dexter!

Dad It's orange juice.

Dexter Good old Dad. You know all the ads, don't you, Dad?

Dad What did I tell you? There's nothing wrong with him! He's having a laugh, the little bastard!

Dexter Relax, Dad. Relax with our comprehensive life insurance.

Jack Goodbye, Dexter.

Jill and Jack are about to exit. Mum goes to Jill, grabs her by the arm.

Mum Wait! Don't go! I remember now! I remember the last thing Dexter said!

Jill Sorry. Too late now.

Dad (*to Mum*) Leave it! (*to Jack and Jill*) You two! Out!

Jill exits but Jack lingers, looking at Dexter.

Jack You going to be alright, Dexter?

Dexter Oh yes. I'm loving it.

A beat. Jack looks at Dexter, Mum and Dad, then exits. Silence.

Dexter Hello, Mum. Hello, Dad. How are you? Are you having a nice day?

Dad You happy now? Pleased with yourself, are you?

Dexter I'm loving it.

Mum Oh, Dexter.

Dad Pleased with all the trouble you've caused, are you? Look at your mother, she's a nervous wreck because of you!

Dexter What was the last thing I said, Mum?

Dad Leave it!

Dexter Go on, Mum. Tell us.

Mum Stop it, Dexter!

Dexter You were going to tell them. Why not tell me?

Dad I'm warning you, Dexter.

Dexter All will be revealed. Coming up after the break.

Mum Dexter, just stop it, will you?

Dexter It's a cliffhanger, Mum.

Dad Don't make me do it, Dexter!

Dexter Come on, jog my memory.

Beat.

Why wait? Call your travel agent now!

Mum Dexter, SHUT UP!

Dad raises his fist. Dexter covers his head with his arms, cowers. Mum covers her eyes.

Dexter No, Dad! Don't hit me!

Dad hits him. Dexter falls to the floor. A beat. Then Dexter picks himself up.

I remember now. 'Don't hit me.' That was the last thing I said.

Dad raises his fist again.

EIGHT

Dexter enters, writes BACK IN THE PARK *on the whiteboard and sits. Johnny Smith enters, all in white.*

Johnny Smith Hey, Dexter! What's up, brethren?

Johnny Smith sits next to Dexter.

Nice day, innit? I'm knackered, though. What a day. Totally knackered. Mind you, every day's the same.

Well, it would be, wouldn't it, in my situation? It goes with the job.

Beat.

Hey, Dexter! I hear you're speaking! Respect, bruv! Isn't it great?

Dexter Yes. It's suprisingly stimulating.

Johnny Smith Amen to that! And it just goes on getting better!

Dexter It's surprisingly stimulating at no extra cost.

Beat.

Johnny Smith Not with you, bruv.

Beat.

Dexter Did they lock you up?

Johnny Smith Did they what?

Dexter Did they lock you up? Did they drug you? Did they handcuff you to the bed?

Beat.

Johnny Smith You've been listening to idle talk, my friend. You've been listening to people who have got nothing better to do than badmouth and disrespect others. Remember what I said, Dexter? People talk lies about me 'cos I'm Johnny Smith. Don't listen to their lies.

Silence for a beat or two.

Handcuff me to the bed? Joking! What am I, some sort of pyscho?

Dexter I don't know. Are you?

Johnny Smith Listen, I started talking, alright? I attended the Centre, didn't miss a day, and I took my medication, I *still* take my medication, okay? 'Cept the days when I forget. Nobody locked me up, nobody handcuffed me. And look where I am now. On top of the world!

Dexter 'The words will pour from you in a veritable torrent, and you will be loved and you will be forgiven!'

Johnny Smith What?

Dexter That's what you said.

Johnny Smith I said that?

Dexter Yes.

Johnny Smith Wow. That is *good*! (*Beat.*) That must've been a day I forgot my medication.

Dexter It didn't work. I wasn't forgiven.

Johnny Smith Maybe you poured out the wrong words.

Dexter You didn't mention that. You didn't say, 'You will be loved and forgiven, but only if you pour out the right words.'

Johnny Smith Dexter, my friend, it's obvious, innit!

Dexter 'Hear the words of Johnny Smith!' you said.

Johnny Smith It's not enough to hear. You've got to listen.

Dexter What's the difference?

Johnny Smith stands.

Johnny Smith Come with me, Dexter. I want to show you something.

Dexter Show me what?

Johnny Smith The way forward!

Dexter The way forward?

Johnny Smith Yes, bruv. You're on the way, but the journey is long and hard and fraught with danger. You won't make it on your own, believe me, you need friends around you, good friends who will light the path.

Beat.

Come with me. You will be welcomed with open arms!

Beat.

Just think. You'll have friends, money, respect. You'll wake up in the morning and know what lies ahead. You'll have a life! Be a winner, Dexter! Join us!

Beat.

Come with me, Dexter!

Dexter doesn't move.

Make it happen! Make it happen now!

Dexter doesn't move. Johnny Smith checks his watch.

Well, I got to go. My shift starts at twelve. Come round later, I'll give you free chips.

Johnny Smith goes to exit, then pauses.

Hear the words of Johnny Smith!

Johnny Smith exits. On the back of his t-shirt, in big letters: BURGER WORLD.
   A beat. Then Tats enters.

Tats Alright, Dexter?

Dexter nods.

I hear you're coming back to school. I hear you're talking again.

Dexter nods.

Say something.

Beat.

Go on.
Dexter Be a winner!
Tats Ohmygod! That is amazing! Say something else.
Dexter Make it happen!
Tats That is amazing! Your voice sounds exactly how I imagined it! You've got a lovely voice, Dexter.

Silence.

It's funny. Now you're talking, I don't know what to say.

Dexter Can I come to your house?

Beat.

Tats Maybe. I don't know.

Dexter You asked me.

Tats It's difficult at the moment. My dad's back.

Dexter Has he finished the tour? How did it go? What's his band called? Have they got a new CD out? Does he play the guitar? Or is he a singer like your mum? Or is he both?

Tats doesn't respond.

How's your mum? Is her singing career still going really well? What kind of things does she sing?

Tats It's difficult at home. (*Beat.*) I could come round yours.

Dexter No. It's difficult round mine.

Beat.

Tats My dad isn't in a band. (*Beat.*) He *was*. A long time ago. (*Beat.*) They were unlucky. (*Beat.*) They were ahead of their time. (*Beat.*) He's a minicab driver. He was living with his girlfriend, but now he's moved back with us. (*Beat.*) He'll move out again soon. He always does. Then you can come round. (*Beat.*) My mum isn't a singer.

Dexter What about the kick-boxing?

Tats doesn't answer.

What about your boyfriend who's been on telly?

Tats doesn't answer.

Tats the liar.

Tats Don't say that.

Beat.

There *was* a boy at school. He was cute. He *was* on the telly. But I didn't go out with him. I only spoke to him once. I hung out with Johnny Smith. I didn't actually go out with him. We didn't like *have sex*. Then he stopped talking. Then he got into trouble and left. He's not a div like the others were saying. He works at Burger World now. People from school go there sometimes. He's always trying to get us to work there. You have to start off clearing tables. You have to wear a white uniform. It's really stupid, it gets dirty really easily and you have to get it cleaned yourself. And you don't even get the minimum wage. We can go there if you like. We'll get free chips if Johnny Smith is working. That's all true. None of that is lies.

Beat.

Dexter Open your eyes to a new world of pleasure.
Tats What?
Dexter Taste the quality.

Richie, Bins, Anthony and Chloe enter. They ignore Dexter to start with. 'Alright, Tats?', 'Hiya, Tats', etc.

Richie Alright, Dexter?

Dexter nods.

Bins You coming back to school, Dexter?

Dexter nods.

Chloe You started talking, Dexter?

Dexter nods.

Richie Say something.
Dexter 'Something.'
Richie Say something proper, you geek.
Dexter 'Something proper, you geek.'
Bins That's not funny, man.

Chloe That's so not funny.

Bins He was funnier when he didn't talk.

Anthony He was more amusing in his silent days.

Richie Come on, he's alright. You're alright, aren't you, Dexter? No hard feelings, alright? Shake on it.

Richie extends his hand. Dexter doesn't move.

Friends, Dexter, okay?

Dexter doesn't move.

Come on, geeze. Forgive and forget. I'm offering you friendship. Here.

Dexter doesn't move.

Anthony That's very disrespectful. He's disrespecting you, Richie.

Richie He's right, Dexter. That's what you're doing. You're disrespecting my sincere offer of friendship.

Beat. Eventually Dexter goes to shake Richie's hand, but Richie withdraws his hand at the last moment, makes the 'loser' sign.

Richie / Bins / Chloe / Anthony Loser! Loser boy! (*etc.*)

Richie Only joking, Dexter!

Richie extends his hand again.

Come on, this time for real. On my unborn babies. I promise. Really. Shake.

Dexter stands. Richie, Chloe, Bins and Anthony take a step back.

Chloe Careful, Richie. He might bash you up.

Bins You going to get violent again, Dexter?

Anthony You going to have a fit or something, Dexter? Should I alert the emergency services?

Tats Leave him alone!

Chloe Shut up, Tats.

Tats *You* shut up.

Richie Yeah, shut up, Tats the liar.

Dexter (*to Richie*) You're the liar.

Richie What?

Dexter You're the liar.

Richie Me? I'm the liar?

Bins Richie's the liar?

Dexter You said they handcuffed Johnny Smith to the bed.

Richie What? What's he on about? Anybody know what he's on about?

Bins Johnny Smith? Who cares about that loser?

Dexter You said they locked him up.

Richie Did I? So what? Who cares about that div?

Dexter You were lying.

Richie Maybe it was a joke, geeze!

Bins We were having a laugh, you div.

Anthony Can't you tell the difference between a joke and a lie?

Chloe What a thicko.

Dexter Apologise to Tats.

Richie What for?

Dexter For calling her a liar.

Richie, Chloe, Bins and Anthony laugh.

Richie Joking!

Bins She *is* a liar, man!

Chloe She is such a liar!

Richie Apologise to Tats? That's funny, man!

Anthony That's hilarious.

Tats Shut up!

Dexter Apologise.

Richie No way.

Dexter You want some?

Dexter takes a step forward. Anthony, Chloe and Bins go 'Ooooh' and laugh, but they retreat a step. Richie stays where he is, face to face with Dexter.

Because you deserve it!

Richie Try it. Go on.

Dexter You'll find it surprisingly stimulating!

Richie (*puzzled*) What?

Dexter At no extra cost!

Richie What are you on about, weirdo?

Chloe He's out of control, Richie.

Bins Deck him, Richie. Deck the psycho.

Dexter Pick up the phone now!

Anthony He's losing it!

Chloe Totally losing it!

Anthony Look at his eyes!

Richie is still face to face with Dexter, but increasingly uncertain.

Dexter Discover a wonderful new life!

Richie What are you on about, man? Anybody know what he's on about?

Dexter Why wait? (*Shouts.*) BE A WINNER!

Richie takes a backward step. Dexter follows him.

MAKE IT HAPPEN!

And Dexter charges at them. Richie, Bins, Anthony and Chloe run off. Dexter stops.

(*Calling after them.*) Only joking!

Beat.

Only joking!

Tats goes up to Dexter, touches him on the arm. He turns, puts his arms round her in a clumsy embrace.

NINE

The Teacher writes THE PRESENTATION *on the whiteboard, then sits.*

    Richie, Anthony, Bins, Chloe, Tats, and Dexter at their desks. They stand when speaking, sit when they've finished.

    Chloe stands.

Chloe (*reading*) 'The Little Boy Lost.' (*Beat.*)
  'Father, father! Where are you going?
  O do not walk so fast!
  Speak, father, speak to your little boy
  Or else I shall be lost.'
Bins (*reading*)
  'The night was dark, no father was there;
  The child was wet with dew;
  The mire was deep, and the child did weep,
  And away the vapour flew.'
Anthony (*reading*) 'The Little Boy Found.' (*Beat.*)
  'The little boy lost in the lonely fen,
  Led by the wand'ring light,
  Began to cry; but God, ever nigh,
  Appear'd like his father in white.'
Richie (*reading*)
  'He kissed the child and by the hand led,
  And to his mother brought,
  Who in sorrow pale, thro' the lonely dale,
  Her little boy weeping sought.'
Chloe In the first poem, the little boy gets lost because he
  can't keep up with his father.

    Chloe reads from notes as do all the others except Dexter.

Richie In the second poem, God finds the little boy and takes him back to his mother.

Anthony William Blake uses words like 'lost' and 'dark' to make the poem even scarier.

Bins William Blake was a very religious poet and he wanted to show that God is always near. 'Nigh' is the old-fashioned word for near.

Tats Both poems have the same structure. There are two stanzas with four lines each, with rhymes at the end of the second and fourth line.

Bins For example, 'dew' rhymes with 'few'.

Richie The poems are like nursery rhymes. William Blake wrote them like this in case people were too thick to understand them.

Laughter.

Teacher Shut up!

Tats The rhythm of the poems is like a song. That is so the meaning of the poems has more impact.

Bins And 'light' rhymes with 'white'.

Anthony The first poem starts off with the little boy talking to his father. This is very dramatic and is a way of making us understand how frightened the little boy is.

Bins And 'brought' rhymes with 'sought'.

Chloe William Blake uses lots of symbols. 'Light' represents good and 'dark' represents evil.

Tats In the second poem, the little boy is lost, but there's a light guiding him. It might be God, because God is in white.

Richie There are two fathers in the poems. There's the little boy's actual father, and there's God the father.

Anthony Or it might be 'vapour', which is actually marsh gas which glows in the night.

Tats Maybe the little boy was following the wand'ring light thinking it was his father but it was actually the marsh gas.

Bins The poems also have rhymes which are in the same line, like 'cry' which rhymes with 'nigh'.

Chloe But it doesn't matter because God finds him anyway.

Bins And 'pale' which rhymes with 'dale'.

Anthony William Blake's attitude to the mother is very sympathetic. She's pale and weeping as she looks for the little boy.

Bins And 'speak' which rhymes with 'speak'.

Chloe Duh!

Teacher Quiet!

Richie 'Mire' means a bog or swamp which could be very dangerous.

Bins 'Dale' means a valley.

Tats 'Fen' is marshy land.

Anthony The message of the poems is that you mustn't give up hope, even if you get really lost, because God is always there to help you.

Richie And even if you don't believe in God, it means you must always have a positive attitude to life.

Anthony Marsh gas is actually methane gas which is produced by plants decomposing under water. Methane gas is highly combustible but isn't so dangerous in marshy areas, where it's diluted with air –

Teacher Alright, alright, enough with the methane. Dexter?

No response from Dexter.

Dexter, could we have your presentation, please?

Beat. Dexter eventually gets to his feet.

Dexter (*inaudible mumble*)

Richie (*raising his arm*) Sir, can you tell Dexter to speak up a bit, I can't hear him.

Teacher Don't interrupt, Richie. Alright, a little louder, please, Dexter.

Dexter (*loud*) Put the smile back on their faces!

Laughter.

Teacher Quiet! Dexter, you're supposed to be talking about the poems.

Dexter I am.

Teacher Get on with it, then.

Dexter Put the smile back on their faces!

Giggles.

There's this family, they're all arguing and shouting and crying, the kids are fighting, Dad's shouting at them, Mum's in the kitchen crying, the dog is barking at the cat. Then Mum has a brilliant idea, she phones for pizzas, and the pizzas come and suddenly everyone's eating pizza and they've got these stupid smiles on their faces. Even the dog and cat have got these stupid smiles.

Teacher The *poems*, Dexter!

Dexter In the poems, the dad doesn't lose the little boy by mistake, the dad loses him on purpose, he's fed up with the little boy, he wants to get shot of him. And the mum isn't crying because the little boy is lost, she's crying 'cos she's feeling sorry for herself, she's crying 'cos she's stressed, and anyway she's not really looking for the little boy, she's nowhere near him, she's in the dale which is probably much nicer than the mire which is where the little boy is. (*Beat.*) But it's alright, 'cos God turns up and kisses the little boy. He puts the smile back on their faces!

Teacher Okay, Dexter, thank you very much –

Dexter Eating pizza doesn't make you smile. It's difficult to smile when you're eating, it makes you look stupid. And when you've finished eating, you just start arguing again. So it's a lie.

Teacher That's enough, Dexter. Sit down, please.

Dexter Nothing added but a touch of sunshine!

Richie Sit down, psycho.

Dexter Taste the difference!

Bins Shut up, freak.

Anthony Weirdo.

Chloe Nutter.

Teacher Quiet, everyone! You've made some interesting points, Dexter. Now will you sit down, please –

Dexter How can colour look this natural?

Teacher Alright, I've had enough of this.

The Teacher stands and walks over to Dexter's desk.

Dexter Open the door to a new world of pleasure!

Teacher Dexter, I want you to sit down and be quiet –

Dexter Why wait? You can buy it now!

Teacher Or you're going to have to leave the classroom –

Dexter Taste the quality! Discover the irresistible tang!

Teacher Alright. That's it. Leave the classroom, Dexter.

Dexter You can buy it now!

Teacher Shut up!

Dexter Why wait? Pick up the phone today!

Teacher Shut up!

Dexter Make it happen!

Teacher Shut up!

Dexter holds out his hand.

Dexter Shake.

Teacher Leave the classroom.

Dexter Shake.

Teacher Leave the classroom now.

Dexter SHAKE!

Teacher This minute!

Dexter I'm offering you friendship. Make it happen!

Teacher I'm going to remove you from the classroom, Dexter –

Dexter Put the smile back on their faces!

Teacher WILL YOU SHUT UP!

The Teacher reaches out and lays a hand on Dexter's arm. Dexter hits him. The Teacher falls. Everyone freezes.

TEN

Tats writes VISITING TIME *on the whiteboard, then sits at a table facing Dexter. She takes some sweets out of her pocket, gives them to Dexter.*

Tats Happy birthday, Dexter!

Dexter nods, takes the sweets.

I can't stay long, I've got homework to do. (*Beat.*) We've got to do another presentation. (*Beat.*) 'What invention has had the greatest impact on modern life?' (*Beat.*) It's a pity you won't be there, Dexter. I'd like to hear your presentation about that. I bet it would be great.

Dexter shrugs, mock-modest.

Maybe I'll do pizza.

Dexter nods enthusiastically.

That would put the smile back on their faces.

Dexter grins. Beat.

Are you alright?

A beat. Then Dexter nods.

Have you shut up again?

Dexter nods.

Okay. (*Beat.*) Don't blame you. My dad's moved out again. (*Beat.*) So you can come round. (*Beat.*) If you want to. (*Beat.*) Do you want to?

Dexter nods.

When you can, yeah?

Dexter nods.

I hope that'll be soon.

Dexter nods. Tats stands.

I'll come again if you like.

Dexter nods.

Okay. See you tomorrow.

Tats goes to exit, pauses.

I don't mind you not talking, Dexter. Really I don't.

Dexter gives her the thumbs up.

See you tomorrow, then.

Tats waves. Dexter waves back. Tats exits.
Beat. Dexter sits on his own. Smiles.

Dexter Tat-eee-arna. (*Beat.*) See you tomorrow, Tat-eee-arna.

Fade out.

Silence that Speaks Volumes

Andrew Payne interviewed by Jim Mulligan

Shut Up is a play about a boy who decides to stop talking.
Dexter, the main character, opts for silence, and in the
course of the play that silence becomes more eloquent
than any of the babble that surrounds him.

> Dexter is surrounded by people – parents, teachers,
> classmates, shrinks and doctors – who are talking at
> him all the time, and what they're saying is evasive, self-
> serving and often downright lies. And the background
> to all this babble is television, the incessant, subliminal
> soundtrack in millions of homes, squatting there in the
> corner, seducing, bullying and cajoling us night and
> day. Sometimes we need straight answers, we need to
> be direct with people and we need them to be direct
> with us. That's what Dexter wants. But no one can
> hear him. It's just too noisy. So he shuts up.

Andrew Payne is not necessarily writing a polemic about
the damaging effects of television on our society, but he is
interested in the way the alternative reality of TV bleeds
into and suffuses every nook and cranny of our lives.
Dexter's mum and dad find it easier to engage with the
lives of TV celebrities than their own son. When Dexter
finally speaks, his language is laced with catchphrases
from TV adverts, and this finally gets his Dad's attention:
'Good old Dad. You know all the ads, don't you, Dad?'

> I have a very ambivalent attitude to television. I watch
> it and indeed I write for it, but it scares the hell out of

me sometimes. Sit through two hours of prime-time children's TV and you need to lie down in a darkened room for half an hour. The ads are ruthlessly efficient, targeted with forensic precision, and often highly sexualised. Should we be worried about this? I don't know. Should it concern us that the first words some children utter are global brand names? Again, I don't know. But I like it when Dexter throws adspeak back in our faces. Good for him, I say.

Dexter stopped talking on his last birthday. In the course of the play, it's revealed that a family row culminated in his father hitting him. Whether the beating happens once or is part of sustained abuse is not alluded to in the text.

You can only go by what is on the page. Anything else is speculation, for me as much as for anyone else. But I think Dexter's dad is probably too lazy and too busy watching television to work up the energy for regular beatings. His life is completely bounded by TV and driving his van. He is not engaging with life at all. Engaging with his son would mean that he had to take responsibility for his own life. What is clear is that Dexter's mother betrays her son when, in order to protect her husband, she will not reveal the cause of his silence. That's a big moment, a turning point in the play.

The adults in *Shut Up* tend to be larger than life. Dexter and his fellow-students are more naturalistically portrayed and, in a way, more alert and intelligent than the adults. Witty and manipulative, they fulfil the curriculum requirements with the minimum of effort, recycling secondhand opinions from the internet, which is enough to satisfy their hard-pressed teacher. Dexter is the only student who makes an original analysis of the Blake poems. His analysis, whatever one thinks of it, has the merit of being personal and deeply felt.

Sometimes the writing gods smile on you. I came across the Blake poems by chance, and they were perfect: a small boy is lost, his parents can't find him, but God saves the day! But God ain't going to help Dexter, and Dexter knows it. As far as Dexter is concerned, the poems are no better than the lies trotted out in TV commercials. That is not necessarily my view, but I do find Dexter's take on Blake rather bracing.

Salvation appears to be offered to Dexter by the ambiguous character called Johnny Smith, a messianic figure dressed in white. Johnny Smith urges Dexter to start talking again: 'The words will pour from you in a veritable torrent and you will be loved and you will be forgiven.' Johnny Smith is another disappointment. The salvation on offer is nothing more than a job at the local burger bar.

I am very suspicious of preachers and proselytisers, but I can't help liking Johnny Smith. The poor guy. He's out there preaching salvation and this salvation amounts to getting a job in a burger bar. Join us and you will be saved. Join our church, the church of burgers. Be a winner, not a sinner. Taste the quality. Poor Johnny.

The other chance of salvation comes from television itself. A couple of educational pyschologists express an interest in making a documentary about Dexter. Surely television will succeed in rehabilitating Dexter where all else has failed.

Television has become the last resort, the ultimate therapy: *Brat Camp*, *Fat Camp*, *Neighbours from Hell*, you name it, it'll make good TV, and the more dysfunctional the participants the better. And it's bound to end in hugs because it's on TV, right? Not for Dexter, though. He sabotages his chance of fame by opening

his mouth and talking. No redemption on TV for
Dexter.

The only person who tells Dexter the truth is Tatiana,
a compulsive fantasist known in school as Tats the Liar.
Dexter, however, brings out the truth in Tatiana.

When Tatiana says, 'That's all true. None of that is
lies,' Dexter knows she's telling the truth. I think
Dexter and Tatiana will find some sort of redemption
in their relationship, whatever it might turn out to be,
because they accept each other for what they are.

When Dexter shuts up again, Tatiana says she does not
mind and makes it clear that she will continue to see him.
The last words are Dexter's: 'See you tomorrow, Tat-eee-
arna.' But there's no one there to hear them.

Production Notes

Avoid designing a set involving lots of furniture, since there are many location shifts that can be achieved with a minimal set. The whiteboard is an informal device for visual rather than verbal communication and through which different attitudes can be portrayed by the variety of different characters that write on it. Using the whiteboard will help speed up the transition of the scenes, but the moments at which the characters write on the board are not randomly chosen, so don't overuse it. Any wrong choices that hold up the plot or make the audience question rather than follow the action are a mistake. Make smooth and efficient scene changes. There are constant location changes within the text and you are encouraged to be creative and imaginative when deciding on them. Watch the film *Dogville*, as it is set on a bare stage throughout. The sitting room can be suggested simply. Try out the following exercise.

Sit, Stand and Lie

Place a chair in the middle of the room. Have three actors sit, stand or lie. Make sure they don't adopt a stance or posture that they have had previously. Get them to perform the exercise with constant movement and fluidity. Have the actors hold their positions and get the rest of the group to tell the story suggested by the scene. Keep a steady rhythm between the scenes: different relationships and stories can be built through looking at the still images.

Using this same technique, create stories that include a Mum, Dad and Child. Direct the rest of the group to look at them from every angle. The possibilities of arranging different configurations and finding stories through them are endless, and creating visual stories is easily done without the need for sound or even movement.

MUM AND DAD There is something monstrous about the characters of Mum and Dad, but it is probably more rewarding if the part of Mum is played with sympathy. Mum is interested in her son, but she'd prefer the scene to be all about her. It's generally more interesting for monstrous characters to show some sort of vulnerability.

Mum probably has an easy part-time job that still stresses her out. In several passages of the script Dad talks about driving a van, and it's clear that they don't have much money as a family.

Decide to what degree the relationship between the parents is evenly matched. Find out where the power is at any given moment. Discover how the scene changes when they become aware of Dexter. Decide if he creeps up behind the parents or if they see right through him.

Mum appears fearful of Dad, though he probably isn't violent towards her. She wants everything to be nice and happy. Dexter has given up as he's always ignored.

DEXTER The process of building a silent character for Dexter is no different to one with lines. But a great deal of thought does need to be given to choosing the moments when he reacts. Because there are many scenes in which he is silent, the danger here would be to make his eye-contact and movements repetitive, which could become boring. Choose the points at which he is switched on and when he is switched off. Explore the different levels at which he could be played switched on/off – aggressive or passive, attentive or indifferent.

Since he makes no conscious decisions, Dexter himself doesn't know when he may or may not speak. Many of the characters speak for him – Mum and Tats both interpret his nods as speech, telling other characters, 'He said yes.'

There are a number of occasions in the text when characters such as Tats and Johnny Smith tell him he's a good listener. Make a list of the observations other characters make about Dexter. Decide what is accurate and what isn't. The TV being continuously on is a constant theme and part of his subconscious. Mum constantly blocks Dexter, which in turn affects his behaviour.

Yes and No Exercise

In pairs, sustain a conversation while only being allowed to use the word 'Yes'. Then repeat the exercise using the word 'No'.

Have one partner make a series of offers that require a response – e.g., 'Good morning!' or 'Would you like a pie?' The other partner needs to find a way of verbally blocking the response. You might find the actors become quieter or try to chase for attention.

Now repeat the exercise with all offers made by one partner being accepted.

Repeat the blocking exercise in silence.

THE SCHOOL SCENES

Don't be tempted to change the gender of the characters; making the teacher female, for instance, would alter the dynamic entirely.

While you can have as many classmates and doctors as you like, provided that the main characters aren't lost, don't be tempted to create a chorus or reassign lines because it would spoil the rhythm of the piece.

The school in the play is probably a good one and the teacher is doing his best despite being tired and stressed. The kids in the class are bright.

The school scene is yet another example of Dexter being surrounded by talk. Just as his mother has accused him of making her fat, the teacher in turn accuses him of making him stressed. It is part of the build up and idea of being surrounded by voices. Dexter's silence makes each of the other characters talk more.

Google William Blake: there are many websites devoted to this artist/poet/mystic that you can research. Get the actors playing the students to do a presentation on Blake just as the characters have to. *William Blake: the Complete Illustrated Version* is a good reference, and we recommend you look at William Hogarth's *A Rake's Progress*, in which each tableau focuses on the Rake as a central character but his position is always changing. Like the Rake, Dexter doesn't necessarily have to be placed centre stage to hold the focus. Don't make the classroom a literal classroom – the script is enough of a clue to the location.

A beat is shorter than a pause. Assume a character is going to say something and then stops. Pace can vary, although it can also be exaggerated. The play is intended to be fast-paced and as a result the pauses have the potential to be very effective.

The intention behind Anthony talking about Dexter's past is to show that Dexter has had problems at school but the problems have been exaggerated. The other schoolkids are waiting for him to behave badly, almost surrounding him in his own myth in order to make the fight scene work effectively.

Walking down the Road Exercise

Get everyone up on their feet and moving around the room. The object is to encourage each person to find their partner – moving as close to them as possible. As an added dimension, make sure that there is a person between them and their partner.

Still moving, have them maintain constant eye-contact with their partner while being careful not to bump into other people.

Get them to walk towards their partner maintaining steady eye-contact, again not bumping into anyone else. This requires a combination of spatial awareness and direct focus.

Have each couple maintain as much distance from each other as possible while always being aware of where their partner is in the room. Don't allow the pair to let the other catch them looking at each other. Remind them to keep moving.

Arrange the group in lines facing each other from opposite ends of the room. Ask one couple to walk towards each other, crossing paths. Instruct each couple on how much or how little eye-contact is allowed whilst walking. Variations might include constant eye-contact, both while walking towards each other and away from each other, or unequal contact as one partner maintains eye-contact while the other only looks up every four strides.

Get the group to place stories and relationships on the situations. When eye-contact is maintained, there might be a strong sense of either love or aggression.

The Fight

If you are able to get the eye-contact right in a fight scene, the action follows from there. Every fight anywhere must start with eye-contact. This is more of a non-fight scene, as Dexter tries hard to get away from the situation rather than aggressively lashing out and getting into it.

Stage fighting is a process much like speaking lines. There is a response to every action just as a question demands an answer. The key to all successful fight sequences, though, is the reaction. Dexter is aggressive-passive in this scene because he pushes the bullies out of the way, so is therefore not written as a pathetic figure. Play with the appropriate levels of aggression needed from Richie and Dexter. Focus on replaying good moves, but justify everything.

DOCTORS AND SHRINKS

The adults – Mum, Dad, Teacher, Doctors, Shrinks – aren't real, rather they are archetypes and representations.

Exercise

Everyone in the cast should find someone that looks entirely different to them. Get them to find ways to appear identical – not necessarily in terms of clothing, but rather in a behavioural sense.

Get them to pair up with their 'identical' partner in the room. Seat them in chairs and have each couple create a café scene where the partners sit opposite each other. One of the pair becomes the lead partner. Both partners need to perform a number of identical tasks. Ask them to mime eating and drinking at the same time, then speak the same words simultaneously. Repeat this with a new leader.

Get rid of the chairs and get them up on their feet. Direct everyone to consider a favourite body part, then move around the room wordlessly demonstrating this finest feature to everyone. Repeat the exercise with everyone demonstrating their most hated feature and moving about the space trying to conceal it. Explore this in both an extreme and a subtle way. Repeat the 'Walking down the Road' exercise and get the pairs to alternate between demonstrating and concealing in both extreme and subtle ways. This is a useful way to begin creating archetypal characters and looking at ways to enter into a comedy character.

Run through the doctor scene playing the characters in the subtle and the extreme ways. As the runthrough of this scene develops, introduce clipboards and bananas. Ask the actors to swap their prop throughout the scene whilst performing, yet never leaving the stage. This will allow the actors to further focus on comedic elements. The props allow more freedom to move around the space. If actors have something to do on stage, they are able to keep it going until the action within the scene dictates otherwise.

Run this scene at super speed and have the actors choose whether to play in a naturalistic or extreme style. Prop games are a good way of stopping actors thinking too hard.

JOHNNY SMITH Andrew originally planned for Johnny Smith to be a ghost that only Dexter sees. He was originally constructed around a mad preacher type, 'selling rubbish', which explains the religious language that he uses such as 'Come and join us.'

Although Tats and Johnny Smith have hung out together, they hadn't been going out with each other. Tats is the only person who tells Dexter the truth.

Remember that Dexter hasn't spoken for a year and, when he finally does, he uses language aggressively with his parents but with Tats to deflect emotions.

Decide where the final scene is set. Andrew didn't want to be too specific on this. It could be a Young Offenders' Unit or a hospital of some sort. This last scene contains a very mature, adult conversation. Dexter repeating Tats' name is an echo of the way she tells him to say her name earlier in the story.

Music

Choose wisely, and above all don't allow any music to tell the story twice. Music is effective as a counterpoint to the action. Be careful with your choice, especially if music is played whilst the audience are waiting for the show to open. Don't build a false expectation.

Workshop facilitated by
Suzy Graham-Adriani and Dominic Rickhards
with notes taken by Pamela Wilson

THE SPIDER MEN

Ursula Rani Sarma

Ursula Rani Sarma is a playwright, poet and screenwriter from the West of Ireland. Her award-winning plays have been translated and performed extensively at an international level with recent productions in Germany, Romania, Ireland and the UK. Her previous work for the stage includes . . . *touched* . . . (Djinn and Granary Theatres), *Wanderings* (Djinn and Asylum Theatres), *Blue* (Cork Opera House), *Gift* (Belltable Theatre), *Orpheus Road* (Paines Plough Wild Lunch Series), *When the War Came* (The New Theatre) and *The Dogs Facing the Hare* (translation for the NT Studio). Her radio plays include *Car Four* and *The Fisherman*. She is developing plays for Paines Plough, the Traverse, the Stephen Joseph Theatre, the Abbey, the National Theatre and the BBC, and is also working on an Irish Arts Council commissioned project on Inishlacken Island, off Co. Galway, developing a feature film and editing her first collection of poetry.

Characters

Michael
fifteen

David
Michael's best friend, fifteen

Sarah
David's sister, fourteen

Karen
Sarah's best friend, fifteen

Jacob
David's brother, seventeen

JT
Jacob's boyfriend, sixteen

Darren
boy from school, fifteen

Nigel
boy from school, fifteen

Michelle
girl from school, fifteen

Stoner
boy from school, seventeen

Policemen

SCENE ONE

All the characters march onto the stage in single file.
They march in unison one after the other in a circle, the
beat of their footfalls steady. Sarah is the first to break
away, and one by one they all do the same until they are
standing in their own space, looking about as if trying to
become familiar with their surroundings. Sarah, fourteen,
with a nose ring, wearing a school uniform and carrying
a satchel, steps forward and speaks to us. The others
wander offstage one by one as she speaks.

Sarah I got my nose pierced the day it happened. I'd
wanted to have it done for ages but my mum said my
dad would go insane, although to be honest I don't
think he'd notice if I pierced both my eyebrows, my
lip, my nose, my ears and got a tattoo that said 'Slut'
across my forehead. Because he's not that kind of dad.
He's the kind of dad that works all day and then
comes home and sits in front of the telly and doesn't
talk to anyone for the night kind of dad. It's like my
mum threatens us with him just so we'll think he gives
a shit but we know he doesn't. (*Beat.*) I read in a
magazine about this girl who really wanted to get to
know her parents, she turned fifteen and she wanted
to form an 'adult relationship' with them but as far as
I could see all that meant is that she wanted to talk
about sex with them. I can't think of anything worse
than having to talk about sex with my parents. It's
disgusting. I mean, when you talk about something,
part of you is making little pictures in your head to go
along with it even if you don't want it to. You know,

like if I say to you, whatever you do . . . don't think of a pink elephant. (*Beat.*) What are you thinking of? (*Beat.*) See? So match that with talking about sex with your parents. (*Makes a face.*) It's just . . . disgusting.

Lights up on Stoner who is sitting with his headphones on.

Stoner (*singing Stone Roses' 'I Want to Be Adored'*)
'I don't need to sell my soul . . .
He's already in me . . .
I don't need to sell my soul . . .
He's already in me . . . .
I wanna be adored . . . you adore me . . .
You adore me . . . you adore me . . .
I wanna I wanna I wanna be adored,
I wanna I wanna I wanna be adored . . .'

He looks up suddenly, and takes off his headphones and looks offstage.

Who is it? Is that Michael? (*Beat.*) I can see you behind the tree.

Michael walks on, he looks annoyed to see Stoner.

Michael What you doing here?
Stoner Hanging out, listening to my music.
Michael Out here? Why'd you come all this way to listen to your music?
Stoner Like the trees man, they soothe me, you know? I'd take trees over people any day.
Michael Well . . . if anyone asks, you didn't see me, alright?
Stoner If who asks?
Michael If anyone asks you, you have to say you didn't see me.
Stoner But I did see you.
Michael Fuck sake, just say you didn't, alright?
Stoner Alright (*Beat.*) Do you have five quid for a burger?

Michael No.

Stoner Do you have three quid for a bag a chips and a Coke?

Michael I said –

Stoner What about a fifty pence for a Mars bar? Just fifty pence?

Michael How come you never have any money?

Stoner My mum doesn't give me hardly any.

Michael (*takes out a coin and throws it at him*) I want it back.

Stoner (*picking up the coin*) You're real nice, you know that? You're the only one that listens to me.

Michael Shut up, Stoner.

Stoner It's alright to be nice, you know? It's cool, just because everyone else around here thinks you have to be hard and loud to be respected . . . The meek shall inherit the earth and all that . . . you know?

Michael And what would you know about it? Only person you spend quality time with is yourself.

Stoner (*beat*) Yeah . . . you're nice . . . you're fucking lovely, in fact . . .

Michael Fuck off, Stoner. (*Goes to exit.*) You didn't see me.

Stoner slips the fifty pence into his pocket and puts his headphones on. Lights down on Stoner as he sings.

Stoner
'I wanna be adored . . . you adore me . . .
You adore me . . . you adore me . . .
I wanna I wanna I wanna be adored,
I wanna I wanna I wanna be adored . . .'

Lights up on Sarah.

Sarah My mum comes into my room that morning, I turn and look at her like, did you knock? I don't think so. She sits on the edge of my bed, without asking, and

watches me do my hair, so I say, 'What you want?'
And she says, 'Sarah,' in that fucking horrible way that
makes me hate my name, 'Sarah, are you smoking
marijuana?' And they way she said it, 'm-a-r-i-j-u-a-n-a',
and the stupid way she looks at me like I might
actually confide in her. That's a joke . . . confide . . . in
her? I tell her no, and get out. She won't go so I say,
'Seriously, get out, I mean it.' She says, 'I'm worried
about you, the school has sent a letter, there are kids
smoking between classes.' I say get out. And she won't
go, so I scream, 'Get out!' I say, 'You think I couldn't
smoke fucking crack if I wanted to, but I don't, I chose
not to, I chose life, alright, now get out!' (*Beat.*) Now
she thinks I smoke crack (*Beat.*) Fuck her.

*Lights down on her and up on Jacob and JT, standing
at a bus stop. Behind them on the wall are graffiti,
fuzzy at first, but gradually sharpening focus into* FAGS
BEWARE *and* DEATH TO HOMOS.

JT I dunno, I think it's alright actually.

Jacob It's not alright, she should have stuck to singing
bloody hymns . . . church music . . . Doesn't make any
sense her running around all tarted up . . . I mean,
she's not Kylie is she?

JT She must have been under a lot of pressure though,
don't you think? I mean she sold millions of CDs,
millions.

Jacob Well, she should have just stayed the way she was,
people liked the way she was.

JT You think she should have stayed that way for ever
just so everyone would still like her?

Jacob (*beat*) No . . . I just think . . . I mean, she was really
good at that . . . singing hymns . . . my gran had all her
CDs . . . She saw a picture of her in the paper last
week with her tits hanging out and she was really
disappointed . . . threw out all the CDs and all.

JT Yeah, but when you think about it, she was just a kid when she was doing all that church music.

Jacob So?

JT So she didn't have any tits to get out.

Jacob What?

JT She's not a kid any more, so why should she spend the rest of her life pretending she was? I mean, don't you think it would be really fucking weird to see this grown woman dressing like a little kid singing hymns for grans? She'd be an absolute freak if she didn't change in some way.

Jacob Yeah, but . . . I just think . . . she shouldn't have . . . I dunno.

JT Gotten drunk at some club and wore a dodgy outfit?

Jacob Yeah.

JT What teenager you know hasn't done that?

Jacob I suppose.

JT You can't spend your life worrying about what other people think of you. Most of the time they're not even thinking of you at all. Look at us, standing here, chatting about her, you think she gives a shit what we think? She doesn't even know who we are.

Jacob Yeah, but you want . . . you want people to like you, don't you?

JT Do you?

Jacob Well . . . don't you?

JT (*beat*) Depends on the people.

Lights down on JT and Jacob.

Sarah (*beat*) After Mr Curtain confiscated my MP3 player and I had my lunch money nicked from my locker I ended up in the bathroom pushing my fist through the mirror. I just stood there looking at myself in the cracked glass, looking at a hundred little me's looking back at me, completely stressed out, and that's when I decided, fuck the lot of you. Told Karen that

I'd meet her after lunch by the chipper and we'd go round to the piercing place and have it done, although I knew she wouldn't go through with it. Once, when we were kids, she came up with this idea to play a trick on a substitute teacher. She said we should swap names around when the new woman asked us, so she asked me first, and I said Karen and then she asked Karen and Karen said her name was Karen. I mean, seriously, so for three whole weeks I had to pretend my name was Karen. She's just like that, she has these wicked ideas but she can't follow them through. (*Beat.*) The guy who did my nose was kind of cute, so I went bright red, even my ears. I'm really bad around boys who I fancy, I turn into a vegetable, I think of a million witty clever sexy things to say and then when I'm actually there I blurt something out and sound like an idiot. Karen says it's a good thing because guys don't like to be threatened by intelligent women, they like them kind of dull. But I wouldn't fancy a guy if he only liked me because he thought I was dull. So I just didn't say anything at all while this guy pierced me. I figured it was pretty impossible to look good with a metal stapler shoved up your nose, so why bother trying. (*Beat.*) To be honest, I thought about Michael when the guy was actually doing the piercing. I thought about what it would be like to be his girl, what it would be like if I was older and if he would think of me as possible 'his girl' material. He's only a year older than me, but he still thinks I'm little. Which is stupid. Because I'm not little any more, and this piercing . . . I suppose I thought that maybe he would think I was a little bit older because I had had it done. Like it was an adult thing to do. So I guess you could kind of say that I got it for him. A little bit. Not just because of him. But maybe . . . maybe thirty per cent because of him. And afterwards, when it hurt, I thought about

what he'd say when he saw it, because David would
tease me about it and he'd look at me, I mean he'd
have to look at me to see it. And I thought about that
at home when I was waiting for them to arrive.
Michael always called in and stayed for a little while,
him and David nattering away in his room or in the
kitchen eating all the biscuits. So I changed into my
cool jeans and I waited in the sitting room, watching
whatever crap Dad had on, trying to pretend that I
wasn't waiting. (*Beat.*) But I was. (*Beat.*) I was waiting.

SCENE TWO

*David, fifteen, rebel-without-a-cause type, sits in a wooded
area, beside a stream. He is reading a comic book earnestly.
Michael, fifteen, serious and slightly nerdy with glasses,
arrives.*

David Did anyone see you?

Michael (*beat*) Course not.

David Did they?

Michael No, alright? Just relax.

David What did you bring?

Michael A Mars bar, an orange, some biscuits, but
they're kind of soft so . . . and half a cheese sandwich
from my lunch, you can have that if you want.

David No crisps or nothing?

Michael I've no money, just gave my last fifty pence to
Stoner.

David Thought you said no one saw you?

Michael (*beat*) At school, I gave it to him at school.

David Could have just nicked some from the tuck shop.

Michael Don't like doing that.

David Chicken, everybody nicks stuff from the tuck shop.

Michael I don't. (*Beat.*) You know, my mum runs the

tuck shop in Drumcliff, and she has to buy all that stuff herself. I help her sometimes and we go down to the cash-and-carry. Pick out all the stuff and go to the checkout, pack it into the bags and carry it to the car. Then she has to unpack it at home and sort it all out and mark it for prices, then she has to get up at six to make all the sandwiches and package them and pack them into the car, and then out of the car again at the school. She's real nice to those kids, even asks them what kind of sandwiches they like sometimes so she can make them up special. And then they go and nick them, it really gets her down (*Beat.*) If I nicked stuff from our tuck shop it'd feel like I was nicking it from my mum.

David Alright, alright, didn't ask for a bloody essay on it.

Michael Sorry.

David (*beat*) Give us some of that cheese sandwich so.

Michael passes it to him, David eats, Michael watches him.

What you looking at?

Michael Nothing.

David Well, stop it.

Michael Sorry. (*Beat.*) Just you look like you haven't eaten, you look hungry.

David I am hungry.

Michael Didn't you have your lunch?

David (*beat*) I'm not taking money off her for lunch.

Michael Why?

David Because I hate her, that's why.

Michael Yeah, but not really.

David I just said I did, didn't I?

Michael Yeah, but you don't mean it really, you don't really hate your mum.

David Yes I fucking do.

Michael But she's your mum.

David So what?

Michael So you're not supposed to hate her, I mean you can fight with her, but not hate her.

David finishes the sandwich.

You know? (*Beat.*) She's your mum.

David (*beat*) You're backing out.

Michael No I'm not.

David Yeah you are, you're backing out.

Michael I didn't say that, all I said was –

David Yeah yeah . . . I heard you . . . I should love my mum . . . well I don't, alright? I fucking don't . . . so don't start with that stuff because I don't want to hear it.

Michael All I said was –

David Shut it, I said.

Michael (*takes his glasses off and cleans them*) You don't have to speak to me like that.

David What?

Michael I said you don't have to speak to me like that, I'm on your side, I'm supposed to be your friend.

David Yeah, alright.

Michael You're supposed to be my friend and that's not how you speak to your friends, is it?

David Yeah, alright. I said sorry, okay? Sorry.

Michael looks away.

What? I said sorry. didn't I?

Michael (*mumbling*) Youdidntsayitlikeyoumeantit.

David What?

Michael You didn't say it like you meant it.

David Jesus . . . alright . . . I'm sorry . . . okay? Really, I'm sorry. Was that alright?

Michael It was better.

David Good, I'm so glad.

Michael puts his glasses on and smiles at David.

What? What you smiling at?

Michael You . . . saying sorry . . . twice . . .
David Fuck off . . . pass me the Mars bar . . .

Michael passes it to him, still smiling.

And stop smiling.

Michael stops smiling.

Michael Which one is it?
David (*eating*) Huh?
Michael (*pointing at the comic*) Which one?
David (*excitedly*) One where Peter Parker is sent to get his aunt's medicine but he ends up having to fight off the Tokkits with Thor instead and she almost dies and he feels really guilty and –
Michael He's always guilty.
David What?
Michael He's always feeling guilty over one thing or another, isn't he?
David Well . . . no . . . he felt responsible for his uncle's death and now he feels responsible for his aunt.
Michael Yeah, but it wasn't his fault, was it? He didn't kill his uncle.
David You don't understand.
Michael Of course I understand, I just think –
David Spiderman is the greatest, coolest, most fantastic superhero that ever was and if you think any differently then you don't understand, get it? You don't understand.
Michael (*beat*) Don't you think we're getting a bit old for Spiderman? (*Beat, looks at him fearfully.*) I mean . . . well, you know what I mean.
David No . . . I don't know what you mean.
Michael Forget it.
David What?
Michael Just forget it.
David People collect comics all their life.
Michael I know.

David As a hobby, they collect them even when they're old.

Michael I know, I'm sorry.

David You should be.

Michael (*takes off his glasses and cleans them again*) What do we do now so?

David (*beat*) We wait.

SCENE THREE

Karen and Michelle are in the dressing room of a clothing store, Michelle is behind a curtain, changing.

Karen All I'm saying is, I don't know why you care.

Michelle I'm not saying I care as such, I'm just saying she's a liar.

Karen But so what if she is?

Michelle (*peering out from behind the curtain*) Because . . . you shouldn't be a liar should you? I mean – (*disappearing behind the curtain*) – I used to hang around with her all the time when we were little, her mum and mine worked together, and she was always round at mine or I was over at hers.

Karen Really?

Michelle Yeah . . . I mean when we were young . . . She had ten Barbies and I had twelve and we just had the best time . . . we had hundreds of outfits and shoes and handbags . . . We swapped them and made up different reasons for them all to get together . . . little Barbie conventions . . . (*Peers around the curtain.*) I mean, we were very young, obviously.

Karen S'alright, I still have my Barbie, play with her all the time.

Michelle (*delighted*) You do? Me too! You should come over some time, I can get out all the clothes and . . .

Karen looks at her like she's crazy.

You don't, do you?

Karen No, I bloody don't, I'm fifteen in case you didn't know.

Michelle I know . . . yeah . . . I mean . . . I was just kidding . . . I don't . . . either . . . play with . . . you know . . .

She goes back behind the curtain, embarrassed.

Karen So how come you didn't stay friends, then?

Michelle Just didn't, she stopped coming over and then we went to different schools for a while and by the time we were both back in the same one she acted like she didn't know me. Bitch.

Karen You really have it in for her, don't you?

Michelle No, I'm just saying – (*Peers around the curtain.*) – even if she hasn't . . . done what she says she's done . . . why does she dress like that? I mean, it's embarrassing . . . the teachers don't know where to look half the time because she just has everything . . . hanging out . . . and she hasn't one girl friend, they're all boys and –

Karen But why do you care?

Michelle I don't know . . . (*Beat.*) She used to be alright, you know . . . used to be really happy when she came over . . . Mum used to say . . . you and Jane . . . two peas in the one pod. My Mum wouldn't let her in our house now . . . way she is.

She pulls across the curtain and steps out, dressed head to toe in pink.

What do you think?

Karen It's . . . it's . . . very . . . pink.

Michelle It's gorgeous, isn't it? It's just perfect for the end-of-year do, you think I look sophisticated?

Karen Erm—

Michelle I think it makes me look like a pop star or an actress . . . like Cameron Diaz.

Karen God, I hate her.

Michelle She's gorgeous.

Karen She's alright . . . but she's a rubbish actress and she's always giggling like an idiot when she's on the telly . . . like she's got half a brain . . . and she's always posing . . . all the time . . . posing . . .

Michelle Well, she's still gorgeous.

She skips back behind the curtain. Karen stands and goes over to the full-length mirror. She looks at herself for a moment, touches her hair, smoothes down her clothes.

Karen You ever think . . . how weird it is . . . that in five or six years you go from dressing a couple of dolls to dressing yourself?

Michelle (*beat*) I don't get you.

Karen Well . . . I mean . . . it's not real, is it . . . dressing a Barbie . . . it's not anything like real . . . (*She lifts the hem of her skirt.*) I mean, the outfits that you put on dolls . . . doesn't matter if they're stupid or tarty or nerdy or . . . whatever . . . no one's going to judge her on it, you know? No one's going to think that it reflects her personality or how cool she is or . . . you know . . . we have to figure all that out for ourselves.

Michelle (*coming out from the dressing room in her own clothes*) What you going on about?

Karen (*beat*) Nothing. (*Beat.*) I gotta go . . .

Michelle (*going back into the dressing room*) See you later so.

Karen (*beat, looks in the mirror*) Yeah, see you. (*Beat.*) Michelle?

Michelle Yeah?

Karen You hear about the wristbands?

Michelle Yeah.
Karen (*beat*) You gonna wear one to the end-of-year do?
Michelle I dunno, you?
Karen (*beat, worried*) I dunno . . . see ya.

Lights down.

SCENE FOUR

Darren and Nigel are kicking a football back and forth to each other. Stoner is seated nearby, watching.

Nigel So what does the yellow one mean, then?
Darren That she'll let the guy snog her.
Nigel And the red one?
Darren Red one means . . . that she'll go further.
Nigel How much further?
Darren Well . . . like, she'll let the guy . . . have a feel . . .
Nigel Where?
Darren Upstairs.
Nigel Seriously?

Darren nods.

What about the blue?
Darren What do you think?
Nigel Downstairs?

Darren nods.

And the green?
Darren All the way.
Nigel Fucking hell . . . and they can't wear a colour they haven't done already?
Darren That's what I heard.
Nigel Fucking hell . . . that's just . . . that's great, isn't it?
Darren I dunno.

Nigel What you mean, you dunno? Means you won't be wasting you're time with one who won't . . . you know . . . do anything.

Darren Would you wear one?

Nigel Thought you said it was just the girls?

Darren It is . . . but if it wasn't . . . would you wear one? Let everyone know exactly how . . . exactly what you've been doing?

Nigel (*stops and thinks about it*) Yeah, but it's different for a guy, isn't it?

Darren Is it?

Nigel Yeah, I mean . . . I can do what I like with whoever I like but if a girl . . . you know . . . puts it out a bit . . . well, a lot . . . then that's just not attractive, is it?

Darren says nothing.

Would you wear one?

Darren Dunno.

Nigel (*sees Stoner staring*) What's he watching us for?

Darren I'm not sure he's watching.

Nigel Of course he's watching, he's looking over here, isn't he?

Darren I don't know . . . I mean . . . I can't really tell with him . . . sometimes he's just staring off into space, you know . . . you think he's looking at you but really he's just kind of frozen . . . like he's been frozen by Mr Freeze.

Nigel The what?

Darren Mr Freeze, the ice man in *Batman*.

Nigel *Batman*?

Darren Yeah.

Nigel Batman sucks, he can't fly or anything.

Darren He's cool, he's the best one.

Nigel He is not. Superman, he could fly, had X-ray vision, burn things with his eyes.

Darren Yeah, but Batman is just a guy, just a regular guy with a vengeance, everything he does you or I could do, that's what makes him cool . . . or Spiderman.

Nigel Yeah, Spiderman was cool.

Darren Yeah.

Nigel (*beat*) He's still staring.

Darren I'm telling you he's not, it's like, you know . . . like when a computer crashes on you and everything freezes . . . the mouse won't even move . . . like that . . .

Nigel What are you on about?

Darren All I'm saying is, if we were to walk over there and go right up to him we'd see that he's just looking our way . . . but not really . . . he's just picked a point over in our direction.

Nigel Right, so –

Darren What?

Nigel Let's go and have a try of that then.

He walks over towards Stoner, followed by Darren. They get right up to him. Stoner doesn't react.

Hey.

Stoner doesn't react, like he's asleep with his eyes open.

Hey.

Darren Stoner.

Stoner (*looks at them, seeing them for the first time*) Hey Darren, hey Nigel.

Nigel Hey.

Darren You want to have a kick about with us?

Stoner How do you mean?

Darren You know, with the ball, have a kick about?

Stoner Me?

Nigel Fuck sake.

Darren Yeah.

Stoner Thanks . . . thanks and all, but . . . I don't know how.

Nigel How can you not know how? It's just kicking a
football.

Stoner I've five sisters . . . never had a football.

Nigel You never kicked a football . . . ever?

Stoner No. (*Takes out his gear and goes to make a joint.*)
You guys want a smoke?

Darren Alright.

Nigel Darren.

Darren What? (*Sits down beside Stoner and watches him
skin up.*) How many of these you doing a day, then?

Stoner Six . . . maybe seven.

Nigel Bullshit.

Stoner What?

Darren Why you smoking so much?

Stoner Dunno.

Darren I mean, it's one thing to have a smoke with
the lads, after school or whatever . . . but . . . six . . .
I mean . . .

Stoner Look, man, I just keep to myself, I don't bother
no one, do I? I don't pick on the small kids, I don't
chat up no one's girl.

Nigel You don't chat to anyone.

Stoner Well . . . what about it? You know . . . I'm happy.

Nigel Are you?

Darren How do you know when you're happy?

Stoner I've seen you smoke, the pair of you, different
times, don't be acting all judgemental on the Stoner.

Darren We're not being judgemental, we're just . . .
interested.

Stoner See, what the rest of you boys don't get is that
when you're not the one doing all the talking you hear
an awful lot, when you're the one sitting back and
observing, you observe an awful lot, you get me?

Nigel (*to Darren*) Come on.

Stoner I'm like the daddy longlegs.

Nigel looks at him like he's crazy.

You know . . . bumbling about . . . no one takes him
seriously . . . keeps to himself . . . but he is in fact the
most deadly of all the spiders . . .

Nigel What are you on about?

Darren He's right . . . daddy longlegs are supposed to be
very poisonous . . . just their fangs aren't long enough
to bite through human skin.

Nigel looks at him like he's mad.

Stoner Too right . . . but the quality . . . of what he has to
give . . . was he given the right opportunity to give it . . .
is top rate.

Nigel Come on, Darren, I can see Finlay doing his
rounds.

Darren Well, you know . . . you can come over and chat
to us . . . sometime . . . if you like . . .

Stoner About what?

Darren About whatever it is you want to talk about . . .
you know?

Stoner Alright.

Nigel I'm going, you want to get yourself expelled
because of this fruit-loop that's your business.

He exits.

Stoner (*finishing his joint, looks up at Darren*) You're
not gay are you, man?

Darren What? No . . . fuck sake.

Stoner Well, what you being nice to me for?

Darren Just . . . just because . . . no one should be on
their own all the time . . . if they don't have to be.

Stoner I don't want to try and compete with no one.
I just keep to myself.

Darren It's not competing . . . it's just . . . just friends . . .

Stoner All I see is people competing . . . friends and all.

Darren Well . . . (*Beat.*) You coming to the end-of-year
do?

Stoner Dunno.

Darren You hear about the wristbands?

Stoner Yeah, fucking twisted, man . . .

Darren (*beat*) You really have five sisters?

Stoner I have and all.

Darren So are they good-looking or all butt-ugly like
you?

Stoner looks up at him. Darren smiles.

Stoner Fuck off.

Darren Yeah . . . see you around.

SCENE FIVE

*David is sitting reading his comic, Michael is reading a
book.*

Michael (*looks up*) This is good, isn't it?

David Huh?

Michael Just the two of us . . . hanging out.

David still reads his comic book.

You know what I was thinking would be cool?

David reads.

If we were to drive across America . . . like the whole
way across from one side to the other . . . wouldn't
that be cool?

David What you on about?

Michael You and me . . . driving across America . . .
from one side to the other.

David When?

Michael When we're old enough.

David When we're old enough? When are you and me going to have enough money to drive across America? To fly over there and then buy a car and then put petrol in the car to drive across America? Who's going to teach us how to drive?

Michael (*disappointed*) My dad says he'll teach me next year . . . He's let me steer a few times when we're in our driveway . . . He says I'm good . . . says I'll be very good . . . (*Smiles.*) I'll drive us.

David You know how long it takes to get your licence? You know how much insurance costs?

Michael Fucking hell . . . I was just saying . . . I was just looking to the future . . . looking forward to something.

David I'm just saying you have to be practical, you have to think things through.

Michael (*beat*) Well I'm going to do it, some day, maybe I'll take my girlfriend.

David goes back to his comic.

Your Sarah's nice.

David She's a pain in the ass.

Michael Oh yeah . . . I know . . . but . . . for a girl . . . she's nice . . . nice enough.

David (*worried*) You got a crush on our Sarah?

Michael No . . . no . . . I was just saying –

David (*lashing out*) 'Cos she wouldn't touch you . . . she wouldn't . . .

Michael (*hurt, looks at him*) You think?

David (*weakening*) Well, I don't know, do I? (*Beat.*) Just would be weird if you did . . . she's my sister and all.

Michael I don't.

David It would be just fucking weird.

Michael I don't, I said. (*Beat.*) She going to the end-of-year do?

David Suppose, always there with her mates isn't she, dancing to fucking Britney?

Michael She going to wear one of those wristbands?

David Dunno, think it's stupid.

Michael Yeah, guess Jane will be wearing a green one then.

He laughs, David looks away.

Sorry, what – you still like her? I thought you said –

David I never said I liked that slag, did I?

Michael You went with her, though, didn't you?

David What's it to you?

Michael I'm just saying, you did, you said you liked her, you went for chips with her and . . . well you went with her, didn't you?

David Who said that?

Michael Look, it doesn't matter.

David I didn't know she was going to go with the whole fucking class, did I?

Michael No.

David She seemed like a nice enough person, she was nice, easy to talk to and that.

Michael Why won't you just say that you liked her?

David Because . . .

Michael I mean the fact that you liked her . . . liked her a lot . . . that's one thing . . . the fact that she's a slag . . . that's another . . . You liking her doesn't make you stupid or nothing.

David Of course it does. (*Beat.*) Nobody is what they're supposed to be any more, people are just fucking shells.

Michael Huh?

David Shells . . . hollow, you know?

Michael (*not getting it*) Oh. (*Beat.*) My mum met my dad when they were in school . . . she was only fifteen . . . now she's ancient . . . Imagine . . . you could just have a crush on someone now . . . just fancy them a bit . . . want them to like you . . . want to hang out . . . go for chips . . . and then thirty years later you could be married and have three kids with them . . .

David Or they could turn out to be the biggest fucking slag on the planet.

Michael looks hurt, looks away. David looks at him.

You know, you're too soft for a guy, you're always getting your feelings hurt and making me feel guilty about it.

Michael No I'm not.

David You are, you're walking around looking at everything like it's brilliant and fantastic and you don't see any of the shit and when I point it out to you, you get all . . . all . . . hurt.

Michael I see the shit.

David Yeah?

Michael Yeah . . . but what's the point in looking at it? It's just shit.

David (*beat*) I didn't mean it in a bad way. (*Beat.*) Just wish I couldn't see it. (*Beat.*) You know, I'm glad you're here, its important to me and . . . well . . . (*Goes back to reading his comic.*)

Michael Which one is it?

David (*looks up*) It's the one where he finds out who the Green Goblin really is.

Michael Who is he?

David You don't know?

Michael Can't remember.

David It's his best friend.

Lights down.

SCENE SIX

Jacob and JT are sitting at a café table.

Jacob I've said I'm sorry.

JT I know.

Jacob I know you're mad at me but I can explain.

JT I don't know if I want you to explain anything, I don't know if I even want to be sitting here talking to you.

Jacob Well, why are you then?

JT Because that's the kind of person I am, Jacob, I'm not the kind of person who would walk out of here just because you've said something I don't like.

Jacob I want to come, I do.

JT Yeah, right.

Jacob I do, I swear. I mean, I am nervous, they are your parents and all and I know how big it is for you and for me too, but . . .

JT But what?

Jacob (*beat*) My dad knows your dad.

JT What?

Jacob My dad, turns out he knows your dad, they work together sometimes, your dad's company uses my dad's company for something, they know each other.

JT So?

Jacob So he'll put the pieces together when he meets me and the next time he meets my dad he'll say it to him, he'll say it.

JT So?

Jacob (*beat*) It's not as easy for me as it is for you.

JT How do you know?

Jacob You don't know my parents.

JT Yeah, and why is that? Is it because you've never introduced me?

Jacob Look . . . they're stressed out at the moment . . . my little brother's acting all weird and they're all worried about him . . . taking him to a therapist and everything . . . and that's my dad's way of dealing with things . . . Something's broken . . . get it fixed.

JT Yeah, but you're not broken are you?

Jacob (*beat*) Look, I just don't want to stress them out any more right now . . . I don't want them to have to worry about me too.

JT (*beat*) It's my birthday and I'd like you to be there.

Jacob (*beat*) I'm sorry, I'll make it up to you. (*Takes a small box out of his pocket and leaves it on the table in front of him.*) I'm sorry.

JT What is it?

Jacob You'll have to open it and see.

JT (*opens the box and takes out a leather wristband*) It's lovely, thanks.

Jacob And I have one too, so we both have the same one, so it's a way of showing that we're together.

JT A way that no one knows else knows about.

Jacob (*beat*) I'm sorry. (*Beat.*) I am.

Michelle comes over, dressed as a waitress.

JT Can we have the bill, please?

Waitress Sure, will you be paying together or separately?

Jacob Separately.

JT (*overlapping*) Together.

Waitress (*confused*) Right . . .

She walks off. Jacob looks at JT. He looks away.

SCENE SEVEN

Sarah and Karen are in two neutral spaces, on the phone.

Karen So, did she completely freak out?

Sarah No, I don't think she even noticed it.

Karen What?

Sarah Well, she didn't say anything all night, don't think she even looked at me, and my dad was watching the telly so. I was kind of disappointed, actually, was looking forward to . . . I don't know . . . rebelling against the system.

Karen Yeah . . . sorry I didn't get one too.

Sarah Yeah.

Karen Maybe I'll go down next week, yours looks really cool. What did Michael think?

Sarah Nothing.

Karen He didn't say anything?

Sarah He wasn't here, they haven't come home yet. Mum is pretty pissed.

Karen It's almost twelve.

Sarah I know, they probably went into town and missed the last bus. She'll kill him, though, they're not getting on as it is.

Karen I came home after ten one night, my dad nearly gave himself a stroke shouting.

Sarah My dad doesn't care.

Karen I wish mine didn't.

Sarah (*beat*) No you don't.

Karen (*awkward*) Yeah . . . I guess . . . so where do you think they are?

Sarah I don't know.

Karen Maybe they're meeting some girls.

Sarah I doubt it.

Karen Well, whatever it is, I bet it's more exciting than lying in their pyjamas talking on the phone.

Sarah Yeah.

Karen What you wearing to the end-of-year do?

Sarah Dunno.

Karen Everyone's talking about the wristbands.

Sarah Yeah.

Karen You get some yet?

Sarah No.

Karen pulls up her sleeve to reveal four wristbands, yellow, red, blue and green.

Karen Me neither. (*She takes them off one by one.*) Saw Jane in town, wearing hers already – no prizes for guessing what colour.

Sarah Green?

Karen Couldn't be greener . . . it's weird, letting everyone know how far you've . . . what you've done . . . isn't it? I mean, letting people you don't even know . . . know . . . letting them judge you for who they think you are and not who you actually are.

Sarah Don't think I'll bother with it.

Karen Jane says anyone who doesn't wear it hasn't done anything at all.

Sarah Yeah well . . . fuck Jane.

Lights down.

SCENE EIGHT

David and Michael are sitting huddled together in the dark.

Michael It's gone out again.

David That was the last match.

Michael But I'm cold.

David I know you're cold, I'm bloody cold and all.

Michael I thought you said you could build a campfire.

David I said I knew how to build a fire – I watched my dad do it loads of times when I was little, before we got the gas fire, but it's different out here.

Michael No fire-lighters?

David You being funny?

Michael No – we don't, do we?

David No . . . thought you were being funny . . .

Michael I'm freezing.

David Stop going on about it, will you?

Michael I want to go home.

David What? We can't go home, we're making a point.

Michael I know, but –

David We're making a point, and if we go home now it will be ruined.

Michael I don't care any more. I want to be warm, I want hot chocolate and biscuits, I want my bed.

David They'll never learn then.

Michael Never learn what?

David They'll never learn to respect us.

Michael They'll respect us if we stay out all night in the freezing cold?

David That's not the point.

Michael Well, what is the point, because I can't feel my feet any more?

David The point is that we're teaching them a lesson . . . we're telling them that it's not just on their terms . . . that it's on our terms too . . . that they can't just dictate and shout and impose their ideals on us just because we're their offspring. We're individuals and we have to assert our right as individuals so that they will respect us as individuals.

Michael (*beat*) Can't we be individuals in the morning?

David No, you're missing the point.

Michael (*beat*) Thing is, I don't mind if sometimes they think I'm still a kid . . . because I kind of still feel like being a kid . . . you know?

David You're backing out.

Michael I'm not, I mean it. I still like to play games and stuff and adults . . . well, they don't play, do they? I mean, it's not considered normal for a grown man to play, but I like playing still, I like my computer games and my *Star Wars* figures – what if they start treating us like grown-ups and they take away my *Star Wars* figures?

David I knew you would back out.

Michael I'm not, I said . . . I just . . . I just don't want them to worry about me.

David That's how they learn, understand?

Michael Kind of.

David Fuck sake.

667

Michael Well, maybe my brain has frozen solid and
   that's why I can't understand.
David Fuck sake. (*He walks off.*)
Michael Where are you going?
David For a piss, alright?
Michael Don't be long.

> *David doesn't answer.*

Don't be long, I don't want to be left on my own. David?
   David?

> *Beat. He looks around nervously, takes out his phone
> and starts texting. David comes back.*

David What are you doing?
Michael (*guilty*) Nothing.
David Are you texting someone?
Michael No.
David (*holds his hand out*) Give it to me so.

> *Michael doesn't.*

Give it to me, I said.
Michael No.

> *David overpowers him and takes the mobile phone
> from him.*

No . . . I said no . . . Ow . . .

> *He holds his hand, which has been hurt.*

That hurt . . . that hurt, you know.
David (*reading*) 'Tell Mum I'm fine.' (*to Michael*) Tell
   Mum I'm fine'? What the fuck is this?
Michael I just don't want them to worry.
David If they don't worry, then it won't work.

> *He opens the back of the phone and takes the battery
> out.*

Michael What are you doing? David? What are you –?

David (*tossing him back the phone*) It's for your own good.

Michael You've taken out the battery.

David So you won't be texting Mummy and Daddy to come and find you.

Michael Give it back.

David Don't you get it? This is serious, this is, really fucking serious, and you just don't get it, you just don't get it.

Michael (*beat*) I know you get cross with your mum sometimes and I think it's crap, I do, and I know you get headaches a lot and that it makes you even more stressed out, but . . .

David But?

Michael But I'm not like you. I get on with my mum and dad, we have a right laugh at dinnertime, sitting around the table, my dad making stupid faces to make my mum giggle and me giving the dog bits of food under the table and he licking the back of my hand, and they did all that tonight . . . without me . . . and I don't want them to worry about me because I wouldn't like to be worrying about them. (*Beat.*) So . . .

David So go on, then.

Michael What?

David Go on then, go on home to Mummy and Daddy, go on running home to them, see if I care.

Michael (*beat*) But you'll be on your own.

David So? You think I'm afraid of being out here? I've been out here loads of times on my own.

Michael Not at night.

David Well, it's the same place, doesn't matter if it's the daytime or the night time (*Beat.*) Go on then.

Michael (*beat*) Won't you come with me? You can stay at mine, I can sneak you in the back door and your parents still won't know where you are, you could be anywhere (*Beat.*) Come on, we can play Resident Evil all night, we don't even have to go to sleep. (*Beat.*) You're not coming with me, are you?

Beat. He sighs and sits down.

David What are you doing?

Michael I'm staying.

David No you're not, you're going home, go on, clear off.

Michael No, it's alright.

David But I don't want you here.

Michael You asked me to come, you're just lashing out at me because you're pissed off with everyone else.

David Yeah, but that's before I knew what a chickenshit you were. I mean, I always knew, but . . . didn't realise how much is all.

Michael is upset.

You're always hanging off me, anyway, slowing me down, cramping my style, I should have known better than to ask you to get involved in this because you don't understand . . . you're too much of a child to understand . . . too much of a baby.

Michael Don't call me that.

David (*beat*) Baby.

Michael I said don't call me that.

David Baby. (*Beat.*) Baby baby, big fucking baby.

Michael (*beat*) Why are you being so mean to me?

David Baby baby baby baby baby baby –

Michael I'm staying here.

David (*beat*) No you're fucking not, go home.

Michael No.

David (*getting angry*) Go home, I said.

Michael (*beat*) I'm staying here, I'm not leaving you on your own.

David (*more angry*) I said get out of here, I don't want you here, you're ruining it.

Michael stays seated. David kicks him. Michael does nothing. David kicks him again, then grabs him aggressively and shouts.

I said get out of here, or I'll really hurt you, I'll hurt you badly, I swear it.

Michael (*shaken, stands slowly*) I don't know why you're so . . . mean to me (*Beat.*) I'm the only one who'll even talk to you any more.

David Fuck off, I said.

Michael turns and leaves, David picks up the orange and throws it at him as he leaves.

You better not breathe a word about this, about where I am, if someone comes down here looking for me I'll come looking for you and I'll cut off your dog's head and leave it on your doorstep.

Michael turns and looks at him.

Fuck off, I said . . . (*screaming*) Fuck off.

Lights down.

SCENE NINE

Jacob is sitting looking out to the audience. There are four policemen, dressed in hats and long trenchcoats, sitting in chairs facing him.

Jacob I don't know where he is, I've told you loads of times. The last time I saw him was yesterday at breakfast and then he went to school and I haven't seen him since.

Policeman 1 Would you say you're close with your brother?

Jacob No. Well, not really. Not close, but we get on okay. He's not really close to anyone, except Michael.

Policeman 2 Has your brother been unhappy recently?

Jacob A bit, sometimes, he gets frustrated.

Policeman 3 Frustrated with what?

Jacob Everything . . . anything . . .

Policeman 4 Has he ever been aggressive?

Jacob Sometimes. (*Beat.*) Sometimes he can't really . . . control his . . . He put his head through the kitchen door before . . . It's glass . . . he had to get stitches.

Policeman 1 And why did he do that?

Jacob Dunno, we don't know really, he was just . . . just frustrated . . . like he couldn't explain himself so he . . . just did that instead.

Policeman 3 Was he ever aggressive towards you?

Jacob No . . . He tried once . . . but I wouldn't hit him back, so he stopped . . . He can be a bit nasty at times.

Policeman 2 To his friends?

Jacob Yes, no, well, just to Michael, I think.

Policeman 4 Why?

Jacob I don't know why. He just is. He doesn't really have any other mates, so . . .

JT appears and dials a number on his mobile phone. Jacob's phone rings; he looks at it and hangs up. JT looks at his phone weirdly, then tries again.

To be honest, I think he's doing this on purpose, because he does things like that, he does something to make you react to it.

His phone rings.

Can I answer my phone – it's ringing?

Policeman 4 You should have switched it off.

Jacob Well, I'm supposed to meet someone – how much longer is this going to take?

The four policemen look at each other, then stand.

Policemen (*speaking together*) That's quite enough, for now.

They exit, taking their chairs.

Jacob (*speaking after them*) You think he's alright, don't you? I mean, he will turn up, won't he?

JT tries again.

He's probably having a laugh at our expense.

Beat. His phone rings, he answers it.

Hey.

JT Where are you?

Jacob At the police station.

JT Yeah, right.

Jacob I swear it, I am. My little brother stayed out all night and my parents are freaking out.

JT Where is he?

Jacob I don't know – with his mate Michael, they both headed off somewhere after school yesterday and never came home. My mum's in a state.

JT (*beat*) So I take it you're not coming over, then.

Jacob I want to, but I have to help look for him.

JT I thought you said you didn't even get on with your little brother.

Jacob Yeah, but still . . .

JT Still what?

Jacob He's still my little brother, we might fight all the time and he might drive me mad but he's still my brother.

JT So you're not coming, then?

Jacob I can't.

JT Well, do you want me to help you look, then?

Jacob doesn't say anything.

Do you want me to come around and meet your family and introduce me to them as your boyfriend?

Jacob says nothing for a second.

I take it that's a no, then.

Jacob I'm not sure this would be the best time.

JT I don't think there's ever going to be a good time, is there?

Jacob Of course.

JT There's never going to be a good time.

Jacob Look, you don't know my dad, he's very . . . stressed out . . . like, on a normal day he's stressed out, on a day like today he's extra stressed out, he's already kicked in the television and we've had to put the dog in the bathroom because he's tried to bite him twice.

JT Who has?

Jacob What?

JT Who's tried to bite who?

Jacob My dad.

JT Your dad has tried to bite the dog?

Jacob No the dog – look, he gets stressed out. (*Beat.*) I have another call coming in, might be home, might be about my brother.

JT Yeah, right.

Jacob Look, I'm sorry about all this.

JT Don't be.

Jacob No, I am, I'll make it up to you.

JT Don't bother.

Jacob What?

JT Don't bother, I don't want to see you any more, do I? Don't want to be hanging around with someone who doesn't want to be seen hanging around with me. (*Hangs up.*)

Jacob What? JT? JT? (*He presses a button on his phone*) Hello? Hello? David? Is that you? I can't hear you? David?

Jacob looks scared.

Are you alright? I can't hear you? David? David?

Lights down.

SCENE TEN

Nigel, Darren, Karen and Michelle all sit on chairs facing the audience. Stoner is behind them writing on a blackboard. Michelle is blowing bubbles with bubble gum, Karen is reading a book, Darren is staring at Karen, and Nigel is making a paper aeroplane. During this scene Stoner writes the following on the blackboard:

> *If you were free you'd know it,*
> *If you were free you'd show it,*
> *You'd fly to beautiful places,*
> *You'd see only beautiful faces,*
> *You'd be a shining star.*
> *Don't be another follower,*
> *Don't be another borrower,*
> *Be exactly the one you are.*

Nigel I can't get the wing bit right, think I need a different type of paper, thicker paper would do the trick, would sort us out.

He gets no response and looks at Darren.

Darren?
Darren Huh?
Nigel I said I need to get some thicker paper, you think you can nick some of your dad's? He's got that good paper for drawing on, hasn't he?

Darren is still staring at Karen.

Darren?

Darren Huh?

Nigel Can you get us some of your dad's paper? The stuff he uses for his architecture?

Darren I'll try.

Michelle Aren't you a bit old to be making paper aeroplanes, Nigel?

Nigel Aren't you a bit old to be blowing bubbles, Michelle?

Michelle Good comeback.

Nigel Who's interested in your opinion, anyway?

Michelle Lots of people.

Nigel Like who?

Michelle Like lots of people, grown-up people.

Nigel I'm grown-up.

Michelle Bet you still wet your bed and all.

Nigel I do not.

Karen (*looks up at Stoner*) Stoner, what are you doing?

Stoner (*looks around at her*) Huh?

Karen What are you doing? Is this homework?

Stoner I'm waxing.

Nigel You're what?

Stoner I'm waxing . . . lyrical . . . you know?

Karen Waxing what?

Stoner Poetry people . . . lyrics . . . prophecies . . .

Michelle He's just going to make you wipe it off.

Stoner So what? Doesn't make the creation of the words any less vital, you get me?

The other characters look at each other in confusion.

Karen You are so odd, Stoner, you're like . . . from another planet or something.

Michelle Hey, why do they call you Stoner, anyway?

The others look at her in amazement.

What? What? It's just a question.

Stoner goes back to his writing. He writes the text below, while the others talk.

To look beyond the ordinary,
To do something extraordinary,
To live beyond your confines.
I see the light inside,
All this dreary human kind,
I bask in the sunshine.

Karen (*to Darren, who is looking at her*) Darren, you're doing it again.
Darren (*looks away*) Sorry.
Karen I don't mind it sometimes, it's kind of nice. I'm glad you think I'm good-looking and all, but other times, other times it's just kind of creepy.
Darren Sorry.
Karen That's okay.

Goes back to reading her book, Darren stares at her again.

Darren!
Darren Sorry.
Nigel Suppose you'll have bought your wristband already, Michelle, or won't be wearing one at all maybe.
Michelle I'll be wearing one.
Nigel Yeah, sure . . .
Darren You wearing one, Karen?
Karen Dunno, don't think I'll bother going.
Darren Right.

He looks ahead, then stands and looks out a window.

There's loads of them, isn't there? Four cars with two officers in each, that's . . . that's . . .
Nigel Eight . . .

Stoner stops writing and listens to them.

Darren Eight officers . . . they look pretty tough . . . pretty cool . . . I could be a cop.
Stoner Cops? What they want?

They ignore him.

Nigel It's not like in the movies, Darren.
Darren I know.
Nigel It's dangerous.
Stoner What the cops want?

They ignore him.

Darren Here? What's so dangerous about here?
Stoner (*louder*) What do the cops want?
Nigel To see if we know anything.
Michelle But we're not even in their year, what would we know?
Stoner Know what?
Karen About David and Michael.
Stoner What about them?
Nigel Jesus, Stoner, you don't know they're missing?
Stoner Since when?
Nigel Last night, I can't believe you don't know this.
Karen They're asking everyone, in groups of five, just in case anyone saw where they went – why do you think we're here?

Stoner looks worried. He tries to write more on the board but can't.

Michelle Poor Sarah, she must be worried. Is she worried?
Karen Yeah.
Michelle I wonder if a news crew will come here, you know, and interview students. I should have straightened my hair this morning – this could be my big break.
Nigel You're not going to be on the telly, Michelle.

Michelle How do you know?

Nigel Because you're not. You didn't even know them, why would they ask you?

Michelle Because . . . because I'm good-looking . . . and that gets you places in this world . . . gets you on the telly . . . No one likes looking at geeky four-eyes on the telly . . . they like looking at pretty faces . . . like mine.

Nigel (*mumbles*) I don't think you're pretty.

Michelle Well, you wouldn't be able to tell, would you? You're too much of a child to recognise a real woman.

Karen I don't want to be on the telly, I wouldn't know what to say.

Darren You'd be great on the telly, Karen.

Karen I think I'd just freeze up, might even start crying, not because of the boys being missing, just because I feel I should start crying, people are always crying on the telly when someone goes missing. I'd have to cry, wouldn't I?

Michelle I'll do it, I can cry on the spot, instantly.

Darren I wonder where they are.

Michelle They're just hiding out somewhere, looking for attention, probably been planning this for ages, David's so weird.

Nigel You think everyone who doesn't fancy you is weird.

Michelle I do not.

Darren I like Michael, he's in the chess club with me and Freddy, he's pretty good too, he's better than me.

Karen I didn't know you could play chess.

Darren My mum taught me, we had a lot of time in the hospital so . . .

Michelle Is your mother sick, Darren?

Darren (*embarrassed*) Eh . . . she was . . . She . . . she died.

Michelle That's really shit. I don't know what I'd do if my mum died, she's great, more of a friend than a mum, takes me shopping and everything, reads the same magazines and all. Last summer we went to the Canaries together, just the two of us, and we had a right laugh.

Karen Michelle.

Michelle What?

Karen That's enough about mums, I think.

Michelle What? (*to Darren*) You don't mind me talking about my mum, do you?

Darren (*shaking his head*) N . . . n . . . no.

Karen I'm really sorry your mum died, Darren.

Darren Thanks.

Stoner My dad's dead.

They all look at him. Beat.

Well, I think he is, went off ages ago, went to put a bet on a horse in the Grand National . . . didn't come back.

After a few moments, David appears. Only Stoner can see him. He walks slowly around the room, stopping in front of characters occasionally. He is very pale. Stoner watches him, terrified.

Nigel (*beat*) What if they don't come back?

Michelle Huh?

Nigel David and Michael, what if they're not messing, what if something actually happened to them?

Michelle (*afraid*) Like what?

Nigel I don't know.

Darren Well, what usually happens to kids when they go missing?

Karen I don't want to think about it.

Michelle Think about what?

Nigel Well, they could have been abducted, by paedophiles or something.

Michelle But they're not kids, they're sixteen, paedophiles go for little kids, not teenagers.

Darren Maybe not paedophiles then, maybe just some crazy guy with a gun.

Karen Stop.

Nigel Maybe there were two crazies in a van and they just pulled up and made them get in.

Darren (*acting our pulling a gun*) Pulled out the gun and made them get in.

Nigel (*joining in, pointing his make-believe gun at Michelle*) And made them do things.

Darren (*pointing his gun at Michelle*) Horrible things.

Michelle whimpers.

Karen Stop, will you.

Darren Sorry, Karen.

Michelle (*freaked out*) I want to go home.

Nigel What?

Michelle I want to go home. I'm scared. (*Starts to cry.*) I want my mum.

Karen It's okay, Michelle.

Michelle I want my mum, I want my mum, I want my mum.

Nigel Don't be such a baby.

Michelle (*louder*) I want my mum, I want my mum, I want my mum.

Darren (*standing and looking as if through a glass panel in a door*) Keep it down, they're coming.

Michelle (*shaking*) I don't want to die.

Karen No one's going to die.

Michelle Promise?

Karen Promise.

Darren Here they are. Don't say anything stupid.

Michelle I'm scared.

Darren You alright, Stoner?

Stoner Huh?

He is still staring at David, who watches him as he exits.

Darren Look like you've seen a ghost.

Lights snap down as all five sit up straight and look forward.

SCENE ELEVEN

Lights up on Sarah, with her schoolbag over her shoulder.

Sarah I went back down to the tattoo place, didn't really leave school heading there, just kind of didn't want to go home and kept walking until I ended up right outside it. Everyone thinks my nose-piercing looks really cool. (*Beat.*) But it doesn't matter, because the one person I really wanted to see it hasn't . . . the one person I really wanted to think it was cool – (*Beat.*) – is missing. (*Beat.*) I've been feeling pretty bad about it, about the fact then when I feel worried for them, it's Michael I'm worried for. And David is my brother, and that just makes me feel like I'm the worst sister in the world. I mean, he's my brother, I've known him all my life, I've lived with him all my life. (*Beat.*) But it's hard . . . he makes it hard to love him. He's not very . . . loveable . . . I don't think any of us are . . . we're just that kind of family. When I'm in Karen's house for a sleepover, and it's time for bed, I start to freak out, I'm watching the telly or chatting to her parents, but I'm not really listening or watching because I'm watching the clock. I know that we'll have to go to bed soon . . . and in Karen's house . . . the parents kiss and hug you goodnight. (*Beat.*) Goodnight, in my house, we don't even say 'Goodnight,' we don't even say 'See ya,' we just leave the room. And I get so nervous, because I know I'm going to have to kiss Karen's parents on the cheek and give them a goodnight hug. I used to make excuses, like I'd go to the bathroom and brush my teeth and just wait in the room for Karen to come up, but her mum would just come in and tuck me in. (*Beat.*) Tuck me in (*Beat.*) I cried that night, after Karen had fallen asleep and I didn't know why I was crying. I knew it had something to do with the fact that she had hugged me, and kissed me on the cheek, and fixed my pillow and brushed my hair out of my eyes, and she smelled like mums should smell . . . like floral perfume and moisturiser, and she smiled all the time . . . and it made me want to cry. (*Beat.*) And I did . . . for ages . . . and I liked it . . . 'cos even though I was crying . . . I was feeling something . . . like I'd woken up for a second and I didn't want to go back to sleep, so I kept crying . . . to hang on to that goodnight hug. (*Beat.*) I didn't even really want to get a tattoo. (*She starts rolling up her sleeve.*) It was just something to do to wake me up. The girl was nice, she gave me books and books full of pictures, and I ended up picking this one. (*She rolls up her sleeve to show a tattoo with* MUM *in a heart.*) But it's not really for my mum, you know? It's just for mums in general, and that tucked-in feeling. And the whole time she was doing it, I was hurting and thinking about Michael and holding back tears and it felt good. (*Beat.*) It felt really really good.

SCENE TWELVE

David sits alone in the dark, he's shivering and staring into space. He is trying to read his comic book by the light of his mobile phone, but it's difficult. He hears a noise offstage and looks up.

David I said fuck off, yeah?

*No answer. David goes back to reading. We hear
another noise, louder and closer this time.*

Fuck off, I said (*Beat.*) Well alright so, come out (*Beat.*)
I said come out, I know it's you. (*Beat. He stands and
ties up his jacket.*) I know it's you, too scared to go
home in the dark, were you?

Michael enters.

What are you doing?

Michael I'm not leaving you here on your own.

David (*surprised*) I kicked you, I said I was going to kill
your dog.

Michael Yeah, but . . . didn't mean it, did you? I mean . . .
you didn't . . . did you?

David What you come back for?

Michael Told you, not leaving you on your own.

David I'm doing just fine on my own, just fine. Don't
need you here to make me feel safe, you know. You're
nothing without me, I'm a natural leader, people like
you are just meant to follow us about.

Michael You don't mean it, this isn't even you talking,
this isn't what you really want to say to me.

David It is.

Michael This is the other you, the one that comes out
when you're all angry and stressed out and you can't
handle it . . . but it's not the real you . . .

David What the fuck are you going on about?

Michael Like Spiderman . . . and Peter Parker . . . or his
friend . . . Yeah his friend, the guy who is his best
friend but then turns into the Green Goblin and tries
to kill him . . . but that's not really him . . . he's really
his friend . . . he doesn't really want to kill him it's just
the mask he puts on . . . it makes him want to.

David If anyone around here is Peter Parker, it's me, you
got it?

Michael You go around behind this mask being shitty to everyone, being shitty to me, but I know that's not what you're really like, you're a good person, you're a good friend.

David takes a knife from his pocket and walks over behind Michael. He catches him from behind and holds the knife to his throat.

David You don't know the first fucking thing about me, about what it's like to be me, about who I am. You think you know me, you think I need you, I don't fucking need you. No one fucking needs you because you're nothing, you're nothing, you're the in-between person, the one no one notices, no one cares about, never does anything worth remembering. (*Beat.*) You think I'm a good person now? (*Presses the knife into his flesh.*) Do you?

Michael Yes.

David (*lets him go*) You're like a dog, aren't you? Just keep coming back for more.

Michael Tell me that you won't be coming over to mine to apologise, tell me you won't be saying how sorry you are, that sometimes you just get so down you have to take it out on someone and I'm always around, tell me you won't be crying and saying I'm the only one who you can talk to, the only one who understands you, tell me that you won't turn up saying if I can just forgive you this one time that it will be the last time, because I always forgive you, David, I always do. (*Beat.*) That's why I keep coming back, I care about you and you don't think I should, you don't think anyone should, but I'm giving you this last chance. (*Beat.*) If this is the real you, the real person, who wants me to fuck off and who believes all those things you've just said about me, then tell me and I'll go, I will. But that's it, then, last life used up, game over.

David (*beat, looks at Michael*) That's it, I meant it.

Michael That's it?

David Said it, didn't I? That's it.

Michael And this is you? This is the real you?

David It is.

Michael And you think I'm a dog and I'm weak and pathetic?

David (*beat*) I do.

Michael Right then.

David What you waiting for? Fuck off so.

Michael (*beat, looks at him*) That's it, then.

David Fuck off, I said.

Michael I will . . . I am . . . I'm fucking off. (*Looks at him again, walks off.*)

David (*shouting after him*) I knew it, thing is you're nothing without me, I'm a natural leader I am, people like you are just meant to follow us about. (*Paces back and forth, hears a noise.*) Follow us about, I said, what, you coming back for more? (*Hears another sound, kind of relieved.*) I said stop it, just come out will you, I won't go for you don't worry, you've learnt your lesson now, you know who's boss.

Silence. David looks about, getting a bit worried. Beat.

Michael? (*Beat.*) Stop being such a prick, come out, I said. (*worried*) Don't make me come in there after you, 'cos I will, I'm not like you, I'm no baby, I'm not afraid of the dark.

Another noise. David stretches out his hands as if to push something in front of him away.

You think this is funny, do you? Do you? Trying to scare me? Well, you can't, I don't get afraid, I don't get scared, do I? (*Beat. Angry now, voice loud.*) It's you who gets scared, isn't it? Isn't it? It's you who's the bloody baby?

Another noise. He crouches down, as if trying to dodge something.

Was that you? (*Beat.*) Did you just touch me? Michael? (*Beat.*) Something just brushed past me and if it wasn't you then who was it? Michael? Who the fuck was it? (*Beat.*) Okay, I'm sorry, I'm sorry, alright? I shouldn't have had a go at you like I did (*Beat.*) I shouldn't have, alright?

Another noise. Michael is very afraid now.

So come out, alright? Please? (*Beat.*) Come on, mate, please? You know I didn't mean it, I didn't mean anything at all.

Beat. Another noise. He reacts as if something has touched him again, falls to his knees, afraid, and puts his hands over his head protectively. He shouts:

Michael! Michael! Michael!

SCENE THIRTEEN

Darren and Karen sit on a wall, Karen is holding a birthday present which is wrapped up and tied with a bow.

Karen Thanks for walking me.
Darren No bother.
Karen Didn't feel like walking on my own.
Darren I don't mind, nothing else to do.
Karen Sarah was supposed to come with me but . . .
I guess she won't be doing anything for a while.
Darren I guess.
Karen I don't even want to go myself now.
Darren Which house is it?
Karen (*pointing*) Around the corner.
Darren How come you don't want to go?

Karen Just don't feel like going to a party, feel like going home, watching telly.

Darren So don't go.

Karen I have to.

Darren Why?

Karen (*beat*) Don't want to say.

Darren Why not?

Karen Just don't.

Darren Alright.

Karen (*beat*) I'm supposed to kiss Fergus Lynch.

Darren What? He's a tosser.

Karen Because of the last time, at Jane's house, for her birthday they were playing spin-the-bottle and it landed on me and Fergus and I didn't want to, so I said I had to use the bathroom and then I climbed out the window. (*Beat.*) Everyone's been having a go at me since. I told them I was sick. but they didn't believe me. They said if I came to Suzy's and kissed him then they'd leave me alone. (*Beat.*)

Darren If you don't want to kiss him then don't.

Karen It's not that I don't want to, or that I want to . . . I just want to get it over and done with.

Darren To get what – oh . . .

Karen Yeah? So? So I've never kissed anyone, what's wrong with that?

Darren Nothing.

Karen I mean, I've never met anyone I wanted to kiss, what's wrong with that?

Darren Nothing, nothing, I said nothing.

Karen (*beat*) I just wanted it to mean something, not just some snog behind the bike sheds with someone who doesn't care . . . I wanted it to be something I could look back on as the perfect first kiss and the longer I waited the more of a deal it became. It's stupid.

Darren I don't think it's stupid.

Karen (*beat*) Have you?

Darren What?

Karen Snogged.

Darren (*embarrassed*) Yeah.

Karen (*disappointed*) You have not.

Darren I have too.

Karen Who?

Darren When I was in France with my parents, her name was Audrey, I have a picture.

Karen What, you carry it around with you?

Darren S . . . sometimes.

Karen Well, go on, then.

> *He takes a picture from his bag and hands it to her. She looks at it.*

She's pretty.

Darren She's alright.

Karen (*hands it back to him. Beat*) I thought you liked me.

Darren I do.

Karen What you kiss her for then?

Darren I dunno . . . get it over and done with, I guess.

Karen (*she stands, fiddles with the present*) Jane says she's had sex and all.

Darren She's lying.

Karen You think?

Darren Yeah, she lies about everything, she said her dad was a navy seal to me before.

Karen Is he not?

Darren Sure he can't be, he's not even American.

Karen So what does he do then?

Darren Well I don't know, but he's not a bloody navy seal, is he? Probably works for Tesco or something.

Karen Probably (*Beat.*) She's been wearing her wristband all week . . . I wasn't going to wear any, but now they're saying that anyone who isn't wearing one hasn't done anything, they're going to write all the names down on a sheet and copy it and leave them all around school. (*Beat.*) Why does it fucking matter, anyway? How does a stupid wristband say everything you want to say about yourself? Doesn't tell you anything about a person, does it? It's not like 'I've had sex' means anything, it's just something you've done, like skiing or bungee-jumping. I mean, if you didn't want to bungee-jump you wouldn't, would you? You wouldn't do it just so some strangers you'd never met will think you're cool.

Darren No point getting upset over it.

Karen Can't help it, can I? (*Beat.*) I have this feeling.

Darren What?

Karen I've had this feeling, since . . . since the boys went.

Darren What sort of feeling?

Karen I dunno . . . like a panic feeling in my stomach . . . like something is wrong.

Darren You're just worried.

Karen Like maybe they're not okay, maybe they won't be back . . . ever . . . Maybe they're dead.

Darren Don't say that.

Karen Imagine that, imagine your life ending now, now? Things are only just starting to get interesting, but imagine that was all you got.

Darren But it's not.

Karen But what if it was? (*Beat.*) What would you be saying as you died? Would you be thinking of all the things you should have done? Would you be wishing you'd done things just to do them?

Darren I dunno.

Karen (*fiddles with the present*) That's the only reason I said I'd come to this stupid party. (*Beat.*) I keep thinking that if someone has taken them, both of them, if someone was able to overpower the pair of them, then maybe they'll come and get one of us. Maybe you, maybe me. I saw this documentary about

these guys that went around in a van and abducted
loads of people and sold them off in foreign countries
as slaves . . . Some of them died on the way, they didn't
even make it as far as there, they died on the trucks on
the way over. (*Beat.*) When Sarah told me they hadn't
come home I didn't think anything of it, but then . . .
then I woke up last night and I thought about it and
thought about it . . . and then I heard a noise and
I thought he was downstairs.

Darren Who?

Karen I don't know, this guy that I've made up, this big
ugly guy who's taken the boys, it's stupid, but I could
really see him, see him downstairs in the kitchen,
coming up the stairs. I was terrified, I didn't sleep all
night. (*Beat.*) All I wanted to do was run into my
parents' room and climb in between them, like I used
to do when I was small, but I can't do that now, can I?
They'd think I was having some kind of breakdown or
something. (*Beat.*) It sucks . . . what do you do when
you're not a kid any more but you're still scared?
(*Beat.*) It's the only reason I came to this stupid party.

Darren What is?

Karen (*embarrassed*) I guess I . . . I don't want to die
without . . . without having done anything . . . without
being kissed . . .

Darren Oh. (*Embarrassed, but trying to build up his
courage, he stands in front of her.*) Stand up.

Karen Why?

Darren Just stand up.

He kisses her. She drops the present.

Darren (*pulling back*) How was that?

Karen Dunno . . . got nothing to compare it to.

Darren Oh.

Karen Was alright, I guess . . . was nice . . .

Darren (*beat*) Good. (*Beat.*) Still want to go to the party?

Karen Nah . . . doesn't seem to matter so much now . . .
(*Beat.*) Doesn't matter at all.

*He smiles and picks up the present. They walk off
together. Blackout.*

SCENE FOURTEEN

*Stoner, Jacob and Sarah are sitting in a room. Stoner is
sitting between them, facing out; they are seated facing
him.*

Jacob You have to tell them where he is, my parents are
worried sick, we're all worried sick. It's not a game,
you know, whatever kind of stunt you think you're
playing, it's not funny. It's serious, it's very fucking
serious.

Beat. Stoner stares out.

Are you listening to me? You better be, because any
minute now they're going to come back in here and
they're going to expect you to answer their questions,
do you understand?

He stands up abruptly. Stoner and Sarah flinch.

I said do you understand, you little fuckwit? (*He grabs
him.*) Well? Well?

Sarah Let him go.

Jacob Tell me where he is.

Sarah Let him go, I said.

Jacob He's my little brother, you know, he's nothing to
you, just a friend, that's all, just someone to play with,
he's my brother.

Sarah That's enough.

Jacob lets him go. He paces around them.

Jacob (*looks at him*) Do you know where he is?

Stoner shakes his head.

Then why did you tell Darren you did?
Sarah Jacob, sit down, you're only making things worse.
Jacob (*beat*) Ask him.
Sarah Stoner.

Stoner looks at her.

Do you know something?
Stoner I . . . I don't know.
Jacob What do you mean, you don't know? What's the matter with him?
Stoner I saw him.
Sarah Who?
Stoner Michael.
Jacob Where?
Stoner In the woods.
Sarah When?
Stoner After school, he asked me not to tell.
Jacob Why?
Stoner I don't know.
Jacob What did he say?
Sarah Jacob . . . relax . . . What did he say to you? It's important.
Stoner He told me not to tell, he gave me fifty pence for a Mars bar and he told me not to tell.
Jacob Tell what?
Stoner That I'd seen him.
Sarah Which way did he go?

Stoner looks down. David enters and walks up to him, walks before him, makes a gun from his right hand and aims it at Stoner's head. Stoner looks up and sees him; no one else does.

Stoner What?

Sarah Which way did he go?
Stoner (*to David*) Do you want me to tell them?
Jacob Tell us, you little shit.
Stoner Do you?

> *David takes his hand away, looks at him and nods, then exits.*

I can show you.
Jacob Can you show the police?
Stoner I can. (*Beat.*) Now I can.

> *Lights down.*

SCENE FIFTEEN

The woods, Michael walks back in. He's been crying and looks hungry and dirty.

Michael David? (*He looks around for him.*) David? You there? (*Beat. He walks over to the pile of comics and lifts them up.*) I'm waiting here till you come out. Okay? (*Beat.*) I'm waiting.

SCENE SIXTEEN

The Policemen are sitting on metal chairs with their backs to us. They are all wearing dark hats and coats, interrogating Michael, who sits facing them.

Michael We had a fight.
Policeman 1 What did you do?
Michael We had a fight and I left. I didn't want to, but he made me. (*Beat.*) He made me.
Policeman 2 When did you see him?
Michael Last night, he took my phone, he said I didn't

understand what he was doing and he said I had to go.
(*Beat.*) It was dark. (*Beat.*) I didn't want to leave him
there. (*Beat.*) But he hit me.

Policeman 3 I thought you were friends?

Michael We were, he just . . . hits me sometimes . . .

Policeman 4 Did this make you angry? Make you want
to hit back, maybe?

Michael No.

Policeman 5 Go on.

Michael He hit me so I left. (*Beat.*) But I was scared, it
was so dark and I'd never been there that late before.

Policeman 6 Been where?

Michael In the woods.

Policeman 7 You'd never been to the woods before?

Michael Never that late, never in the dark. (*Beat.*) I tried
to come home, but I couldn't . . . I didn't want to
leave him there on his own, so I tried to find my way
back, but I couldn't . . . I couldn't . . .

Policeman 8 Couldn't what?

Michael I couldn't find him.

Policeman 9 Where is he now?

Michael (*upset*) I don't know . . . I don't know . . .

Policeman 10 It's okay.

Michael I didn't want to leave him . . . he made me . . .
he made me . . . He was shouting . . .

Policeman 4 Where did you leave him, Michael?

Michael I promised.

Policeman 8 Promised what?

Michael I promised I wouldn't tell.

Policeman 2 You have to.

Michael But that's the thing . . . he's not there anyway.

Policeman 7 Not where?

Michael As soon as it got bright I found my way back
but he wasn't there . . . His bag was and his phone and
his comics and everything . . . but he wasn't there . . .

Policeman 9 You have to tell us where.

Policeman 3 He might be in trouble, Michael, he might be hurt.

Michael But I promised.

Policeman 4 (*losing his temper*) Where is he? Where is he? (*grabbing him*) I'm warning you, where is he?

Michael (*upset*) In the woods. (*Beat.*) Near the lake.

Policeman 10 (*as he exits*) You have to take us there right away, do you understand? Right away.

Michael puts his head in his hands.

Policeman 1 You did the right thing, Michael. (*Beat.*) You did.

Lights down.

SCENE SEVENTEEN

Michelle, in the spotlight, is being interviewed by a TV crew.

Michelle Oh yeah, we were like best mates, best best mates, we hung around together all the time, all the time. Yeah . . . yeah, I guess you could say that . . . we were kind of boyfriend-girlfriend . . . it's all very . . . very . . . sad . . . (*She feigns some tears.*) but you've got to be strong, you know? Got to get on with your life, that's what David would have wanted. Oh yeah . . . he was a great guy . . . real personality . . . a born leader, you know? I used to look at him and think . . . now there's a guy who's really going to go somewhere with his life . . . to make something of himself. Like me. (*Big smile.*) I can see the ladder of success and I'm going all the way to the very top. Sure . . . sure . . . the school has three counsellors, and we get time off class if we want to go and talk to them about it . . . It's mostly for the weaker kids, though, you know . . . the ones who can't handle it. Me? Of course, I can handle anything . . . I am going to sing at the mass, though . . . personally I think it's kind of weird to have a funeral for someone who you don't know for sure is dead, but – yeah they found his jacket, but . . . that doesn't mean he's dead . . . Yeah, but they don't know for sure that it was his blood – oh, they do? Oh . . . well he must be dead then . . . It's so . . . so . . . sad. (*Feigns a few more tears.*) What do I think happened? I dunno, some of the kids at school say he was abducted by aliens, but I don't believe in all that crap . . . I think there's enough extra-terrestrials right here on earth, if you know what I mean. (*Beat.*) I don't know why anyone would want to hurt him, though. (*Beat.*) Why would anyone want to hurt someone they don't even know? (*Beat.*) Is that it? I can say more if you like? (*She pulls up her sleeve to reveal several green wristbands.*) Sure, I have stories about him, I have tons. Are we ready, tell me when.

Beat. She flashes a smile as the recording continues, lights down.

SCENE EIGHTEEN

Nigel and Jacob are washing graffiti off a wall. It says JACOB WILSON IS A FAG *over and over again.*

Nigel I'm real sorry about David. (*Beat.*) I mean, I didn't know him all that well, but . . . still . . . I'm sorry.
Jacob Thanks.
Nigel Are you okay?
Jacob I guess, don't really know what to think about it.
Nigel Yeah. (*He continues to wash.*) Sure was mean of whoever this was, though, I mean, taking into account

what's just happened, they could have picked on
someone else, you know?

Jacob Yeah.

Nigel You don't seem that pissed off about it. I mean, I'd
be, I'd be real pissed off about it, if it was me, that is.

Jacob says nothing.

Not that I mind helping you out, hey it's better than
double French anyway, so thanks!

*He laughs, looks at Jacob, who is serious. He stops
laughing.*

But seriously, man, I'd be really fuming about now, this
school the way it is, they'll be teasing you for weeks.

Jacob Maybe there's worse things.

Nigel Huh?

Jacob I said maybe there's worse things than being teased.

Nigel Yeah, I guess.

Jacob I bet you get it all the time.

Nigel Get what?

Jacob Teased . . . 'cos of your specs.

Nigel Yeah, sometimes.

Jacob Do you let it get to you?

Nigel No . . . not really. I mean, that's the way I am . . .
not my fault . . . Them teasing me isn't going to make
a difference . . . they kind of stop once you don't let it
get to you, anyway . . . that's what you should do,
man . . . you just shouldn't let them know that it gets
to you, and then they'll leave you alone, that's the
trick. (*Beat.*) Still though, be nice to know who did it,
could get them back at least.

Jacob I know who did it.

Nigel You do?

Jacob I do.

Nigel What you going to do about it? You going to get
them back?

Jacob No.

Nigel Why?

Jacob Because my little brother just disappeared and I've just realised that I didn't really know him and that he didn't really know me and that seems more important right now than revenge.

Nigel Sure . . . of course . . . But I mean, still . . . you have to do something . . . don't you?

Jacob No.

Nigel But don't you want to get them back for it?

Jacob Not really.

Nigel Why not?

Jacob Because the person who did this is my ex-boyfriend and I love him and I was too afraid to tell people so he did it for me.

Nigel You're kidding, right?

Jacob Nope. (*Stands back and looks at the wall.*) I am indeed a fag.

Nigel (*doesn't know what to say, goes back to washing the wall*) Oh . . . alright . . . That's, I mean . . . that's cool . . . that's . . . cool.

Jacob and Nigel continue washing. Nigel takes a sidestep away from Jacob before the lights go down.

SCENE NINETEEN

Michael is standing downstage, making a speech to the audience as if they were the congregation at the funeral mass. The other characters sit in a row facing him. They all have a flower in their hands.

Michael (*beat*) David was my best friend. (*He stops and clears his throat.*) David was my best friend and I miss him. (*Beat.*) I wish he was here (*Beat.*) His parents have asked me to say something about him . . . because

I was his best friend . . . I was. (*Beat.*) And I guess I'm happy that he thought of me like that, because I wasn't really sure if he did . . . sometimes. David liked playing video games, Resident Evil was his favourite, one time we played it for twelve hours straight and I was afraid to walk home so he walked me. Me and David were like that a lot, we'd do something or watch something and I'd get real scared and he'd have to walk me home. David was brave. David was funny and smart and sometimes . . . well, he could be mean sometimes, too. I guess that's the one thing I didn't like about David, he'd get real frustrated with something and then he'd be mean. But I understood it so I didn't mind it so much most of the time. I understood that he had to get it out somehow, and I thought that in some way maybe that's why he kept me around. David liked reading comics and *Spiderman* was his favourite. He always said if he could be any superhero it would be Spiderman, and he said I could be the Green Goblin because he was his arch enemy and superheroes are always best friends with their arch enemies. David was brave, funny, smart, mean but kind too. When I was failing maths last year he stayed at my house all night trying to teach me algebra so I wouldn't have to stay back, and when my dog went missing he walked all over town with me and he never complained. (*Beat. He looks up.*) That's all I wrote. (*He fiddles with the paper.*) I don't know where David is or what happened to him. (*Beat.*) I think I was a good friend to him, as good as I could be. (*Beat.*) I hope he's happy, I hope he's not angry any more . . . I hope I didn't let him down.

He stands down and sits beside the rest of the characters, who all turn in their chairs to face the audience. David comes out and stands behind them.

Michelle I hope my hair doesn't get frizzy in the rain – why does it always rain in graveyards? And what's the point in burying a pile of old comics anyway?

Nigel Shut up, Michelle.

She looks at him in shock.

You heard me, shut up.

Jacob I didn't think you'd come.

JT I didn't know if you'd want me to.

Jacob I did.

JT I'm sorry . . . I didn't know . . .

Jacob I know.

JT Well . . . I'm just sorry.

Jacob Don't you want to meet my family?

JT What, now?

Jacob No time like the present.

Darren What do you mean?

Karen I mean . . . hang around more.

Darren Like . . . like your boyfriend?

Karen No, not like my boyfriend . . . actually my boyfriend.

Darren Oh.

Karen Well?

Darren (*beat*) Alright.

Stoner walks up to them.

Alright, Stoner.

Stoner Alright.

Darren You coming for a burger?

Stoner With you two?

Karen Why, what's wrong with us?

Stoner Nothing, just . . . yeah . . . I'd like that, yeah . . . Wouldn't mind . . . a chat . . . you know.

Sarah walks forward and the others turn round.

Sarah The day we knew David wasn't coming back
I went around the tattoo store, only this time I actually
meant to go there, didn't just walk and find myself out
there, looking at all the designs on the window. This
time I went down there myself, on purpose. I knew
I wanted something, something to mark the day and
what had happened because I knew if I didn't, then it
wouldn't seem real. Wouldn't seem like it actually
happened. (*She pulls up her T-shirt to show a belly-
ring.*) This is for David, to remind me of that day, the
day when he wasn't coming back any more. (*Beat.*)
I felt it then and now I feel it every time I touch it,
because the only ones that know about it are me and
him, wherever he is. At least he knows that I did
something for him, just for him, for us, something to
tie us together. (*Beat.*) I miss him most in the evenings,
just to make faces at or to have a mess, or walking to
school, stupid things that I didn't even think I enjoyed,
but I did. I miss having him as a brother, I miss knowing
that he'll look out for me whatever, I miss having to
pick his socks off the landing and having no milk for
cereal because he's drank it all. I miss the bad stuff.
I miss it all. But at least I have this, and it's the last
one, my last trip to the tattoo store. (*Beat.*) Because
that in itself means something. (*Beat.*) Doesn't it?

Michael walks forward.

Michael Are you ready?
Sarah I guess.
Michael I like your piercing.
Sarah You do?
Michael Yeah, it's cool.
Sarah Cool.
Michael Cool.

They turn and walk upstage. As they walk past, David enters and walks to centre stage; they both drop their flower at his feet as they exit. David stands in a pool of light on the floor. He is reading from a Spiderman *comic. Michael joins him and Sarah continues to exit.*

Michael But I don't want to be the Green Goblin

David You have to be.

Michael But he's stupid – Dr Octopus is much cooler, he's got all those arms.

David But he wasn't Peter Parker's friend – the whole point of it is that it is his arch enemy. It has to be his friend too . . . It's only when they put on their masks that they are mortal enemies.

Michael Why?

David Because the mask lets them do whatever they want to do, act however they want to act, without anyone knowing what they're really like. If everyone knew he was Peter Parker they'd just go round and kill all his family and friends. Without the mask, he's vulnerable.

Michael I don't know.

David Trust me, you don't want to be Dr Octopus, he's just another bad guy – you want to be the Green Goblin, his closest friend.

Michael Alright then.

David Brilliant . . . There's no point in playing if you're not going to do it properly – you have to go all the way, you know?

Michael I know.

David Okay, I'll count to twenty, you go.

Michael Okay.

David And no climbing trees, that's not fair.

Michael Alright.

David sits. Michael stands and watches him.

David One . . . two . . . three . . . four . . .
Michael David –
David What?
Michael Nothing.
David Go on, will you? Five . . . six . . . seven . . .
eight . . .

David continues to count as Michael walks away.
Michael turns and looks back at him, then exits.
Lights down on David counting.

The End.

Without the Mask We Are Vulnerable

Ursula Rani Sarma interviewed by Jim Mulligan

The closed world of *The Spider Men* starts and finishes with Sarah visiting the tattoo shop. The first time she drifts there to get a nose-ring that will impress Michael, the boy she fancies. But he is not there to see it, and the members of her family do not notice it either. At the end of the play, on the day of the funeral, she shows us her new belly-ring and tells us, 'This is for David to remind me of that day, the day when he wasn't coming back any more.' The visits encapsulate the story: two fifteen-year-old boys stay out all night; one comes back, the other does not.

> I was interested in the effect of a child going missing on the psyche of the kids in that community, trying to imagine what would happen within this close-knit world if two young people went missing and one of them didn't come back. What fear would it generate? There would be journalists around, so how would they react to that? 'Maybe the person who took that boy will come and take me.'

The central character in the play, David, lives in a relatively dysfunctional family with his sister, Sarah, and brother, Jacob. The mother is trying to over-extend herself to compensate for the father, who makes no attempt to communicate with the family and who can be violent. Sarah can't stand her mother. David says, 'I should love my mum . . . well I don't, alright? I fucking don't.' Jacob is trying to come to terms with his sexuality. Some time before the play starts, something happens in this family that triggers off the events that follow.

> I didn't want to be too specific about the reason why David ran away. I suppose something happened at home the previous night, something to make Sarah get her piercing and tattoo and to make David snap. I wanted the play to be a response to something we don't know about. I think David needs affection and attention more than Sarah does. He does not know how to go to his mother and say, 'I crave love and I'm not getting it.' And that spills over into his relationships with the other kids. He is unable to process what he is feeling. He is furious.

David turns his fury toward Michael, who is fascinated by this rebel because he is so different from him. In his comfortable life, nobody is forcing Michael to do something he doesn't want to do; he does not mind being treated like a child at times, so he turns to this person who is almost a romantic hero for him.

> In the real world David cannot control anything, so he retreats into the world of comics, seeing himself as Spiderman and Michael as the Green Goblin. As in any abusive relationship, Michael justifies all David's bad behaviour with the knowledge that sometimes he's nice, sometimes he's a good person. And he is proud that he has seen a side of David nobody else has seen. The two of them have all the fights of a couple who have been together too long.

For most of the play the characters are unaware that something terrifying is going on in the woods within walking distance of where they live. They are getting on with their teenage lives and relationships and coping within their families. Both girls and boys are discussing the end-of-year do and the wristbands that will define exactly how far a girl will go. The boys are both fascinated and repelled. As Nigel says, 'If a girl . . . puts it out a bit . . . well, a lot . . . then that's just not attractive, is it?' The girls seem to discuss the matter endlessly. And yet, we ask ourselves, how much of this is bravado? Karen, for one, turns out to be a complete innocent who cannot judge how good a kisser Darren is because she has nothing to compare it with.

> Why do kids have to grow up so quickly? Wearing an external sign to prove what you've done is not much of a leap from what goes on at the moment. Everyone loses their innocence at a certain point, but it seems to be getting earlier and earlier. There are no boundaries any more, and legal age-limits mean nothing. It's not an original concept that young people are taking drugs and having sex, but I wanted to put a tangible symbol in.

Stoner has placed himself outside this teenage world. He is the tramp-figure that appears in older Irish plays, the moral voice of the play. Nobody takes him seriously. Everything he says is what the rest of the play is showing. He can be detached and profound. The quality of what he has to give, if he were given the opportunity, would be top-rate. He tells the boys, 'When you're not the one doing all the talking you hear an awful lot, when you're the one sitting back and observing, you observe an awful lot.'

In *The Spider Men* the only continuing relationship is between Jacob and JT. At the start of the play Jacob has had difficulty making his love public, but the fact that his young brother is not coming back into his life gives him the opportunity to re-evaluate his position.

> There's something lovely about two young men, still at school, who have found a very normal, healthy

relationship. I think young people want the opportunity to discuss things openly, not to hint at them but to say the words. They need to relate things to themselves in an accessible and tangible way. This may be a threat to parents and teachers, but the play is not for them. If adults feel something in this play is risqué or not accurate or is in there as a shock factor, I would have to disagree. Everything in the play comes from the characters. After all, what's comfortable about being a teenager? The liberation for the young people in the play is the challenge for parents and teachers.

Production Notes

For several years, Ursula Rani Sarma had been thinking about writing a play that dealt with the subject of missing people. Her interest lies in the impact on community, friends and family when young people go missing. She started writing when she was just out of her teens, which is perhaps why she captures the teenage register so well. She was interested in the two worlds: that of the missing person, and that of the world for those left behind. David's story is at the heart of it – specifically his sense of fear – while other people's responses and how the media seize such tragedies are also explored.

She also wanted to write about the loss of innocence – how it appears to happen at such a young age. The idea of the wristbands seemed a logical response to the pressure to be sexually promiscuous. Stoner is a 'tramp character', as in Irish plays at the turn of the twentieth century – a character with a lower social status who is the moral voice of the play, but to whom no one listens. There is a stillness about him, and a grain of truth in what he says when he does speak. Ursula was charmed by him as a character and the humour of the play is important to her.

She didn't intend there to be a homoerotic relationship between Michael and David, but it could be taken as such if you want. Ursula doesn't want to say what she imagines happened to David in the woods. She makes a comparison to the movie *Jaws* – because we don't see the shark, we instead imagine one of our own which is far scarier than the one we do eventually see. She makes the link between this and the fact that it is more frightening *not* to know what happened to David. But you will need to decide. Theatre audiences are amazingly imaginative – no matter how specific you are, they will still overlay a story of their own, and this is as it should be.

This play is robust: it won't fall apart on the way from the page to the stage, but it has been very finely timed, right down to how it is punctuated.

Ursula's stage directions and her actions – such as David reappearing after he has died – are crucial. Every stage direction is character-driven, and so gives an insight into the characters. Even if, for example, the production ends up ignoring the suggestion that Michael wears glasses, there should be an awareness of the inference behind it. This is grounded in David seeing Michael as an example of the weaker of the species, in a Darwinian sense.

Slow pacing is the most dangerous trap to fall into, and will kill the play. But this doesn't mean that the actors should just speed up – it's about human interaction. The change from the end of Scene Twelve to Scene Thirteen could be one of the most tricky, as it's the transition from the height of David's terror to a light-hearted and very long scene between two characters that we don't know too well. So Scene Thirteen needs to have an underlying energy and tension in order to convey that sense of submerged panic. A big question is how to get David off stage at the end of that scene.

Transitions between the scenes are vital – production decisions need to be made about whether to put music in or not, and above all, there needs to be an awareness of the different needs of the changes. Some scene changes, such as the one between the wristband scenes, have to run on for it to be clear in the following scene that we are talking about the same thing. The great skill here is how to use time, to give the audience a surprise. You have to use the changes as part of the storytelling, rather than just getting from one scene to another. Again, the stage directions give a hint. 'Lights up, lights down' may perhaps be hard to achieve with your lighting plot, but it makes clear that the writer intended an abrupt, guillotine-like ending to the scene.

FINDING A STYLE FOR THE PRODUCTION

Look at moments that are difficult, such as the opening stage directions. The opening is a stylistic device that is never referred to again. In production, go for a unified style. The first few minutes are like a lesson: this is how we'll tell this story. Surprise is a key: you want to make your audience sit forward.

Ask questions such as: *Are they on stage as actors or as the characters they are playing? Why are they coming on together? Are they re-telling this story? What does the marching mean?* Here, as elsewhere, the stage directions give clues: the characters are named, indicating they are not just neutral actors preparing to tell a story. This opening section establishes Sarah in a different time frame to the play, slightly ahead of the action.

There is a problem of location, in that, although the wood is a constant, the other settings change, and are generally different each time. Potentially this could be a fantastic play to do promenade-style, with the audience moving and the actors setting up the furniture behind them while another scene is going on.

Unless you can achieve a perfect blackout, you will have to decide what happens to David and Michael in the woods in between scenes. Phone calls are another issue – do they mime a telephone, or have one in their hands?

Do they have radio microphones? Try not to show anything you don't have to.

Casting is a huge part of making the play work – Ursula deliberately denies the audience easy hand-holds in the dialogue, such as the characters' names, which are revealed relatively late. Therefore each character must be clearly identifiable as an individual from their clothing and physicality.

You might wonder whether David is a ghost when he appears to Stoner. Is Stoner hallucinating or imagining it? This obviously affects the timing of the play – if he is a ghost, then the next scene is a flashback. David's phone call to Jacob at the end of Scene Nine could be seen as a voice from the present, past or future.

You can use games to give the actors ownership of the characters. Try hot-seating, or a system of lists. Make one list of facts you know to be true about that character, along with concrete actions in the stage directions, a second of everything the character says about him/herself, a third of anything they say about other people, and a fourth of anything other people say about them.

When rehearsing you could visit similar locations. Get the actors who play Michael and David out into the woods. Get props like the wristbands into rehearsals as soon as possible, so that the actors have ownership of them.

NOTES ON THE SCRIPT

David's parents are dysfunctional in the extreme – no genuine affection reaches the three kids. Sarah, perhaps because she is a girl, is the most aware of this, and she is addicted to the pain of being tattooed and pierced because she wants to feel something.

David can't process what's wrong, or deal with it at all, which is why he puts his head through the glass door. He hates, because he can't love. David's pain shows how we all need to be loved, and to be a child in that kind of relationship with adults.

It's important that the actors playing David, Sarah and Jacob all have the same parents in their head. David needs to decide what the row was about – the superficial one, the tip of the iceberg that caused him to run away, because he would be replaying the scene in his head in the forest. He might be a depressive – it has certainly been projected onto him (he's been sent to see a psychologist) and all three kids are very imaginative.

Ursula kept the parents out of the play because she didn't want the actors to have to play grown-ups – the policemen are adult but appear fleetingly; they have trench coats on and their backs are to the audience. As to the other characters in the world of the play who don't appear, this is largely because they are representative. They provide colour though. Jane doesn't have to appear – she's a reference point, for what she represents. Finlay is a schoolteacher, and Fergus Lynch is a kid in their class.

Every character has a different drive, which informs the play's world. Nigel, obsessed with getting his paper aeroplane just right, is the kind of guy who would ride up the corporate ladder. He juxtaposes well with characters like Stoner and Jacob. Michelle is about how you can sell your soul for fame, but also has a lot going on behind this.

The title resonates on many levels. *Spiderman* is about fantasy, and heroes, but this is reality. Spiderman is a nerd, encapsulating the myth of being weak in real life, and then suddenly becoming strong. Spiderman's parents weren't around either: he was brought up by his aunt and uncle. *Spiderman* returns them to childhood, and Michael and David probably had the best relationship when they were children, playing. On another level, the title could refer to globalisation, making us all insect-like.

For reference, check out www.spiderfan.org

PROBLEM-SOLVING

Focus on: Sarah's monologues; Michelle's speech to the camera; a big two-hander like Scene Thirteen; and the policemen sections. Decide what environment the characters are in, whether they're in the same space, possibly each in their own room, or together in a timeless zone. Ask if there's an entrance to the space. This poses the question of lighting, and how to light the set, what to give away before the start of the play.

Treat the word 'Beat' with respect, as it is a clue to what is going on in the heads of the characters. Pinter now regrets ever having used 'Pause' as a stage direction – 'Beat' is more what he meant. Respect the stage directions. Ursula is very sparse with hers, and rarely indicates the character's emotions before a line ('angrily', etc.) When she does, therefore, it is important.

Punctuation Exercise

Ask someone to read Sarah's first speech, and have the rest of the group, sitting in a circle around her, clap for a full stop or an exclamation mark, click for a comma, click three times for three dots, and clap when she leaves a pause for a beat. A voice teacher rule: only allow the actor to take a breath for punctuation – a new thought is indicated by a breath. Different characters are punctuated differently in this play. The punctuation allows the audience to laugh, and brings out the humour.

Ball Exercise

To point out that any young person could believably say 'so' at the end of a line, try this. Get the actors to stand in a circle and say the line 'Give us some of that cheese sandwich, so,' throwing a ball on the final word, 'so'. The word will probably be used differently every time, but it is most effective when used dynamically rather than swallowed – though this is actually unlike the Irish usage, which is quite light.

Physical Punctuation Exercise

Have someone stand in the centre of the circle, with three people on chairs, in a triangle around her/him. Get the actor to address the line to a person on a chair, changing the person addressed on a full stop, moving position on a comma, and turning on the spot, silently taking in every audience member on a *beat*. Get the actor to be rigorous about this. (With young actors it may be best to use this exercise when the speech is already quite familiar.)

There are three circles of concentration when you speak to anyone:

The inner – talking to yourself. The guy in the corner of the pub, muttering. He's not a threat to anyone.

Direct one-on-one contact with someone – this is what we want in life, when someone absolutely talks to us. This *is* a threat in the pub – the guy threatens someone directly.

Talking to people en masse – again, if the guy in the pub says 'I want to kill you,' but is talking to the whole room, he is not a threat.

For a speech, highlight which parts belong to which circle, to see the light and shade, and what's below the surface. This is especially useful for Sarah's speeches.

Dialogue Scenes

These are about a contraction and expansion of space, and an investigation of safe distances. If the scene's going to end with a kiss, you want to keep the characters as far apart as you can for as long as possible. If you're performing in-the-round, you need to find a way to get the two people to reverse positions, because otherwise they block each other, and the audience won't believe them unless they've seen the eyes of both partners.

For Michelle's speech in Scene Seventeen, you have to decide with your actress which are the breaks when a reporter asks a question, and which are her own, to change the subject. What questions are being asked, and where?

Question exercises

Get an actor to stand in the middle of the circle. Ask everyone in the group to crowd around her, move and shout questions at her like paparazzi: try to make her life hell. She might have to turn to face a different way on each question. • Ask the group to do the same thing again, this time just miming the photographers. • Have the director move around the space and clap hands where the questions are coming from. Get the actor to wait, and imagine the question before answering. • Have the actor seated. Have the director indicate the directions the questions are coming from. The actor should play it for real, like an audition speech, believing what she's saying, as if she knew nothing about the character.

Michelle's tragedy is the brightness built out of her sadness. Grief is played in different ways, and this extrovert behaviour is her way of dealing with the situation. It is important to look at the lines with beats in them: you have to get the sense that she's pushing through on each line, not pausing.

The section in Scene Thirteen between Darren and Karen is one of the hardest in the play. The two characters are meant to be sitting on a wall. Get them to sit opposite each other on chairs, then to read the whole scene through and split it up into bits to work on. Karen's mini-soliloquies could be like a stream of consciousness, with the speeches almost pouring out of her. There's barely a line or a speech that has a full stop in it: this scene is intended to flow.

Punctuation exercises

Still sitting opposite each other, get the actors to have a beat of eye contact with each other after every line of dialogue, as well as on a comma, a full stop, and look at each other for twice as long on an ellipsis, before they look down at their scripts to see what their next line is. They should try only to perform to each other, and ignore the audience.

This exercise should make them connect, and release the subtext. The most human way to seek information from someone is through the eyes. Encourage them to share eye-contact rather than feel threatened by it. Having done the whole scene in this way, they should bond – it could be a shorthand to intimacy.

Actioning

Actioning is another technique that you might use, going through the entire scene attributing a transitive verb for every single line – 'I want to thank him/to blame him/to bond' etc. – never re-using a verb within the scene. This is useful because it makes the way you play the line objective, and you can only use a verb you know. You have to be specific, which is useful for lines you don't understand, or where plays have difficult language.

It is good to talk to actors about what else is in the scene –
what direction the party is in, for example – so that they
can look that way. If Darren starts on the opposite side of
the wall, you want to keep him there as long as possible –
his move will be a big change in dynamic and it is
worthwhile making the most of this.

Sometimes there will be a line in a scene where a character
gives away their subtext, as when Karen asks, 'What do
you do when you're not a kid any more but you're still
scared?' The kiss is the answer – you find yourself a
partner. The kiss is not about a loss of innocence, but
about Karen holding on to something that is important
to her, so that her first kiss actually means something.

Status Game

Give a group of five a number, secretly, where one is the
lowest status and six the highest. Without dialogue, they
should position themselves in a space according to their
status. We instantly know that a high status person gets
on a table, and a low one on the floor. Status 6 people
will sometimes stand in a corner on their own. The most
interesting scenes are often between people of similar
status.

The classroom is fraught with status areas and objects –
the teacher's table, the blackboard, etc. Looking out of
the window is middle status. Actually, there are more like
twenty statuses rather than six, and it can become very
complex.

Workshop facilitated by Edward Kemp
with notes taken by Sophie Lifschutz

Participating Schools and Companies

Academy Youth Theatre
Action Transport Theatre
Ad Lib Theatre Company
Alderbrook Actors Theatre
Arnold School
Ashcroft High School
Astor College for the Arts

Behind The Scenes Youth
 Theatre
Berzerk Productions
Best Theatre Arts
Birchwood High School
Bishop Thomas Grant School
Bishop's Stortford College
Blatchington Mill School
Blue Coat CE Comprehensive
 School
Bodmin Community College
Boston Spa Comprehensive
 School
Bournemouth School for Girls
Brentwood Youth Theatre
Brewery Arts Centre
Brewery Youth Theatre
Bristol Old Vic Education
Brune Park Community
 College
Bryanston School
B-Tizzles
Buckingham School
Burton Borough School

CADA Performing Arts
Caerleon Comprehensive
Caister High School
Callington Community College
Camborne Science &
 Community College
Castledon School (Special
 Needs)
Castleford High School
 Technology College
CATS Youth Theatre
Catteral Hall, Giggleswick
Cavendish School
Centre Stage School of
 Performing Arts
Centrestage Theatre Group
Chadwell Heath Foundation
 School
Chafford Hundred Campus
Charlton Outreach Theatre
 Company
Cheadle and Marple Sixth
 Form College
Chester Gateway Live! Youth
 Theatre
Christelijk Gymnasium Utrecht
Christ's Hospital School
City College Norwich
Clacton County High School
Claremont High School
Coleg Sir Gar
Company of Teens

Coopers' Company and Coborn
  School
Cork School of Music Youth
  Theatre
Coulsdon College
Craigholme School
CRE8
Crofton High School
CYTO – Croydon Youth
  Theatre Organisation

Dartford Grammar School for
  Girls
Dolman Youth Theatre
Downe House School
Doyl'y Arts
Dumont High School Youth
  Theatre
Dunraven School

E0.45 Theatre at West Suffolk
  College
Education in Stage and Theatre
  Arts
Ellesmere College
Erith School
Far East Theatre Company
Fernhill Secondary School
Fisher More Theatre
  Company
Floorless Productions –
  William Morris Academy
Fortrose Academy
Francis Combe School –
  Daffodil Drama

Galway Youth Theatre
George Heriot's School Drama
Glenthorne High School
Grays School

Great Baddow High School,
  Chelmsford
Greenwich & Lewisham Young
  People's Theatre
Grenville College
Guiseley School

Halewood Performing Arts
  College
Harrogate Theatre HT2
Hatfield Visual Arts College
Headington School
Headstrong Young Peoples
  Theatre
Helene Lange Schule
Hemel Hempstead School
Hemsworth Arts and
  Community College
Hertfordshire County Youth
  Theatre
Heysham High School
Hillingdon Youth Arts
Hope Valley College
Hreod Parkway School
Huddersfield Technical College

Ian Ramsey Church Of England
  School
Independent Youth Theatre
Innovaters
International School Milan
Ironduke, Wellington College
Isle of Skye Youth Theatre
ITV Junior Workshop
Ivybridge Community
  College

Jigsaw Youth Theatre
  Company

John Cleveland College

Kaskenmoor School
Kennet School
Kent Youth Theatre
Kidbrooke School
Kildare Youth Theatre
@ Crooked House
King Edward VI School
King's School

Langdon School
Leyton Sixth Form College
Lightbulb Youth Theatre
Lingfield Notre Dame Senior
School
Littlehampton Community
School
Llanelli Youth Theatre
Longdean School
Lookout Theatre Company
Lyceum Youth Theatre
Lyndon School

Malmesbury School
Marple Hall School
McEntee School
Methwold High School
Millfield School
Mold Players Youth Works
More House

Nescot College
New Bridge Integrated College
& Twiglet Theatre Company
Nightingale Productions
NoName Theatre Company
Nuffield Youth Theatre
Nunthorpe School Youth Theatre

Old Palace School of John
Whitgift
Oslo International School,
International String of Lights
OUDS (Oxford University
Dramatic Society)
Oulder Hill Community School
and VI Form Centre

Park Community School
Park High School
Parsons Mead School
Peacehaven Community School
Pencoed School
Penrice Community College
Performance Academy
(Newcastle College)
Performance Lab @
Roundabout Youth Theatre
PerformerZone
Phoenix Theatre Company
Pilot Youth Theatre
Players & Faces @ Barnwell
Plumstead Manor School
Polka Theatre
Portlaoise Youth Theatre
Preston Manor High School
Pump House CYT

Quad Theatre Company
Queen Elizabeth School
Queen Elizabeth's Community
College
Queensbridge School

Range High School
Razed Roof
Regent College/Leicester Hay-
market Theatre Young Blood

Ricards Lodge High School
Rickmansworth School
Riding Lights Youth Theatre
Royal West of England School
for the Deaf

Saint Felix School
Saint Martin's
Salisbury Playhouse Stage 65
Youth Theatre
Sandringham School
Scarborough YMCA Youth
Theatre
Shetland Youth Theatre
Shotton Hall
Sir Bernard Lovell School
NIPA
Sir Frederic Osborn School
South West Youth Theatre
South Wight Youth Theatre
South Wirral High School
Southwark College
Southwell Minster School
St Aelreds Technology College
St Augustine's High School
St Bede's School
St Catherine's School
St Edmund Arrowsmith High
School
St Edward's School
St George's College, Weybridge
St Gregory Youth Theatre
St Julian's School
St Mary's Youth Theatre
St Monica's High School
St Wilfrid's RC Comprehensive
School
Stage by Stage Music Theatre
School

Starfruit Youth Theatre
Company
Stephen Joseph Theatre
Stoke Sixth Form College
Stokesley School
Straight Up Theatre Company
Sussex Downs College

Tamarside Community College
Tanglin Trust school
The Albany
The Bishop's Stortford High
School
The Castle Arts Centre
The Company – Theatre in
Training
The Croft Drama Group
The Eastwood School
The Garage Project
The Harefield Academy
The Harrodian School
The International School
The Lady Eleanor Holles
School
The Lindsey School &
Community Arts College
The Loft Theatre Group
The Mirfield Free
The Mountbatten School
The Northampton School for
Girls
The Petersfield School Senior
Youth Theatre
The Plume School
The Princess Helena College
The Rawlett School
The Ridgeway School
Theatre Antidote
Theatre Cap-A-Pie

PARTICIPATING SCHOOLS AND COMPANIES

Theatre Royal Bury St
   Edmunds Youth Group
Theatre Royal Young Company
Thomas Hardye School
Thornden School
Thurrock & Basildon College
Truro School Theatre
Tunbridge Wells Grammar
   School for Boys

Varndean School
Vienna International School

Wakefield City High School
Wellacre Technology College
Wellington School
Whickham School
Whitstone School

Whizz Kids Theatre Company
Wilmington Youth Theatre
Winchmore School
Wired Youth Theatre
Woodcote High School
Woolston Community High
   School

Xpress Theatre Company – The
   Camberley Theatre

Yateley School
Young Actors Theatre
Young North Theatre Company
Ysgol Aberconwy
Ysgol Glanaethwy
Yvonne Arnaud Youth Theatre:
   Interval

REGIONAL PARTNERSHIP THEATRES

The Albany
Brewery Arts Centre
Brighton Dome
The Castle Arts Centre
Clwyd Theatr Cymru
Drum Theatre Plymouth
Everyman Palace Theatre
Greenwich Theatre
The Lowry
Lyric Hammersmith
Norwich Playhouse & The Garage
Nuffield Theatre
Royal Lyceum Theatre
Stephen Joseph Theatre
Theatre Royal Bath
Theatre Royal Newcastle
Watford Palace Theatre

The Connections Series